D0297897

MODERN DEVELOPMENTS
IN ELECTRON MICROSCOPY

Contributors to this Volume

DON W. FAWCETT

CECIL E. HALL

PAUL KAESBERG

EDWARD KELLENBERGER

D. W. PASHLEY

KEITH R. PORTER

ANTOINETTE RYTER

BENJAMIN M. SIEGEL

Modern Developments in Electron Microscopy

EDITED BY

BENJAMIN M. SIEGEL

Department of Engineering Physics and Materials Science
Cornell University
Ithaca, New York

1964

ACADEMIC PRESS • New York and London

ACADEMIC PRESS INC.
111 Fifth Avenue, New York 3, New York

United Kingdom Edition published by
ACADEMIC PRESS INC. (LONDON) LTD.
Berkeley Square House, London W.1

LIBRARY OF CONGRESS CATALOG CARD NUMBER: 63:16977

PRINTED IN THE UNITED STATES OF AMERICA

List of Contributors

Numbers in parentheses refer to the pages on which the authors' contributions begin.

DON W. FAWCETT, Department of Anatomy, Harvard Medical School, Boston, Massachusetts (257).

CECIL E. HALL, Department of Biology, Massachusetts Institute of Technology, Cambridge, Massachusetts (395).

PAUL KAESBERG, Department of Biochemistry, University of Wisconsin, Madison, Wisconsin (99).

EDWARD KELLENBERGER, Laboratoire de Biophysique, Université de Genève, Genève, Switzerland (335).

D. W. PASHLEY, Tube Investments Research Laboratories, Hinxton Hall, Nr. Saffron Walden, Essex, England (83 and 149).

KEITH R. PORTER, Harvard Biological Laboratories, Cambridge, Massachusetts (119).

ANTOINETTE RYTER, Services de Photomicrographie et de Physiologie Microbienne, Institut Pasteur, Paris, France (335).

BENJAMIN M. SIEGEL, Department of Engineering Physics and Materials Science, Cornell University, Ithaca, New York (1).

Preface

The use of the electron microscope in research has reached a stage in which this instrument is providing one of the most powerful means of investigating the complex organization of matter at the molecular level. No other method provides such a direct observation on the manner in which the individual molecules are arranged in the intricate building-up of the components of the biological cell, or in the ways in which the defects occurring in the regular arrays of crystalline matter are distributed and interact. The growth of electron microscopy in research has been phenomenal in the past few years. We are no longer limited to the primitive techniques of the early years, and with the development of the refined techniques of ultrathin sectioning for biological material and the preparation of thin foils for studies of crystalline solids has come the improved engineering of the electron microscope itself. Several different commercial instruments are now available which, when properly adjusted, will enable the skilled investigator to utilize the electron microscope as an effective research tool.

This volume presents a critical evaluation of a wide cross section of current developments in electron microscopy. In the past few years the uses of the electron microscope have expanded at a very rapid rate, and a number of volumes and review articles have now appeared dealing with the application of the instrument to particular fields. Excellent as some of these contributions are, the expert in one field who confines his attention to applications in his own speciality does not acquire the perspective of the versatility inherent in this instrument or an appreciation of the rich diversity of techniques and methods which are still developing. The present volume is directed primarily to the research worker who has only recently started to apply the electron microscope in his research. For him the acquaintance with excellence in various fields of application, which this volume presents, should provide an important broadening of understanding of the utilization of the instrument, suggest methods from other fields which may apply to his particular problems, and set standards for his own work.

Each contribution has been written so that it will be understandable to research workers outside the particular discipline. The technical vocabulary of the specific fields could not be avoided entirely, but none is so intricate that reading a given contribution would be impossible or without profit. What we hope is that as the examples of some of the best current work in a given field are presented and critical evaluations are made on the achievements and limitations of the applications in this field, readers from other disciplines can apply these experiences to their own research. In each field the examples of electron microscopy have been chosen with regard for the high standards of achievement which research workers should apply to their own work.

The volume contains three sections and they deal with the physics, the techniques, and the applications of the electron microscope. The first section presents a descriptive evaluation of the current problems in the physics of the electron microscope. An attempt has been made to present the basic physical phenomena without detailed mathematical treatment and in a manner which would make the subject understandable to a person with only an introductory background in physics. While the implications of the evaluation can be better understood by the physicist, all who use the instrument will be interested in where the development of the instrument now stands. An appreciation of the present limit of our understanding of the nature of image contrast is especially important. A stage has been reached where it now appears possible to achieve or exceed the limits of resolution set by an oversimplified theoretical description. It is hoped that the presentations in this volume will be helpful in understanding the current status of the subject. The physicist will then want to go to more extensive treatments such as are available, for example, in the "Handbuch der Physik" Volume XXXIII, or in a new book by R. D. Heidenreich, "Fundamentals of Transmission Electron Microscopy."

The section on techniques is brief, but places emphasis on the critical evaluation of some of the techniques now available in electron microscopy and on their limitations and the direction of needed development. In some cases additional techniques are described or evaluated in chapters on the special applications. Such an overlap was unavoidable for often the evaluation of the application of the electron microscope to a particular field is intimately bound up with the current techniques available. The need for detailed descriptions of procedures has been made much less necessary with the appearance of satisfactory works which provide that information, such as the volume edited by D. Kay, "Techniques for Electron Microscopy" (Oxford, 1961) and some of the publications given in the reference sections of the various chapters.

The section on applications has a somewhat arbitrary selection of subjects. Each of the applications represented here deals with a field in which important contributions to research have been made with the electron microscope. Each chapter presents excellent examples of the manner in which this instrument has been utilized at its highest level of competence. To have included all fields in which significant contributions have been made would have enlarged the volume beyond reasonable size. The reader whose interest is primarily in fields not represented in this volume is referred to reviews or monographs on specific applications of the electron microscope which are now available. The applications which are represented in this volume do provide a wide cross section of examples. From each there is something to be learned.

The Editor wishes to thank the contributors to this work, and especially for their patience with the long delays in bringing the volume into being. I also wish to thank the Hebrew University of Jerusalem for the generous facilities which provided me with such a pleasant and congenial atmosphere in which to complete my task. The cheerful help of the many in my laboratory who work with me, and in particular, Mrs. Frances A. McHenry, is gratefully acknowledged.

Ithaca, New York   BENJAMIN M. SIEGEL
December, 1963

Contents

Chapter 1.   The Physics of the Electron Microscope

BENJAMIN M. SIEGEL

SELECTED METHODS AND TECHNIQUES

Chapter 2.   Thin Metal Specimens

D. W. PASHLEY

Chapter 3.   Particulate Materials

PAUL KAESBERG

Chapter 4.   Ultramicrotomy

KEITH R. PORTER

SELECTED APPLICATIONS OF THE ELECTRON MICROSCOPE

Chapter 5.   In Physics

D. W. PASHLEY

Chapter 6.   In Histology and Cytology

DON W. FAWCETT

Chapter 7.   In Bacteriology

EDWARD KELLENBERGER AND ANTOINETTE RYTER

Chapter 8. *In Studies on Biological Macromolecules*

Cecil E. Hall

CHAPTER 1

The Physics of the Electron Microscope

BENJAMIN M. SIEGEL

I. Electron Optics

A. Introduction

The focusing effect of electric and magnetic fields on electron beams was first described in optical terms in 1926 by H. Busch (*6a*). In a most elegant manner it was now possible to make a direct application of the theory developed by William Korvan Hamilton in 1831 (*20a*) to the trajectory of an electron in the electromagnetic field of an electron optical system. The "Hamiltonian analogy" described the path of light rays through media with continuously varying refractive index in terms of the trajectory of material particles in potential fields. Here was the direct analogy realized in a physical system, and development of electron optical instruments followed, using analogous optical thinking based on this fundamental similarity of the two fields.

Electron optics took over the terminology and descriptions of light optics and the fundamentals of electron optics were developed in analogy to familiar light optics. The Hamiltonian theory is most general and elegant, establishing the fundamental mathematical foundation common to all optical systems. But its generality and the mathematical complexity of its formulation puts it in the realm of the theorist and it becomes too complex for treatment of most practical problems. In practical electron optics it is more useful to develop analogies, first describing the geometric optics of electron lenses in terms of electron trajectories and then the analogous wave optical phenomena that produce the diffraction effects which set limits on the ultimate resolution of an instrument such as the electron microscope.

The analogies between geometrical light optics and electron optics carry over through a wide range of practical applications to optical components and systems, but some differences and limits of applicability should be pointed out. Light optical instruments are composed of suitably shaped surfaces of solid media which abruptly refract or reflect the light. Electrons are refracted or reflected by electric or magnetic fields which act continuously over a finite length. Electron optical design will consist of suitably shaping electric or magnetic fields to refract electrons and produce the desired imaging. There are some rather severe limitations on the electron lenses which can be designed by shaping electrodes for the electrostatic lenses or the pole pieces of high-permeability magnetic material in the magnetic lenses. Axial symmetry of a refracting media can be shown to be a sufficient condition to produce imaging of the first order; thus lenses in general have rotational symmetry about the optic axis. Light lenses with surfaces having both positive and negative curvature, made up of media of different refractive index, can be designed to give convergent or divergent lenses, and can be corrected for higher-order aberrations. Electron lenses having axial symmetry can only be convergent, and it has been impossible to shape fields to give systems free of spherical and chromatic aberrations. These severe limitations have led to designs of electron optical systems without axial symmetry which may be of considerable importance in the future.

The analogies in the wave optics of light and electrons are based on wave mechanics, and, of course, in the complete treatment could be developed as a unified theory. Classic treatment of physical optics is, however, an adequate and very useful method of describing imaging in optical systems and the limits of resolution imposed by diffraction phenomena. In considering image formation by electron lenses it is not necessary to go beyond certain approximations in classic diffraction theory which have been well formulated for light. Thus, here again, it will be useful to take over the terminology, concepts, and methods of light optics and apply them to electron optics.

The analogies have been carried further. In considering image formation in the electron microscope, the scattering of the electrons by the matter of the object has been treated in a first approximation as an analog of the absorption of light in the microscope objective. A word of caution must be introduced. The nature of the interaction of electrons with matter and light with matter are so different at the level of interest in the respective optical instruments that it is misleading to think only in analogous terms. Especially in the exciting new field of observations of crystalline materials with the electron microscope, the electron interaction with the periodic lattice is completely different than any considerations required for light microscopy. Here analogies with photon scattering in the x-ray region may provide a useful starting point for discussion based on an established subject in physics, but an adequate treatment of the electron interactions will require an independent approach.

The discussions on the physical aspects of the electron microscope, the imaging and image contrast obtained in electron optical systems, will follow these general divisions which provide such convenient analogies with the established methods of physics. Electron optics will first be considered in rather simple terms based on the concepts of goemetrical optics. A very useful description of image formation in the electron microscope can be presented in these terms and provides an understanding of the function of the different optical components. Wave optics will then be used to describe the limiting conditions which determine the resolution of the electron optical system. Finally, image contrast and the ultimate performance of the instrument will be considered both in terms of optics and the quantum mechanical scattering phenomena which determine the manner in which observations must be made at atomic dimensions.

B. Geometrical Optics

In geometrical optics, light can be treated as a ray in its passage through an optical system and this ray is represented geometrically as a line. The refraction of the light ray in passing from a medium of one refractive index n_1, to a medium of different refractive index n_2, becomes the basis of lens action. Snell's law, $n_1 \sin \phi_i = n_2 \sin \phi_r$, relating the refractive indices, the angle of incidence ϕ_i that the ray makes with the boundary between the two media, and the angle of refraction ϕ_r, provides the necessary information for tracing a ray through any system of surfaces of different curvature and media of different refractive index.

The problem of geometrical optics is now to shape the refracting surfaces of an optical system in such a way as to give imaging; that is, a one-to-one correspondence between points in an object plane and an image plane.

Figure 1 illustrates the manner in which geometrical imaging can be described for refracting surfaces in the region $L_1 \, L_2$. If the refracting surfaces in the region $L_1 \, L_2$ are all surfaces of revolution about the axis Z, or in other words are an axially symmetric refracting system centered on the axis Z, symmetry requirements will show that a point in the object plane at P_o with coordinates x_o, y_o will be imaged at a point P_i with coordinates x_i, y_i in the Gaussian image plane in first approximation.

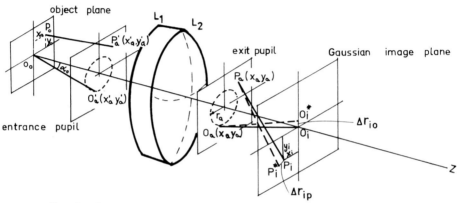

FIG. 1.   Geometrical imaging by axially symmetric refracting system.

The approximation required is the paraxial approximation that the rays make only small angles with the axis so that $\sin \alpha \simeq \alpha$. Then we have a linear correspondence between object and image,

$$x_o = Mx_i \quad \text{and} \quad y_o = My_i \tag{1}$$

where M will be the lateral magnification of the optical system.

In actual optical systems the extra-axial rays must be considered, and then deviation of these rays from the Gaussian image point can be described in terms of the location of the object point in the object plane and an additional parameter, the intersection of a given ray with the aperture plane in image space, or exit pupil, of the axially symmetric refracting system, or usually less conveniently, its conjugate plane in object space the entrance pupil. A ray from P_o will be refracted so that it intersects the aperture plane at P_a and the Gaussian image plane at P_i^*. The deviation Δr_{ip} of P_i^* from the paraxial ray image point P_i represents the aberration of the system and can be expressed in higher-order terms added to the relations in Eq. (1).

In electron optical systems used in electron microscopes only the next higher terms must be considered. The important aberration is spherical aberration occurring when the object points are near the origin O_o, and the rays begin to make angles in which the approximation for $\sin \alpha = \alpha - (\alpha^3/3!) + (\alpha^5/5!) - (\alpha^7/7!) + \ldots$ must include the third-order terms. The paraxial rays will be imaged at the origin O_i in the Gaussian image plane, but the extra-axial rays will intersect the Gaussian plane at O_i^* producing an image figure of radius Δr_{io} which is given by

$$\Delta r_{io} = C'_s \, (r_a/f)^3 \qquad (2a)$$

where C'_s is the spherical aberration coefficient, a constant for a given refracting system imaging at a given magnification, r_a the radial separation of the ray from the axis where it intersects the aperture plane, and f the focal length of the system. It is customary to refer the image aberration figure back to the equivalent dimensions at the object and thus we have

$$\Delta r_{oo} = C_s \alpha_o^3 \qquad (2b)$$

where C_s is the spherical aberration coefficient with the proper magnification factor and α_o is the angular aperture of the system.

A satisfactory general description of the geometrical imaging of an optical system is obtained by considering the Gaussian image given by the paraxial ray approximation. Only when a detailed investigation of

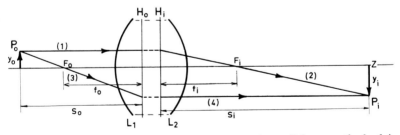

FIG. 2. Cardinal points of a thick-lens system and parallel-ray method of image tracing. The *principal planes* H_o, H_i and the *focal points* F_o, F_i define the imaging properties of the optical system L_1 L_2 in the paraxial (Gaussian) approximation. To locate the image, y_i, of the object, y_o, produced by the optical system, a ray (1) from a point, P_o, on the object is drawn parallel to the axis in object space to the *object principal plane*, H_o. This ray projects at unit magnification to the *image principal plane*, H_i, and is refracted as the ray (2) in image space, passing through the *image focal point*, F_i. Another ray (3) is drawn from P_o passing through the *object focal point*, F_o. This ray is again projected from its intersection at the *object principal plane*, H_o, at unit magnification to the *image principal plane*, H_i, and continues as ray (4) in image space parallel to the axis. The intersection of these two rays, (2) and (4), defines the image point, P_i, conjugate to object point, P_o.

the image figure produced by the optical system is undertaken must we go beyond this first-order approach. Then it will also be necessary to consider diffraction effects which can only be described in terms of wave optics. We shall see that a more satisfactory approach will be to describe the effects of aberrations in terms of the wave picture as well.

The first-order Gaussian imaging properties of a simple or complex axially symmetric system can be very conveniently described by the *cardinal points* of the system. Image formation using the *cardinal points* (*focal points* and *principal points*) is illustrated in Fig. 2, and a description of the parallel-ray method is given in the caption.

C. Electron Lenses

The first-order geometrical imaging of electrons by electron lenses is determined by the cardinal points of the electron lenses in just the same way as for light lenses. Once the focal points and principal planes of a given electron lens or a system of lenses are known, the imaging by the system can be determined in the paraxial ray approximation. The trajectory of the free electron can be taken as the analog of the ray in light optics. To determine the cardinal points of an electron lens, the trajectory of an electron incident on the lens parallel to the axis in object space must be followed through the lens. The manner in which electric and magnetic fields refract electrons must be established. Light rays are treated as refracting discontinuously at the boundary between media of different indices of refraction. Electric and magnetic fields will act on electrons over finite distances, and in determining the path of the electron ray or trajectory this fact will play an important role. As already pointed out, the elegance of the "Hamiltonian analogy" is that it describes the path of rays through media of continuously varying refractive index. While electron optical systems provide the only general case for such a treatment, the mathematical methods needed are advanced and the physical model is difficult to follow on an elementary level. Once the fundamental analogy between light and electron optics has been established, it is much clearer and simpler to describe the trajectory of an electron through the electric or magnetic fields of an electron lens in terms of the dynamics of a charged particle in an electric or magnetic field. Then we need only the elementary equations describing the force on a charged particle moving through an electric or magnetic field to obtain the trajectory of given electrons through the lens. The electron which is incident on the lens parallel to the axis in object space then defines the ray that gives the image focal point and principal plane. As in light optics, the first-order imaging, or Gaussian image, is obtained by making the approximations which are valid for the paraxial rays.

1. Electrostatic Lenses

In electrostatic fields the electron is acted upon by a force directly proportional to the field and dependent on the direction of the field. In practice it is convenient to describe the electrostatic field in terms of a potential distribution. The force on an electron is then perpendicular to equipotential surfaces, and the velocity to which an electron has been accelerated is given by a function of the potential. By convention, zero potential is taken as the potential at which the electron has zero velocity.[1] Thus

$$v = \sqrt{2eV/m} \tag{3}$$

where v is the velocity, V the potential, e the charge of the electron, and m the mass of the electron.

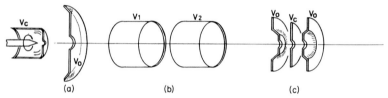

FIG. 3. Electrostatic lenses produced by axially symmetrical configurations of electrodes: (a), electron gun; (b), two-cylinder lens; (c), unipotential lens.

Since the electrodes of the lenses must be equipotential surfaces, they can be conveniently shaped to produce axially symmetric field distributions and thus give first-order imaging. Three systems of electrodes used to produce different types of electrostatic lenses are shown schematically in Figs. 3a–c.

---

[1] The force on the electron is given by: $\mathbf{F} = -e\mathbf{E}$. The field $\mathbf{E}$ is described by

$$\mathbf{E} = -\text{grad } V = -\left(\frac{\partial V}{\partial x} + \frac{\partial V}{\partial y} + \frac{\partial V}{\partial z} \right)$$

Then $d(mv)/dt = e \text{ grad } V$. In one dimension $\mathbf{E}_x = -[(dV/dx)]$, and integrating for the nonrelativistic case

$$m \int_{v_1}^{v_2} v_x \, dv = e \int_{V_0}^{V_a} dV$$

$$\tfrac{1}{2} m(v_2^2 - v_1^2) = e(V_a - V_0)$$

Since by convention, $V_0 = 0$ when $v_1 = 0$

$$v = \sqrt{\frac{2eV}{m}}$$

The electrodes themselves have axial symmetry about the optic axis. Figure 3a is an example of the arrangement used in electron guns to produce an electron beam of small effective source diameter and low angular divergence, giving illumination of the extremely high brightness required for critical electron microscopy. The two-cylinder lens of Fig. 3b is not used in high-resolution electron optics, but may be found in such electron optical devices as the cathode-ray tubes used in television application and image intensifiers. The few electron microscopes which do use electrostatic lenses in their imaging systems use unipotential lenses such as illustrated in Fig. 3c. A high-quality lens can be produced, but limitations are set by the maximum field strengths which can be obtained between electrodes before breakdown and the restriction imposed of keeping the physical object or specimen out of the region of high fields. The best designs of unipotential electrostatic lenses have spherical aberration coefficients which would give an ultimate resolving power of an electron microscope at least a factor of two times poorer than the best magnetic lens (2, 14).

2. MAGNETIC LENSES

The critical lenses of the electron microscopes in general use today are magnetic lenses. Electron-ray tracing using simple dynamics to determine the trajectory of the electron in a field is not complicated for electrostatic fields where, as we have seen, the force on the electron is proportional to the charge times the magnitude of the field and is in the direction of the gradient of the field. But the motion of an electron in a magnetic field is more complicated because the direction of the force on the electron is perpendicular to both the velocity of the electron and the field, and the magnitude of the force is proportional to the velocity and the sine of the angle between the velocity and the field. In vector notation:

$$\mathbf{F} = -e\mathbf{v} \times \mathbf{H} \qquad (4)$$

where e is the charge on the electron taken as negative, $\mathbf{v}$ is the velocity vector, and $\mathbf{H}$ is the vector representing magnetic field intensity. Field intensity $\mathbf{H}$ may be used instead of $\mathbf{B}$, the magnetic flux, since $\mathbf{B} = \mu\mathbf{H}$, and μ, the permeability, is unity in free space, the only condition of interest in the electron motion in lenses. The vector product is represented by $\mathbf{v} \times \mathbf{H}$, and the force must be perpendicular to the plane made by the two vectors. The magnitude of the force is

$$|F| = evH \sin\theta \qquad (5)$$

where θ is the angle between the vectors $\mathbf{v}$ and $\mathbf{H}$, and v and H are their respective magnitudes.

Describing the motion of electrons in the axially symmetric fields which form the magnetic lenses is thus complicated by the directional dependence of the force on the electron moving in a magnetic field. Practically, the problem is not too difficult to treat because it is possible to describe the imaging of a magnetic lens as though it were an equivalent electrostatic lens which produces the same image except for a rotation of the image as a whole. When this separation of effects is made the analytical treatment is, in fact, somewhat simpler for the magnetic lens than the electrostatic lens.

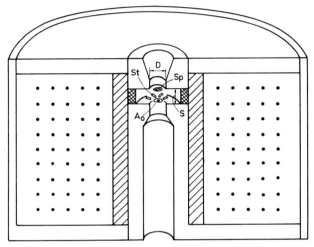

Fig. 4. Magnetic objective lens. Cross-section schematic shows location of yoke and windings which produce magnetic field in pole-piece gap, S, and bore of diameter, D. The relative locations of specimen, Sp, stigmator electrodes, St, and objective aperture, A_o are indicated.

A physical description of the trajectory of the electron through a typical magnetic lens will be helpful in understanding how this separation of effects can be made. A cutaway drawing showing the construction of the essential magnetic components of a typical objective lens is given in Fig. 4. All of the structures associated with apertures, specimen stage, etc., which usually make this component of the electron microscope a complicated piece of engineering have been omitted. The cross-section of the gap between the pole piece is shown on an enlarged scale in Fig. 5, where the dashed lines represent the magnetic field intensity $\mathbf{H}$. The field is, of course, axially symmetric about the z axis. At any point the field $\mathbf{H}$ may be represented by its two vectorial components H_z and H_r. An electron entering the field from the left and parallel to the axis, will be parallel to H_z and no force will act upon it from this component of the field. However, the velocity vector of the electron is perpendicular to the H_r component of the field and a force on the electron will act to move it out from the plane of the paper. This force will accelerate the electron in a direction perpendicular to z and now the electron will have a component of velocity v_θ, about the axis, which will interact with the field component H_z. The force produced by this interaction will deflect the electron toward the axis. The actual motion of the electron entering parallel to the axis will be a rotation about the axis and a deflection toward the axis as it proceeds through the lens field. This motion can

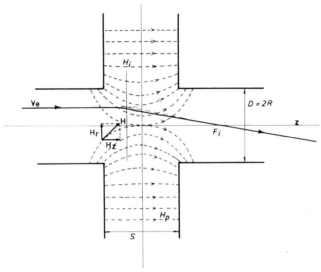

FIG. 5. Magnetic lens schematic showing pole-piece configuration with bore of diameter, D, and gap, S.

be separated into two components, the deflection toward the axis and the rotation about the axis. The deflection toward the axis is the radial trajectory of the electron and will give the information necessary to describe the imaging of the lens. The rotation will represent only a rotation of the whole image and can be treated separately. The representation of the radial trajectory can be simplified by imagining the electron to be rotated back onto the plane of the paper. The trajectory shown in Fig. 5 gives all the necessary information for locating the cardinal points of this lens. The image focal point F_i and the principal plane H_i are obtained by tracing the radial trajectory of an electron entering the lens parallel to the axis in object space. The point at which the electron crosses the axis is the image focal point and the projection back to the intersection of this ray with the entering parallel ray locates the image principal plane. Since the lens must be symmetrical, the object focal point and principal planes are also determined.

This separation of the radial trajectory and the rotational motion can be expressed analytically by deriving two separate equations, one for the radial parameter, r in terms of z, the distance along the axis, the other equation for θ as a function of z. By introducing the paraxial ray approximation, only terms in the first or lower powers of r and (dr/dz) are retained, the radial equation for an axially symmetric magnetic field in a region of constant electric potential V_r, reduces to:

$$d^2r/dz^2 = -\left(\frac{e}{8mc^2V_r}\right)[H(z)]^2r \tag{6}$$

where $H(z)$ is the magnetic field intensity on the axis, V_r is the value of the potential to which the electrons have been accelerated, and c is the velocity of light required when e is given in esu and H in emu.

The equation which describes the rotation of the whole image is

$$d\theta/dz = \sqrt{\frac{e}{8mc^2V_r}}\,H(z) \tag{7}$$

or

$$\theta - \theta_0 = \sqrt{\frac{e}{8mc^2V_r}}\int_{z_1}^{z_2} H(z)dz \tag{8}$$

Thus the rotation of the image can be treated independently of the refracting properties of the lens system. The fact that the image is rotated as a whole by the magnetic lens is important in practical observations with an electron optical system, for example, in alignment procedures set up for adjusting the electron microscope or in determining the axis of tilt in taking stereomicrographs. But for a determination of the optical parameters of the lens, the focal points, principal planes, magnification of the system, etc., only the radial separation of the electron trajectory need be considered.

To solve Eq. (6) and obtain from the solution the parameters which will give the values of focal length and the location of the focal points and principal planes requires that the magnetic field on the axis, $H(z)$, be known. The axial fields produced by the arrangement of pole pieces used in the conventional magnetic lenses have been measured and when plotted have a characteristic shape described as "bell-shaped." A typical plot of $H(z)$ as a function of z is given in Fig. 6.

Zero on the abscissa is taken as the midpoint between the pole pieces which must have equal bore diameters to give this symmetrical distribution about the midpoint. Measuring the field intensity on the axis, a maximum value H_o is found at the midpoint between the pole pieces. Defining a parameter a, the distance from the midpoint at which the field has dropped to one-half maximum, an analytical expression which closely describes the actual fields which have been measured is

$$H(z) = \frac{H_o}{1 + (z^2/a^2)} \qquad (9)$$

With this function, Eq. (6) can be integrated and the desired solutions obtained which will describe the optical behavior of a magnetic lens.

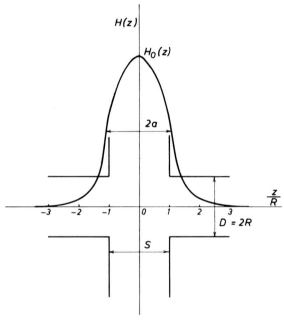

FIG. 6. Axial magnetic field distribution, $H(z)$, in pole piece of bore diameter, D, and gap, S. $S/D = 1$. [Liebmann and Grad (37).]

Glaser (11, 13) carried out in great detail the description of magnetic lens behavior based on the solution of the paraxial ray equation using the bell-shaped field approximation of Eq. (9), calculating not only the first-order behavior, but the third-order aberrations of the magnetic lens. These calculations are extremely helpful in describing the behavior of the magnetic lens in general, but for any particular lens require an actual experimental determination of H_o and a for the particular pole-piece geometry.

A very valuable contribution to practical electron optical design of magnetic lenses was made by Liebmann and Grad (37). In later publications (34–36) Liebmann extends the analysis to universal curves and evaluation of optimum conditions for certain types of application. An analog method was used for measuring $H(z)$ in terms of the actual physical dimensions of the pole pieces in magnetic lenses. The basic configuration of the pole pieces at the gap and the physical parameters are represented in the cross-sectional schematic in Fig. 4. At this gap the refraction of the electrons takes place and hence this configuration can be taken as the schematic of the magnetic electron lens. From the published data of Liebmann and Grad (37) the performance of any given lens can be determined if the pole piece bore diameter ($D = 2R$) and gap S are known. Given these physical dimensions, the performance of the lens is determined for any given field excitation H_p and accelerating potential V_r. The parameter H_p is the magnetic field intensity that would be produced across the gap in the pole pieces if there were no axial bore. This field is produced by a current I in the lens coil of N turns, and is given by

$$H_p = \frac{4\pi NI}{10S} \tag{10}$$

I in amperes and S in centimeters gives H_p in oresteds. This is actually the field intensity which does exist between the pole pieces far from the region of the bore as shown in Fig. 4. Actually only the axial magnetic intensity maximum H_o (at the midpoint for the symmetrical system) must be known to obtain the first-order parameters for a pole piece with a given S/D.

An excitation parameter K^2 is defined

$$K^2 = 0.022\, H_o^2 (R^2/V_r) \tag{11}$$

The parameter, V_r is the potential to which the electrons have been accelerated, corrected for relativistic effects by the relation $V_r = V_o (1 + 10^{-6} V_o)$, where V_o is the measured voltage. A given lens will have a fixed-bore diameter $D = 2R$ and gap S, setting the shape of the field and thus, H_o/H_p is given for a given S/D. By varying I in the lens coil, various values of K^2 can be obtained. From curves plotted by Liebmann and Grad (37) the performance of any given lens can be determined.

Typical radial trajectories in two magnetic lenses of different excitations are plotted in Figs. 7a and b. Both lenses have the same value of D and S, but different excitation currents giving different field intensities. The distribution of field intensity along the axis $H(z)$ is plotted for each case, indicating a lower excitation or K^2 for the case in Fig. 7a. The electron trajectories actually rotate about the axis, and the radial trajectories plotted in Figs. 7a and b are the projections of the radial displacements of the electron rotated back through the angle $\theta(z)$ as the electrons pass through the magnetic field of the lens. In the case of the trajectory in the weaker lens plotted in Fig. 7a, the image focal point is given at F_i, and the image principal plane, H_i, is located by the projection of the emergent refracted ray, r_i, back to its intersection with the incident ray, r_o, at point P_i. Since the lens is symmetrical about the midpoint of the gap ($z = 0$), the object focal point and principal planes

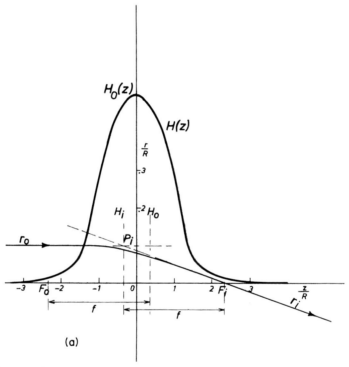

(a)

<figure>Fig. 7a. Radial trajectory of electron through weak lens with low excitation, $K^2 = 0.3$, $S/D = 1$. [Liebmann and Grad (37).]</figure>

can be immediately located without tracing through the trajectory of a ray entering parallel to the axis from the right.

Characteristics of all axially symmetric magnetic lenses in which there is no electric field are illustrated in this example: (a) The value of the focal lengths are positive, and therefore the lens is always a convergent lens; (b) the image and object focal lengths are equal; and (c) the principal planes are crossed.

If the lens is made strongly refracting as in Fig. 7b, account has to be made for the fact that the electron trajectory of a ray entering parallel to the axis crosses the axis while it is still in the magnetic field and thus is refracted after the point usually designating the focal point. The location of the focal points and principal planes of this lens will depend on how the lens is to be used. If the lens is used as a projector

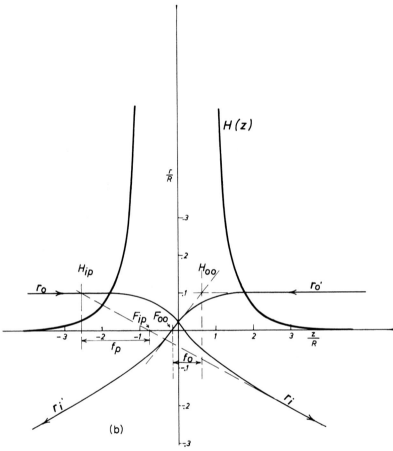

FIG. 7b. Radial trajectories of electrons through strong lens with high excitation, $K^2 = 2$, $S/D = 1$. If lens is used as a projector the image focal point, F_{ip}, and principal plane, H_{ip}, are located from ray trajectory r_o. If lens is used as objective the object focal point, F_{oo}, and principal plane, H_{oo}, are located as indicated from ray, r_o'. [Liebmann and Grad (37).]

lens so the object imaged is an electron image formed by preceding lenses, the whole field of the lens is acting in the imaging process, and the image focal point and image principal plane are those designated as F_{ip} and H_{ip} with a focal length f_p in Fig. 7b. These cardinal points are located by taking the emergent ray in image space, r_i, after it is out of

the field so it is now traveling in a straight line and projecting this
ray back into the lens field. The point at which this ray intersects the
axis locates the image focal point, F_{ip}, and the intersection with the
incident ray, r_o, locates a point on the image principal plane. Thus the
focal length of a given magnetic projection lens will decrease as the
excitation current is increased until it reaches a minimum value, and
then the focal length will increase again with increasing lens excitation,
reaching a focal length $f \rightarrow -\infty$ at the excitation at which the ray

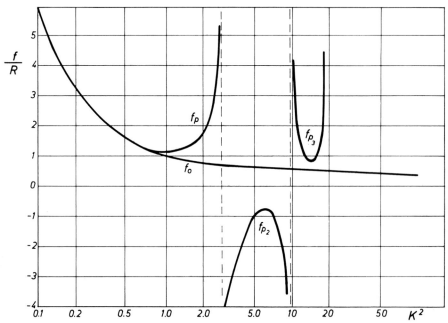

FIG. 8. Graph of focal lengths for projector, f_p, and objective, f_o, as function of
lens excitation $K^2 = 0.022\ H_o^2\,R^2/V_r$. $S/D = 1$. [Liebmann and Grad (37).]

emerges parallel to the axis in image space, but on the opposite side
of the axis as the incident ray. This behavior is shown in the plot of
f_p/R versus K^2 in Fig. 8 taken from the published data of Liebmann
and Grad (37). Increasing the excitation still further will cause the
electron trajectory to cross the axis a second time, giving a resultant focal
length of large negative value which then also goes through a minimum
with increasing excitation. In practice, magnetic lenses are not used with
such high excitations.

  If the lens is used as an objective lens of an electron microscope, a
real object is placed in the optical system. Since the image is to be
formed at a large distance from the lens at high magnification (in prac-

tice $m_o \simeq 100 \times$), the object must be located very close to the object focal point of the lens, approaching the condition of the image being produced at infinity which obtains when the object is located at the object focal point. When the lens has high excitation as in Fig. 7b, the focal point is located inside the magnetic field, so that setting the object inside the field effectively cuts off the section of the field before the object. Thus, only the field after the object is used to refract the electrons from the object. To obtain the cardinal points in object space, an electron entering the lens from the right parallel to the axis is chosen.[2] The effective focal point is now at the point on the axis at which the electron trajectory actually crosses the axis, F_{oo}. The object principal plane, H_{oo}, is located by taking the intersection of the tangent to the trajectory at that point, $(dr/dz)_{r=0}$, and the extension of the parallel ray in image space, r'_o. The focal length for this lens as an objective lens thus becomes f_o. In effect, that part of the field before the object only affects the illumination of the object. Thus, the object focal length continues to decrease with increasing lens current, as shown by the f_o line in the plot in Fig. 8.

D. The Microscope

The description of electron lenses in terms of their cardinal points as developed in Section C, provides the basis for formulating the paraxial ray imaging of combinations of these lenses which characterize complex optical systems. The analogies of geometrical optics carry over to the description of optical instruments. Practical familiarity with the light microscope provides a convenient basis for describing the electron microscope, for here we have similar arrangements of lenses in each instrument and analogous functions of the several components. A brief description of the light microscope will be given first to provide the basic analogies and comparisons to the electron microscope.

1. LIGHT MICROSCOPE

The basic schematic of the light microscope is illustrated in Fig. 9. The optics of the light microscope consist primarily of two lens systems (L_o and L_e in Fig. 9), which give two stages of magnification of a real object (S_p). The illumination is usually provided by an incandescent source (S_c) with a single lens (L_l) and controlled by a lens system (L_c).

---

[2] A condition in geometrical optics is that the ray paths are reversible. While in magnetic lenses the rotation about the axis will be in the opposite direction for electrons entering from opposite sides of the lens, the projections of the radial trajectories will be the same.

The optical function of each component is shown in the ray schematic
on the right of Fig. 9.

The illuminating system must provide illumination over a small
area but into a large angular aperture, that is, provide a cone of illumination which will fill the angular aperture of the objective lens. This

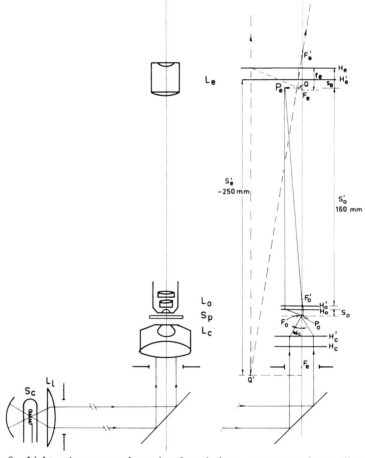

FIG. 9.   Light microscope schematic of optical components and ray diagram.

requirement comes from the factors which determine resolution in the
optical system. Physical wave optics are involved in these considerations,
and at this point of the discussion the criterion of large angular aperture
must be accepted as a requirement to be achieved by proper arrangement
of the geometrical optics.

The incandescent lamp set at the center of curvature of a mirror provides the source of radiation. Using a ribbon filament or extended tight helical coils to give a uniform surface, the mirror reflects back part of the radiation that would be lost. The lens L_l is set with the lamp filament at the focal point of the lens so the rays of the emergent beam are parallel and the image of the source is produced at infinity. The mirror below the microscope condenser reflects this parallel beam on the condenser lens system, which when set at "critical illumination," will have its image principal plane at the focal length distance of the lens system below the specimen. Thus, the image of the source is produced at the object plane of the objective lens, converging at very large angles, a condition desired, when high-dry or oil-immersion objectives are to be used.

The interaction of the light with the specimen is a complicated physical process, but for the present discussion of image formation it will be considered simply as the absorption of light. The selective spectral absorption of radiation in the visible region of the spectrum by different materials and dyes provides one of the most powerful methods of light microscopy for identification of specific constituents of cells, as all biologists know. All points of the object will be illuminated by the image of the source and the effective object will be a variation in the intensity and color of the light as it is transmitted by the specimen.

Following the methods adopted for describing image formation in an optical system, the rays from a given object point are traced by the parallel-ray method (see Fig. 2) to the conjugate image point for the lens system. Referring to the ray diagram schematic on the right of Fig. 9, two rays are traced from object point P_o. The objective lens system which in a highly corrected oil-immersion objective may have as many as eight separate lenses, is represented as a single thick lens system by its two principal planes, H_o and H'_o and two focal points F_o and F'_o. The use of the lenses in the light microscope have been standardized, so that properly adjusted, the objective will produce a real image of the object at 160 mm from its image principal plane. Light lenses are highly corrected for aberrations, and optimum correction for the aberrations involved can only be achieved at one imaging distance. Thus the manufacturers design each lens to be used at a given working distance with a given setting of the draw tube of the microscope. The objective produces an image which is real and inverted, the magnification given by $m = -(160/s_o) \simeq (160/f_o)$, since $s_o \simeq f_o$ for the high magnification employed. For a typical high-dry objective, the focal length is 4 mm and the magnification $m_o = -40 \times$ while an oil-immersion objective of standard focal length $f_o = 1.8$ mm will produce an image which is magnified $-90 \times$.

The second stage of the light microscope is the eyepiece. It usually consists of two lenses set to correct certain aberrations. These two lenses are again treated as a single thick-lens system, and the principal planes and focal lengths are designated in the schematic of Fig. 9. If the microscope is to be used for visual observation, the eye will be another optical system and the lens of the eye will be used to focus the final image on the retina. Under these conditions the eyepiece will be adjusted to produce a virtual image which will be the object for the lens of the eye. Since the eye can accommodate between the "near point" of 250 mm and infinity, the microscope can be focused so the real image produced by the objective lens is formed at s_e either slightly above the object focal point $\{s_e = f_e/[1 + (f_e/250)]\}$ of the eyepiece system or just at the focal point at f_e, giving a virtual image at —250 mm or —∞, respectively.

To obtain a photomicrograph, the eyepiece is either replaced by another lens system set so the image produced by the objective is below the focal point of this lens and the final image is a real image produced on the photographic plate, or the draw table is extended to move the eyepiece into a position at which it will produce a real image.

2. Electron Microscope

The electron microscope is composed of the same set of components as the light microscope: a source of illumination, a condenser system to control the illumination on the specimen, the objective lens as the critical first stage of magnification, and a projector system corresponding to the eyepiece, or more analogous to the lens system used in this stage for photomicrography. The higher resolution available with electron optics does permit higher useful magnification and to achieve this greater magnification an extra stage of magnificaton is now generally introduced in the projector system. Also, to achieve adequate illumination at the high magnifications extra flexibility has been introduced by using a two-stage condenser system.

A schematic of the electron microscope is shown in Fig. 10 illustrating the arrangement of the components. The magnetic lenses have focal lengths of approximately the same values as high-power light objectives and require larger image distances to obtain the high useful magnifications available. The over-all dimensions of the instrument are usually between one and two meters. Most instrument designers have found it convenient to use a vertical column with the components inverted from the order of the conventional light microscope.

Again starting our description with the source of illumination, the electron beam is produced by an electron gun which will be described in more detail in Section III, A, 1. The electron-gun assembly with the anode is analogous to the lamp of light microscopy. The cathode shield and anode function as an electrostatic lens, focusing the electrons from the filament into a beam that is of extremely high brightness. The voltages and geometry of the system give fixed optical parameters. The ray schematic given in Fig. 11 illustrates the case in which an image of the

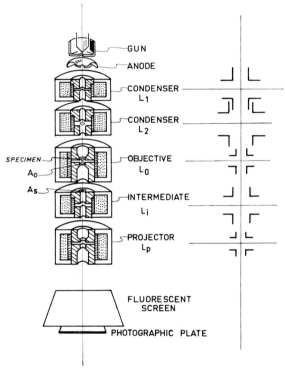

FIG. 10. Electron microscope schematic showing arrangement of optical components. Schematic using pole-piece configuration of each lens shown on right.

source is produced at s_g. The illumination of the specimen is controlled by adjusting the focal length of the condenser lens system. If a double condenser lens is used, as illustrated in Fig. 11, the first lens is used to produce a reduced image of the source and the second lens is adjusted to give proper intensity of illumination. Highest intensity for a given setting of the first lens is obtained when the second lens produces an image of the source at the specimen or object plane. The angular aperture of illumination under these conditions is set by the physical size of the condenser aperture A_{c2}, usually chosen to give an angular aperture of illumination subtending an angle of the order of 10^{-2}–10^{-3} radians.

In practice, the second condenser lens current is set to give a focal length which images the "effective" source either slightly above or below the specimen plane. In Fig. 11 the condition in which the source is above the specimen is shown. The actual specimen area illuminated by

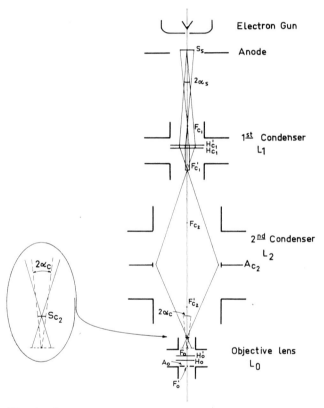

FIG. 11. Illuminating system with two condenser lenses. Schematic ray diagram illustrating reduced image of effective source, S_g, produced above the specimen at S_{c2} giving illumination of angular aperture α_c.

the beam is larger under these conditions and the angular aperture of illumination incident on a point of the object will be smaller.

The imaging by the objective lens, also illustrated in the ray diagram of Fig. 12, is quite analogous to the imaging of the objective lens shown in Fig. 10 for the light microscope. The focal lengths of the two lenses have comparable dimensions, 1–4 mm. While in the light microscope the object must be placed so the image is produced at an axial distance of 16.0 cm from the image principal plane, electron microscopes are designed with no such convention. The object plane of the intermediate lens L_i, in Fig. 13a is usually 10–15 cm below the objective lens. The easy flexibility of focusing the objective lens by varying the current in the coil of the lens makes a range of operating conditions possible. For example, the condition illustrated in Fig. 13b in which the intermediate lens is used at a magnification of less than 1 to provide a convenient method of extending the total magnification of the microscope

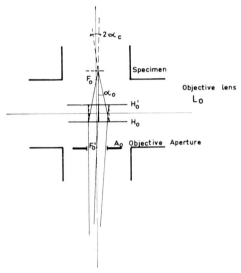

Fig. 12.   Objective lens imaging. Schematic ray diagram showing imaging of object and angular aperture, α_o, defind by objective lens aperture, A_o, located in the plane of the image focal point, F_o'.

to low ranges is a type of operation that has no useful analogy in practical light microscopy. This mode of operation will be discussed later.

A very important difference in the two instruments is the much smaller angular aperture used in the electron microscope objective than the one in the light microscope objective. Ultimate resolution is obtained with light lens objectives by using apertures subtending angles as large as 70–80°. These lenses are highly corrected for spherical and chromatic aberration. Electron lenses used today cannot be corrected for spherical aberration and only very small angular apertures can be used. As we shall see, the optimum angular apertures for electron microscope objectives subtend angles from 5×10^{-3} to 1×10^{-2} radians depending on the spherical aberration coefficient of the given lens. Most electron microscope work is done today with a physical aperture stop (A_o, Fig. 12) placed in the image focal plane of the objective lens. While the actual size of the aperture is often too large to act as a true aperture stop for the lens, contrast is enhanced with this aperture by reducing the background in the image.

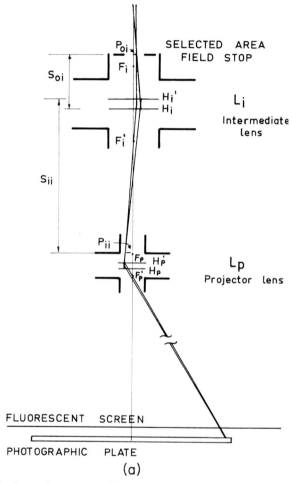

FIG. 13a. Projector lens system; high magnification. Schematic ray diagram showing intermediate lens, L_i, giving $|m_i| > 1$.

The intermediate lens (L_i, Figs. 10 and 13) is part of the projector system producing an electron image P_{ii} in the object plane of the projector lens, L_p. If the intermediate lens is used to increase the total magnification of the electron microscope, the focal lengths of the lenses are adjusted in the manner illustrated in Fig. 13a. The lens current in the intermediate lens coil is set so that a real image produced by the objective lens at P_{oi} is imaged at P_{ii}. The plane at s_{oi} provides a convenient position for a field stop in the optical system. An adjustable aperture in this position will define different areas of the specimen imaged by the total optical system.

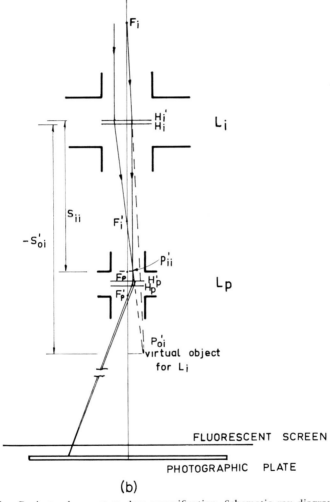

(b)

FIG. 13b. Projector lens system, low magnification. Schematic ray diagram showing intermediate lens, L_i, giving $|m_i| < 1$.

Extending the total magnification below the product of magnifications given by the objective and projector lenses alone is obtained by the mode of operation illustrated in Fig. 13b. For this operation a slight increase in the focal length of the objective lens (weaker lens) will produce the image formed by the objective lens below the intermediate lens at P'_{oi}. This image becomes a virtual object for the intermediate lens which can now be set to image the incident rays at P'_{ii}, the object plane for the projector lens. Since the image distance, s_{ii}, will be less than the virtual object distance $-s'_{oi}$, the magnification will have an absolute magnitude of less than one, giving a reduced magnification for the total optical system.

The imaging of the projector lens is also illustrated in Fig. 13. The lens is operated as a short focal length lens. Since the object for this lens is the electron image produced by the intermediate lens, the whole field of the lens is used and the effective focal length goes through a minimum as described in Section I, C, 2 (see Figs. 7b and 8). It is convenient to operate this lens at the minimum focal length where the maximum magnification is obtained. Characteristic of the imaging in the projector system are the extremely small angular apertures of the pencil of rays defining each image point. The maximum angular apertures used in the objective lens are about 1×10^{-2} radians. With each stage of magnification the aperture of the pencil is reduced by the factor $1/m$, so the image points which produce the object for the intermediate lens have angular divergences of $\sim 1 \times 10^{-4}$ radians. At the object plane of the projector lens the divergence of the pencils may be reduced by another factor of 5–$10 \times$ if the intermediate lens is operated to give increased magnification. Finally the image produced by the projector lens on the photographic plate and fluorescent screen have pencils of rays diverging only by an order of 10^{-5} to 10^{-7} radians. Under these circumstances the depth of focus of the optical system is tremendous. The fluorescent screen and photographic plate can be set at any convenient position below the projector lens and a sharp image will be obtained if the focal length of the objective lens is set properly for the object position of the specimen.

Another consequence of these extremely narrow imaging pencils giving the large depth of focus in the projector system is that the focal length of the projector lens can be changed over a considerable range, effecting only the final magnification but not the sharpness of the image. Switching the intermediate lens from strong-lens operation (Fig. 13a) to weak-lens operation (Fig. 13b) usually requires some adjustment of the focal length of the objective.

Visual observation of the final electron image is obtained with a fluorescent screen and a record is produced on a photographic plate. Both of these transducers are described and evaluated in Section III,F. Visual observation on the fluorescent screens must be made at low brightness levels where visual acuity is low. Considerable enhancement of the ease of observation and the detail which can be resolved is achieved by using a light optical magnifier of about $10 \times$ which can present to the entrance pupil of the eye an enlarged image but of equivalent brightness to that available to the eye by direct observation. Photographic records can be viewed under high light intensity, and fine detail and subtle variations in density in the image can be observed which cannot be observed on the fluorescent screen.

II. Image Formation and Contrast

A. Wave Optics

When the details of the actual image formed by an optical system, whether light or electron optical, are examined, the limitations in the description provided by Gaussian geometrical optics become apparent. There are two categories of limitations to be considered: one introduced by the approximations which have been made for the paraxial ray case, and the other by the fact that light and electrons do not behave strictly as particles traveling on trajectories which can be represented by lines which do not interact with each other.

Treatment of the imaging of rays inclined to the axis at angles which would make the paraxial ray approximation no longer valid, can be considered in terms which are still geometrical in character. In practice, these are the effects already described in Section I,B as geometrical aberrations and are divided into different effects depending upon the way in which a given optical system is to be used. An additional effect which can still be treated in terms of geometrical optics deviating from the perfect image given by the paraxial ray approximation, is the chromatic aberration inherent in any optical system. In electron optics the chromatic effects will be associated with a variation in the potential (voltage V_r) to which the electrons are accelerated and the stability of the current, I, in the lens coils producing the refracting magnetic fields.

In the second category where the approximation of electron trajectories as individual rays is no longer valid, the electron imaging can only be described in terms of waves. For electrons, also, are found to exhibit the same interference and diffraction phenomena as light when the images formed in any optical system are investigated in detail. The dual nature of light was established after first being postulated by Einstein in 1905 and then confirmed experimentally by observation on the photoelectric effect. The dual nature of material particles, such as electrons, was first suggested by de Broglie in 1924 (7a) and has since become the foundation of the whole quantum mechanical description of nature.

According to de Broglie, a particle of mass, m, traveling with a velocity, v, has a wavelength associated with it that can be expressed by

$$\lambda = h/mv \tag{12}$$

The momentum (mv) must be relativistically invariant and thus the mass, m, depends on the velocity, v. However, for the electron energies of interest in the electron optics of the conventional electron microscopes (50–100 kv) only a small correction need be made. The constant, h, is Planck's constant. An electron accelerated by an electric field to a potential V has been shown to have a velocity (see Section I,C) $v = (2eV/m)^{1/2}$.

Thus

$$\lambda = \sqrt{\frac{h^2}{2emV}} \simeq \sqrt{\frac{150}{V_r}} \tag{13}$$

in angstroms if V_r is in volts. Again, $V_r = V_o (1 + 10^{-6} V_o)$ is introduced to correct for the relativistic change in the mass, $m = m_o/[1 - (v^2/c^2)]$. This approximation is adequate for the range of energies used in conventional electron microscopy.

Contemporary quantum mechanics stems from this concept, and analysis of phenomenon on the atomic scale can only be developed completely in terms of quantum mechanical theory. But as is the character of all valid theories of nature developed to explain hitherto unexplained observations, they must contain within them the explanations of all established observable facts which have been explained by previous theories. The older theories are then shown to be only more limited descriptions or approximations of the observed facts. Wave optics must contain within it the observations described by geometrical ray optics and quantum mechanics must contain explanations of classic wave optical phenomena. Within certain limits of observations each of the older theories provides satisfactory working descriptions of the physical properties under investigation.

Geometrical optics can be shown to be a limiting case of wave optics when the wavelength $\lambda \to 0$. Since the value of λ is always finite, in practice geometrical optics becomes a satisfactory working description if observations are made on a scale which is large relative to the wavelength associated with the radiation. If a pencil of rays falls on a screen with a small aperture, the radiation behind the screen will, in first approximation, appear to be sharply bounded by a shadow defined by the geometrical extension of the rays. However, on closer examination the boundary edge will be found to vary in a continuous and oscillatory manner from maximum to minimum intensity. The period of these oscillations are of the order of the wavelength of the radiation. If the effective wavelength of the radiations is very small compared to the dimensions defining the boundaries observed, geometrical optics is a simple and satisfactory method for describing the physical phenomena under investigation.

When it becomes necessary to describe phenomena in the shadow edge, as we must when the resolution of the optical system is under consideration, the wave optical description of nature must be employed. Again, it will be necessary to establish the limits of validity which the approximate wave optical method to be used represents in terms of quantum mechanics. When we are dealing with the refraction of the radiation by the electric and magnetic fields of the electron lenses where the effective aperture stops have parameters large compared to atomic dimensions, the wave optical theory provides an adequate method of description of the phenomena observed. As we shall see, it is satisfactory to apply certain well-established classic approximate methods in the treatment of the diffraction phenomena involved. Only when we are concerned with the interaction of the electron radiation with the atomic lattice of the specimen material must we utilize the more complicated and complete description of the phenomena given by quantum mechanics.

1. RELATION BETWEEN GEOMETRICAL OPTICS AND WAVE OPTICS

The relationship that the ray of geometrical optics has to the propagation of the waves in wave optics or electromagnetic theory is important to an understanding of the methods of both descriptions. Such an analysis is also very useful, for in our discussion the concept of the ray of geometrical optics will still be useful in describing the behavior of wave optical phenomena. In the wave optical description, radiation is conceived as propagated by transverse electromagnetic waves. These may be considered the oscillating electric and magnetic fields described completely by Maxwell's equations. For the purpose of describing the optical systems in which we are interested it is convenient to describe the wave propagated through the system very simply in terms of the sine wave variation of the amplitude of the electric field associated with the propagating electromagnetic wave. This sine wave is characterized by its wavelength, phase, and amplitude (see Fig. 14).

Huygen's construction is very useful in providing a description of the passage of a wave through an optical system. A wave front can be defined for a group of waves being propagated through space, as the surface over which all the waves are in phase. Huygen's construction considers

BENJAMIN M. SIEGEL

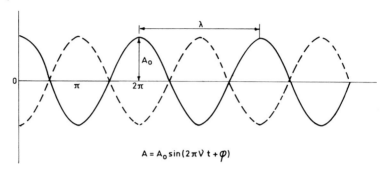

$$A = A_o \sin(2\pi \nu t + \varphi)$$

Fig. 14. Sine wave representation. The wave is described by its wavelength, λ; amplitude maximum, A_o; and phase, ϕ. The amplitude, A, will vary with time, t, as $A = A_o \sin (2\pi\nu t + \phi)$. The frequency, ν, for light is equal to c/λ where c is the velocity of light. The phase, ϕ, of the solid sine wave is $\pi/2$ while the phase of the dashed sine wave is $-\pi/2$. The amplitudes add algebraically so the superposition of the two waves illustrated here would give zero amplitude and an intensity $I = A^2 = 0$.

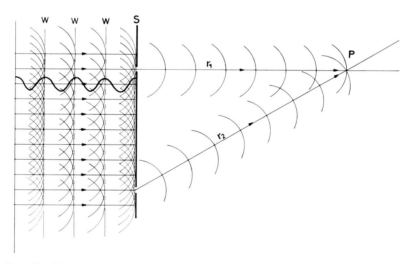

Fig. 15. Wave phenomena represented by Huygens' construction. A plane wave propagated from the left is represented by the dashed lines, W, indicating the wave fronts. The rays of geometrical optics are the arrowed lines perpendicular to the wave fronts. A sine wave is superimposed on a ray to indicate that the wave fronts are separated by one wavelength. The interference phenomena produced by two slits in an opaque screen is shown on the right. At the screen, S, two slits would be sources of spherical waves. The distance r_2 from the lower slit to point P is one full wavelength greater than the distance r_1, so at point P the amplitudes of the two waves add to give an intensity, $I = 4A^2$. A point at which the distances from the slits differ by $\lambda/2$ would cause cancellation of the waves and give an intensity of zero.

every point of a wave front to be a center of a secondary disturbance which gives rise to spherical wavelets, and the wave front at any later instance may be regarded as the envelopes of these wavelets (see Fig. 15). The rays of geometrical optics are lines perpendicular to a set of wave fronts representing the propagation of the waves through the optical system. If the rays are parallel to each other, the wave fronts must be parallel and describe a plane wave. If the rays all pass through a single point, the wave fronts must be spherical surfaces. Thus, through Huygen's construction the rays of geometrical optics are related to the propagation of waves through optical systems. Even when diffraction phenomena are to be considered it will often be helpful and convenient to trace optical paths by the rays that are perpendicular to the wave fronts.

2. DIFFRACTION

The physical phenomenon which sets limitations on the resolving power of optical systems is the same diffraction which produces the oscillatory character in the shadow edge. For our discussion of this phenomenon in electron optical systems it is only necessary to point out the approximations in this well-developed subject in the field of physical light optics which are adequate for the treatment of electron optics. The first extension of Huygen's construction to account for diffraction phenomena was due to Fresnel who introduced a supplementary postulate that the secondary wavelets which arise at each point on the wave front mutually interfere. Kirchoff put the Huygen-Fresnel theory on a sounder mathematical basis and showed that in many cases diffraction phenomena can be described by the formulation of Fresnel but with the addition of an explicit formula for an inclination factor which was undetermined in Fresnel's theory. The approximate diffraction theory of Kirchoff is adequate for application to electron optical systems and provides a method for describing the optical behavior of the electron microscope.

A brief resumé of the method of application of the Kirchoff approximation to imaging in an optical system, light or electron, will be given to illustrate the method. The result to be obtained is the diffraction effects in the optical image. To obtain this image diffraction figure, the transmission between the image point and each element of the wave front emerging from the object is calculated, by the rules of geometrical optics, summing the complex amplitudes and taking into account the inclination factors. Of course, to obtain the wave front emergent from the object, first the wave front from source to object must be constructed measuring equal optical-path lengths along the rays, again by rules of geometrical optics, and then the passage of the wave front through the object. In the case of an object which is an opaque screen, the free part of the wave front is considered as undisturbed in phase and amplitude and the rest as cut off. In the case of a partially transmitting object, which is characteristic of the specimens that are useful objects for electron microscopy, the rays are traced through the changes in phase and intensity introduced as determined by the complex refractive index. This approximate method neglects any diffraction effects in the object, a condition which generally holds for the very thin objects observed with the electron microscope. However, in the observation of crystalline material, dynamic interaction may be involved (see Chapter 5), and this simplified treatment will no longer give the correct wave front emerging from the object into the refracting system.

Actually in any detailed treatment of image contrast as related to the interaction of the electrons with the specimen it is necessary to discuss in detail the electron scattering from the material in the specimen. Relating the interaction to a refractive index of the object will be useful only for extended objects and may not be the most satisfactory method for electron optical imaging.

a. Fraunhofer Diffraction. The step in the previously mentioned procedure in which the figure of the image point is obtained by calculating each element of the wave front emergent from the object and transmitted to the image is ultimately limited by the condition described by Fraunhofer diffraction. This condition means that the limits of resolving power of the electron microscope are set by the Fraunhofer diffraction phenomena which occur in the imaging process of the objective lens. The lens, having axial symmetry, acts as a circular aperture of finite diameter. The image produced has the distribution of intensity which is the same as the diffraction pattern given by a circular aperture illuminated by a plane wave and observed at a distance far from the aperture, the Fraunhofer diffraction condition. A physical description of why Fraunhofer diffraction occurs in the focal plane of a well-corrected lens is illustrated in Fig. 16. Radiation from an infinitely distant point will produce a plane wave incident on an aperture which can be represented by the rays from the left in Fig. 16a. These are the orthogonal trajectories to the wave fronts. Now in Huygen's construction each element of the wave front is the center of a secondary disturbance which gives rise to spherical wavelets. If we construct the waves arising from each point of the aperture, the effect then observed at a very distant point, P, in a given direction can be regarded as that from the superposition of plane waves arising at the aperture and propagated in that direction. Such waves are diffracted waves and would have no existence within the approximations of geometrical optics. The corresponding normals to the diffracted waves are the diffracted rays. If a lens is placed behind the aperture, all parallel rays incident on the lens will be refracted to a point in the focal plane of the lens and thus, as in Fig. 16b, all rays diffracted in a given direction will be brought to focus at P'. Since the geometrical path from a wave front of the diffracted pencil to P' is the same for all the rays, one obtains essentially the same interference effect as in Fig. 16a. Under the conditions used in the microscope, the lens itself is the effective aperture.

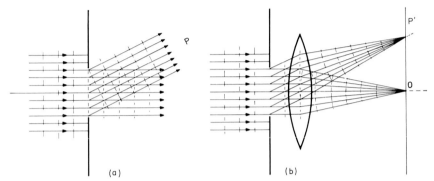

FIG. 16. Fraunhofer diffraction with and without a lens. [After Born and Wolf (5).]

The diffraction figure of interest is thus the Fraunhofer diffraction given by a circular aperture which may be the lens itself. The figure is the well-known Airy pattern. A plot of the intensity distribution in the geometrical image plane (Gaussian) as a function of the radial distance from the center is given in Fig. 17. This figure is a plot of the solution of the diffraction equation which, because of the circular symmetry, gives the intensity in the form

$$I(x) = I_o \left(\frac{2J_1(x)}{x} \right)^2 \tag{14}$$

where x is a function of: (1) the separation distance from the geometrical center of the image; (2) the wavelength of the radiation; and (3) the diameter of the aperture. This relationship is illustrated in Fig. 18 and defined in the caption of the figure. The function $J_1(x)$ is the Bessel function of the order of 1. The pattern consists of a bright disk centered on the geometrical image surrounded by concentric bright and dark rings. The function $\{[2J_1(x)]/x\}^2$ oscillates with diminishing amplitude in a way similar to the more familiar function $(\sin x/x)^2$ but with the minima not strictly equidistant. The secondary maxima are much weaker than the primary central disk and hence only the first minimum is of a real interest. We shall see later how the energy is distributed in the different rings. The first minimum occurs when

$$J_1\left(\frac{2\pi r_a \gamma_i}{\lambda}\right) = 0 \tag{15}$$

which obtains when

$$\frac{2\pi r_a \gamma_i}{\lambda} = 1.22\pi \tag{16}$$

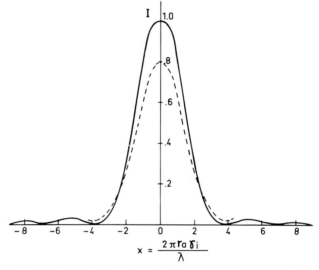

Fig. 17. Fraunhofer diffraction at a circular aperture. Solid line is intensity distribution in Gaussian image plane of perfect lens. Dashed line is approximate intensity distribution produced by lens with spherical aberration of one wavelength, λ, imaged at diffraction focus. For parameters of x see Fig. 18.

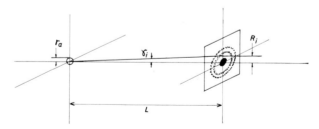

Fig. 18. Parameters defining Fraunhofer diffraction at a circular aperture; r_a is the radius of the diffracting aperture, γ_i is the sine of the angle which the ray makes with the central direction, R_i is the radius in the image figure, L is the effective distance from aperture to image. $\gamma_i \simeq R_i/L$.

Then

$$\gamma_i = \frac{0.61\lambda}{r_a} \tag{17}$$

The fraction of the total incident energy contained within the central disk is of considerable interest for the consideration of the resolution of object in the microscope. This distribution will be found to change when spherical aberration is taken into consideration, and in the final analysis it will be important to consider the optimum distribution that can be obtained with the inherent spherical aberration of the lens is taken into

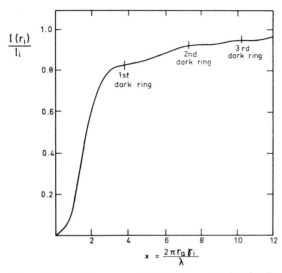

FIG. 19. Fraction of the total energy within given radii in the Fraunhofer-diffraction pattern from a circular aperture. For parameters of x see Fig. 18. [After Born and Wolf (5).]

account. If $I(R_i)/I_i$ is the fraction of the total energy contained within a circle of radius R_i in the Gaussian image plane centered on the geometrical image, a relation due to Rayleigh (43) is obtained

$$\frac{I(R_i)}{I_i} = 1 - J_0^{\ 2}\left(\frac{2\pi r_a\gamma_i}{\lambda}\right) - J_1^{\ 2}\left(\frac{2\pi r_a\gamma_i}{\lambda}\right) \tag{18}$$

where J_0 and J_1 are Bessel functions of the order of 0 and 1. The terms of the argument $(2\pi r_a\gamma_i)/\lambda$ are defined in Fig. 18. This function is plotted in Fig. 19. Since $J_1(x_0) = 0$ at the minimum of each dark ring the fraction of energy outside any dark ring is just $J_0^{\ 2}(x)$ which equals 0.162, 0.090, and 0.062 for each of the first three dark rings. Thus, 83.8% of the energy is within the first ring and 90% within the second.

B. Resolving Power of the Microscope

The resolving power of an optical system such as a microscope can be calculated from the Fraunhofer diffraction figure which characterizes the image of a point object. The requirement is to find the minimum separation of two object points which will be imaged as two diffraction-image figures which can be resolved as separate points.

The actual separation of image figures that can be described as separate depends in the manner of observing the image and, in any case, must always be arbitrary to a certain extent. A useful criterion which

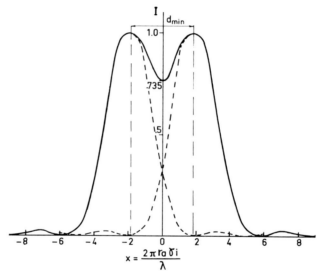

FIG. 20. Intensity distribution defining least resolvable separation of image figures, d_{min}.

allows for a quantitative comparison between different optical systems is the Rayleigh criterion. Two image figures of equal intensity are taken to be resolved when the principal intensity maximum of one coincides with the first intensity minimum of the other. The combined intensity figure of two Airy disks at this separation is plotted in Fig. 20. There is a dip of intensity at the midpoint between the two maxima of some 26.5%. The resolution of the instrument is said to be this minimum distance, d_{min}, between the two points referred to object space. The resolving power of the instrument is then the reciprocal of this distance.

This elementary definition of the resolution of an optical system is based on the assumption that the object points are self-luminous and the radiation from them independent in phase and hence incoherent. In an actual microscope where the object is illuminated with radiation from a source, the situation is more complicated than this simple description allows. In the electron microscope the illuminating beam of electrons, coming from a small effective source and focused by the condenser to give close to axial illumination, can be considered in many cases as an almost plane wave with a certain degree of coherence incident on the object. Some of the wave is transmitted through the object with or without change of phase while the rest is scattered. The particular distribution of matter in the object is an important factor in determining the degree of coherence and contrast given in the beam forming each image point.

The resolution obtained with a given instrument is thus a complicated problem in which the nature of the object plays an important role. The limits of the resolution set by the extreme conditions of self-luminous object points giving incoherent radiation, and perfectly coherent illumination will be discussed to set the limits at which these factors effect resolution.

1. INCOHERENT ILLUMINATION—SELF-LUMINOUS OBJECT

Consider first two self-luminous points P and Q (Fig. 21). The axial point P is imaged on the axis at P'. The ray limited by the aperture of

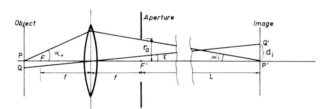

FIG. 21. Parameters defining the resolving power of the microscope.

the system has been taken to represent the imaging of this point, and the angular deviation of this ray from the axis in object and image space is designated by α_o and α_i, respectively. If the radius of the limiting aperture located at the image focal plane is r_a and the image distance is L, then

$$\tan \alpha_i = \frac{r_a}{L} \simeq \alpha_i \qquad (19)$$

The parameter r_a is very small and at high magnification L is large, so $\tan \alpha_i \simeq \alpha_i$. The image of Q at Q' is traced by the central ray which passes through the lens undeviated. The separation, d_i, of the image of P' and Q', will be

$$d_i = (L + f) \tan \gamma \simeq L\gamma \qquad (20)$$

since $f << L$ and $d << L$, so $\tan \gamma \simeq \gamma$.

Taking the Rayleigh criterion that the image figures are to be separated so the maximum of the second falls at the minimum of the first, from Eq. (17)

$$\gamma_i = \frac{0.61\lambda}{r_a}$$

and from Eqs. (19) and (20)

$$d_i = \frac{0.61\lambda L}{r_a} = \frac{0.61\lambda}{\alpha_i} \qquad (21)$$

It is convenient and customary to refer the resolution distance back to the separation in the object plane. For the small angles involved and for lenses in electric field free space (magnetic lenses) the Abbe sine condition reduces to

$$\alpha_i = \frac{\alpha_o}{m_o} \qquad (22)$$

and since

$$d_i = d_o m_o \qquad (23)$$

we have

$$d_o = \frac{0.61\lambda}{\alpha_o} \qquad (24)^3$$

2. COHERENT ILLUMINATION—ABBE THEORY

The factor 0.61 in Eq. (24) is quite arbitrary and follows from the criterion which has been chosen for the least resolvable distance. The same criterion as that taken for incoherent illumination to define the resolvable image figure may also be taken to determine what this factor will be, if we consider an object in which the emergent radiation is completely coherent.

---

[3] This relation may be compared to the equivalent expression for the resolution of the light microscope

$$d_o = \frac{0.61\lambda}{n \sin \alpha} \qquad (25)$$

Here the objective lenses, highly corrected for spherical aberration, utilize large angular apertures, and for the highest resolution immerse the object in a medium of index of refraction, n, greater than 1. Then the denominator, $n \sin \alpha$, referred to as the *numerical aperture* of the system, can have values as large as 1.4–1.5, giving the corresponding decrease in separation that can be observed with the instrument. As we have seen, for the electron microscope objective the uncorrectible spherical aberration sets a very low limit on α and only the extremely short equivalent wavelengths for the electrons make possible the enhanced resolution.

The coherent condition would be realized by a coherent plane-wave incident on an object which according to Abbe may be considered to act as a diffraction grating. The effect of every element of the object on the incident radiation must first be taken into account and then the effect of the finite aperture of the lens to obtain the final image figure. The Abbe construction is illustrated schematically in Fig. 22. The object can be considered to be a diffraction grating on which there is incident a coherent plane wave. This condition would be obtained from a point source at infinity, or a point source focused by a condenser system to give axial illumination. The grating object will diffract the incident

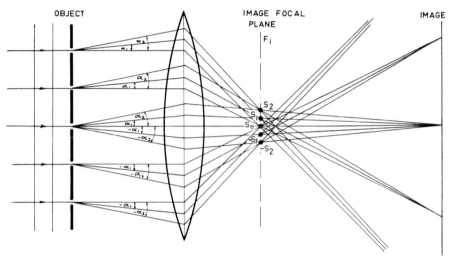

FIG. 22. Abbe construction of image formation in the microscope with coherent illumination.

radiation with maxima of successive orders at the angles . . . , $-\alpha_2$, $-\alpha_1$, 0, α_1, α_2, ... The lens will now refract these rays so that all rays entering at a given angle, α_n, will intersect at a point in the image focal plane, F_i. Thus, in the image focal plane of the lens is the diffraction pattern of the object, each point $-S_2$, $-S_1$, S_0, S_1, S_2 being a center of coherently reconstructed rays scattered from the object at a given angle. The intensity of each point is the square of the summed amplitudes. The rays proceed from the image focal plane to the image plane to be reconstructed as an image of the original object, in this case a diffraction grating. To obtain a completely faithful image, all orders of the spectra must be included in the reconstruction of the image. Since this is never possible with the finite aperture of the optical system, the image will be an approximation of the object even with a perfect lens. The degree of approximation will be determined by the fraction of the total energy included within the aperture of the lens which is used to reconstruct the image. The fact that the diffraction pattern can be considered to be formed in the image focal plane of the objective lens, and that the final image is reconstructed by the recombination of different orders of this diffraction pattern are the bases for selected area diffraction and the lattice-resolution technique.

To obtain a relation for the resolution of two object points in which the radiation from the object is coherent we now refer back to Fig. 21. Assuming that the radiation from P and Q is coherent, the distribution in the image plane arises now from the coherent superposition of two Airy diffraction patterns at P' and Q'. To compare the resolution for this case with the resolution for radiation from two incoherent object points, the separation will be calculated in which the dip of intensity at the midpoint is the same as that for the incoherent case. Now the amplitudes add coherently so at the midpoint R_m, using Eq. (14), the relative intensity is given by:

$$\frac{I\,(R_m)}{I_i} = \left[2 \, \frac{2J_1\left(\dfrac{2\pi r_a \gamma_m}{\lambda}\right)}{\dfrac{2\pi r_a \gamma_m}{\lambda}} \right]^2 \tag{26}$$

The argument of the Bessel function $(2\pi r_a \gamma_m)/\lambda$ contains the same factors as described before, Fig. 18. The parameter γ_m is the sine of the angle that the ray to the midpoint makes with the ray to the central maximum, and thus is a measure of the separation of the midpoint from the maxima for any image distance, L. To obtain an equivalent criterion for the resolution, $I\,(R_m)/I_i$ is set equal 0.735 which is the same relative intensity at the midpoint as in the image from two incoherent objects. The first root of this equation gives $\gamma_m \simeq 2.41\lambda/2\pi r_a$. Then, referring to Fig. 21, the separation of P' and Q' in the image is given by twice the distance from maximum to midpoint of the figure; and as in Eq. (21) with the small angles involved we have to a good approximation:

$$d_i = 2\gamma_m L \simeq \frac{2.41}{\pi}\,\frac{\lambda L}{r_a} \simeq \frac{0.77\lambda}{\alpha_i} \tag{27}$$

Again relating to object space using the Abbe sine condition, Eqs. (22) and (23)

$$d_o = \frac{0.77\lambda}{\alpha_o} \tag{28}$$

Thus the minimum separation which can be resolved under conditions assuming coherent radiation is controlled by the same factors of the optical system, the wavelength of the radiation, and the angular aperture of the system. Only a factor is changed from 0.61 to 0.77. Both these factors are arbitrary, depending on the definition chosen for the image figure which is taken to be that observed as resolved. Since the diffraction figure will also be changed by spherical aberration and the observation of actual images will depend on the relative contrast above background in the image, these relationships (24) and (28) are much more important for the indicated dependence on wavelength and angular aperture than as results giving absolute values.

3. RESOLUTION WITH LENSES HAVING SPHERICAL ABERRATION

The treatment of resolution in Sections II, B, 1 and 2 involved no consideration of the aberrations that play a role in a real electron lens. In actual practice the procedure which has been commonly used is to consider the Fraunhofer diffraction-image figure in the Gaussian image plane which would be produced by a perfect lens free of spherical aberration, but with the finite aperture set by the spherical aberration of the lens. This approach is only a first approximation, but has been generally useful in providing an approximate relationship for the ultimate limit of resolution. The limits set by this simple treatment will be discussed first and will be followed by a discussion of the differences in the results obtained if the effects of spherical aberration are taken into account in a more intimate way. In the more complete treatment we require a wave optical formulation for the passage of the radiation through the optical system using the Huygen-Fresnel-Kirchoff approximation.

In the first approximate method of equating the radius of the geometrical spherical aberration figure to the diffraction figure we have from Eq. (2b), using the more conventional Δr_s instead of Δr_{oo},

$$\Delta r_s = C_s \alpha^3$$

where C_s is the spherical aberration coefficient already discussed in Section I, B. The parameter α is the angular aperture of the lens, the same parameter as α_o, which determines the diffraction figure in the image, already discussed in Section II, A, 2. Thus, the size of the image figures, Δr_s and d_o, depend in opposite ways on the size of the angular aperture. A lens with a given spherical aberration coefficient, C_s, will have an optimum angular aperture at which the highest resolution will be obtained. This optimum angular aperture can be obtained to a first approximation by equating the two figures of Eqs. (2b) and (24);

$$\frac{0.61\lambda}{\alpha} \approx C_s \alpha^3$$

then

$$\alpha_{opt} = \sqrt[4]{\frac{0.61}{C_s}} \tag{29}$$

and substituting from Eq. (29) in either Eq. (24) or (2b)

$$d_{min} = 0.7 C_s^{\frac{1}{4}} \lambda^{\frac{3}{4}} \tag{30}$$

The factor 0.7 is quite arbitrary, depending now not only on the definition of the figure which will be resolved in the image, but also on the very questionable procedure of equating the two figures, given by diffraction phenomena and the spherical aberration. While a somewhat better choice might have been made than merely equating the figures given by the two limiting factors, a really adequate analysis of the actual image figures cannot be made with this approach. The wave optical formation for passage of the radiation through the optical system using the Fresnel-Kirchoff approximation is required.

A treatment of the problem in wave optical terms has been applied to light optical systems with an extensive development in terms of the several factors which must be considered (4, 5, 39). Haine and Mulvey (17) have applied the analysis used by Conrady (7) for the light microscope to the electron microscope [see also Scherzer (44), and Glaser (13)]. In our discussion, a physical description will be given which extracts the important factors that must be considered in obtaining the ultimate resolving power of the electron optical system of the electron microscope.

First we must consider the intensity distribution in the image figure for it has been neglected in the previous approximation. In the absence of aberrations the maximum intensity in the image is at the Gaussian image point where the Airy disk is obtained. On the other hand, ignoring diffraction effects, the "circle of least confusion" produced by the lens with spherical aberration lies two-thirds of the distance along the axial separation between the Gaussian image point where the paraxial rays intersect the axis and the image point of the marginal rays. The maximum image intensity would be produced at this "circle of least confusion." In an optical system in which the spherical aberration figure is limited so as to be of the same magnitude as the diffraction figure, the wave optical method must be used to calculate the intensity distribution in the image figure. With small aberrations present, the maximum intensity in the image will no longer be either at the Gaussian image point or at the two-thirds point, but at a separation midway between paraxial (Gaussian) focus and marginal focus. This position is called the "diffraction focus."

The maximum intensity in the diffraction image will always be smaller when aberrations are present in the optical system than the maximum intensity calculated for the Airy pattern obtained at the Gaussian image point of an aberration-free system. An arbitrary criterion must again be chosen to determine the maximum amount of aberration which can be tolerated to give image figures which can be resolved. Once the criterion is set, calculations can be made on the amount of spherical aberration which can be tolerated and on the intensity distribution in the image figure. From these results, values of the angular aperture of the system and its resolving power can be obtained. The criterion adapted is that the intensity in the central maximum at diffraction focus should be at least 80% of the intensity calculated for the aberration-free system at Gaussian focus.

It will now be useful to describe the spherical aberration in terms of the deviation of the wave fronts from true spherical surfaces. The aberration figure can be treated as part of the total image figure produced by the optical system. Then the combined effects of diffraction, aberration, and defocusing can be obtained. The deviation of the spherical wave front at the exit pupil of an optical system which has a spherical aberration coefficient C_s and is defocused is given by

$$\varphi_s = -\tfrac{1}{4} C_s \alpha^4 + B\alpha^2 \tag{31}$$

The parameter B gives the defocusing in terms of the number of wavelengths from Gaussian focus along the optical axis at which the final image figure is observed. Some of these deviations in the wave fronts are shown in Fig. 23, an illustration from Black and Linfoot (4). At Gaussian focus $B = 0$, while marginal focus is given at $B = -2$ and "diffraction focus" for small amounts of spherical aberration is given at $B = -1$, the point midway between the two. The wave front is seen to have zero deviation at the extremeties in this case. The relation to the geometrical spherical aberration figure is just that the pencil of rays forming the image in the Gaussian plane deviates from a true point within a circle of radius $C_s\alpha^3$ while the wave optical method describes wave fronts which are no longer spherical but are distorted by amount $-\tfrac{1}{4}C_s\alpha^4$ from spherical form. The defocusing effect on the wave fronts can be introduced in a very convenient manner by the factor $B\alpha^2$ in the wave optical treatment.

If the criterion for the required intensity in the image figure with aberration is now taken to be 80% of the intensity of the image at Gaussian focus without aberrations, it is found that the wave-front deviation must be less than 0.94λ or just under one wavelength. The value of optimum α will then be set by the spherical aberration figure

$$-\tfrac{1}{4}C_s\alpha^4 \simeq \lambda \qquad (32)$$

$$\alpha_{opt} = \sqrt[4]{4\,\frac{\lambda}{C_s}} = 1.4\,\frac{\lambda^{\frac{1}{4}}}{C_s^{\frac{1}{4}}} \qquad (33)$$

We are concerned with very small values of α and the value of α_{opt} will not be effected by the defocusing factor $B\alpha^2$. But the optical system is adjusted so that the equivalent of one wavelength of spherical aberration is introduced by the objective lens and the image is observed at diffraction focus to give an image figure which has over 80% of the ideal

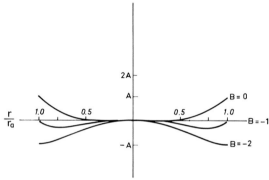

FIG. 23. Deviation of wave front produced by spherical aberration and defocusing. A, wavelengths of error; B, wavelengths of defocusing; $B = -1$, diffraction focus; $B = -2$, marginal focus. [From Black and Linfoot (4), (39).]

intensity given by an aberration-free system. The intensity distribution of the central section of the image figure produced by the lens under these conditions is also remarkably similar to the distribution of intensity in the Airy pattern of the aberration-free lens (see Fig. 17).

Thus criteria for the resolution of two points in an image will be essentially the same as those established for the ideal lens with the diffraction figure limiting the resolution of the instrument. Under these conditions the angular aperture of the lens will be set to limit the abberration figure to the equivalent of approximately one wavelength of spherical aberration, the plane in which the image will be observed will be taken as midway between the Gaussian image plane and the image plane of the marginal rays, and the separation (in the object plane) between the maximum and the first minimum is given by setting α_{opt} from Eq. (33) in Eq. (24)

$$d_{min} = 0.43 C^{\frac{1}{4}}\,\lambda^{\frac{3}{4}} \qquad (34)$$

This relation may be taken as a better approximation than Eq. (30) for the theoretical limit of resolution of the electron microscope. The criterion for resolution taken when only Fraunhofer diffraction was considered was the separation between two points in the object which would give an image figure such that there would be a dip in the intensity of 26.5% at the midpoint between the two image figures. To determine the actual factor in Eq. (34), the coherence of the radiation should again be taken into consideration.

Incoherent radiation is effectively the condition which would obtain with self-luminous object points and would give a resolution essentially that given by Eq. (34). Coherent illumination, the condition more closely approximating the situation in the electron microscope is more complex and, as in the ideal case of an aberration-free lens, the object points which can be resolved must be slightly farther apart than for incoherent radiation.

The resolution of the instrument under all the conditions we have considered always depends on the spherical aberration coefficient to the one-quarter power, $C_s^{1/4}$, the equivalent wavelength of the electrons to the three-quarters power, $\lambda^{3/4}$, and a factor which is given by the nature of the illumination, the plane in which the image is observed, and the criterion chosen as representing the resolved image figure of two object points. The detail with which we have considered the problem is of interest in a consideration of the possibilities of ultimately resolving structure at the theoretical limits of the electron microscope. But before any real evaluation can be made of these potentialities, the nature of contrast in the image must be taken into consideration. We must now consider the scattering and phase delay of the radiation during the interaction of the electron beam with the specimen, and the effects of defocusing in which phase-contrast and Fresnel-diffraction effects occur.

C. Contrast

Among the assumptions made in taking the Kirchoff approximation of the wave optical theory as adequate for application to imaging in the electron microscope was the nature of the transmission of the radiation at the object. The assumption was made that the object is either an opaque screen cutting off part of the incident radiation or, more often, a partially transmitting screen through which the rays or the corresponding wave fronts can be traced by geometrical optics, the changes in amplitude and phase being determined by the complex index of refraction of the matter composing the object. The assumption was also made that the object is so thin that no diffraction effects occur inside the specimen. Such conditions clearly do not hold for crystalline material such as metal foils where dynamic effects are observed (see Chapter 5). However, imaging of noncrystalline materials may be treated without considering dynamic electron interactions and certainly we may expect this assumption to be valid in the imaging of single molecules and atoms at the ultimate limit of resolution of the instrument.

The wave optical method has been applied only in a few special treatments of the subject (15, 33, 44). The more conventional procedure is to treat the interaction of the electron beam with the specimen which forms the object as a particle-scattering process. Of course, since we are dealing with interactions on the atomic scale, a quantum mechanical treatment of the phenomena must be used, e.g., Lenz (31) and Pilyanko-vich (42). The method involves a determination of the angular distri-bution of the electrons after passing through the object, and re-constructing the image with those electrons which have been scattered through angles which are less than the angular aperture of the objective lens. Contrast arises in the image because different regions of the object scatter different amounts outside the limiting aperture. The reconstructed image has contrast related to the scattering in the conjugate-object points, and all that is required to give a description of the contrast observed in the image is a determination of the scattering cross section of the com-ponents of the specimen: e.g., von Borries (51a), Hall (20), Leisegang (28), Zeitler and Bahr (55), and Lippert (40). But this analysis is limited for it gives only the amplitude-contrast effect and neglects the phase relation-ships between the scattered and unscattered beams. Without a knowledge of the phase relationships of the wave fronts corresponding to the electrons scattered from the object, no proper analysis can be made of the imaging by the objective. The wave optical method requires that a complete treatment of the wave from source to image surface be considered, and without such a treatment the ultimate resolution of the complete optical system cannot be evaluated. Important contrast effects observed in the electron microscope cannot be explained on a simple amplitude-scattering basis.

Strong phase-contrast effects are especially evident, for example, in electron micrographs in which an object is suspended above the substrate rather than in contact with the substrate film. This effect is beautifully illustrated in Fig. 24, a micrograph by Westerberg and Hall (53).

In the treatment of image contrast where the effects of the phase relationships of the scattered waves were considered (15, 33, 44), adequate data treating the electron interaction with matter were not available. Only an approximate description of the phenomena could be given in which several assumptions had to be made before obtaining the contrast to be expected if both phase shift and angular distribution were considered in the scattering process.

The problem of describing the electron interactions at the intermediate energy ranges employed in the electron microscope is difficult both analytically and experimentally because of the very small angles of

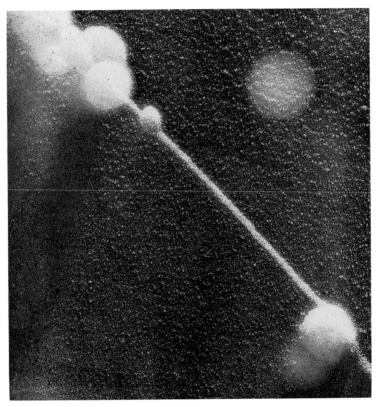

FIG. 24. Strand of DNA (deoxyribonucleic acid) "rope" strung between polystyrene spheres (880 Å diameter) platinum-shadowed at an angle of 1:10. The contrast of the DNA strand is enhanced over that of the DNA deposited on the substrate not only because of the shadowing metal, but also because it is above the substrate. Magnification: $\times$ 150,000. Courtesy of Westerberg and Hall [Westerberg (1962)].

scattering involved (10^{-6}–10^{-3} radians). Lenz (*31*) has extended earlier analytical methods of treating the electron scattering and provided a method for approximating the angular intensity distribution of electrons of intermediate energies (50–150 kv) at very small angles. He has obtained expressions for the atomic form factors, and, from them, the differential scattering cross sections, both for the elastically scattered

48   BENJAMIN M. SIEGEL

electrons which do not lose energy and for the inelastically scattered
electrons which have been found to lose discrete amounts of energy
(some 10–20 ev) in their interaction with matter. Figure 25, taken from
Lenz (31), gives the distribution of electrons scattered from a carbon foil
of mass 1×10^{-6} gm/cm² for 50 kv electrons. The curves indicate that
for carbon the inelastic scattering is at least two orders of magnitude
greater than the elastic scattering at angles of less than 1×10^{-3} radians.
The ordinate is the relative number of electrons scattered per unit
solid angle. The scattering into the larger angles subtends a much

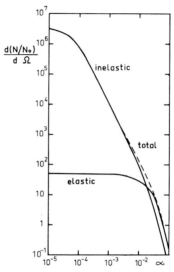

FIG. 25. Fraction of electrons scattered within solid angle (differential scattering
cross section) as funtion of angle, α, from carbon film of mass-thickness 1×10^{-6}
gm/cm²; 50 kv electrons. [Lenz (31).]

larger area, so though the scattering cross section is much smaller, the
fraction of incident electrons scattered at angles of less than 1×10^{-3}
radians is only one-half of the total scattered by the carbon film. Certain
limitations in Lenz's calculations should be pointed out. The atomic
model is one in which the expression for the coulomb potential has a term
representing a screening radius, R, to account for the screening of the
nuclear charge by the electron cloud of the atoms. Lenz takes the values
of the screening radius, R, from magnetic susceptibility measurements.
Later calculations by Pilyankovich (42) using a Hartree-Fock model of
the atom show the screening radius chosen by Lenz to be too large.
Experimental measurements on the scattering cross sections (2a, 25)
also show better agreement if a screening radius smaller than that chosen

by Lenz is taken. Lenz has calculated the scattering for foils of given thickness by taking the sum of the scattering from the total number of individual atoms required to form the film. Any coherent interactions between scattering from atoms is thus neglected by Lenz. Carbon does show diffraction rings representing a C—C spacing, but this effect is weak for evaporated carbon films. But as Kamiya (25) has pointed out, the treatment of Lenz disregards the fact that even if the atoms were randomly distributed there is an interatomic distance of nearest approach and this factor will effect the observed intensity distribution. Lenz (31) has also calculated the ratio of the total inelastic scattering cross section to the total elastic cross section, σ_i/σ_e, for atoms of different atomic number. This data is plotted in Fig. 26.

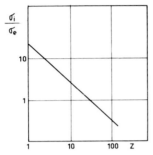

FIG. 26: Ratio of total inelastic scattering cross section, σ_i, to total elastic scattering cross section, σ_e, as function of atomic number, Z; 50 kv electrons. [Lenz (31).]

Lenz's treatment, however, does provide the best basis available for a description of the electron interaction with matter. More experimental data are required to provide a better value of the screening radius, R, and confirm the predictions of the theory. An extension of theory is also required, for while the elastic interaction can be treated adequately within the approximations of this method the inelastic interactions are not actually defined. The inelastic scattering may involve interactions with the bound electrons of the individual atoms, the plasma of free electrons (21a), or phonon interactions (24). While all of these interactions may be expected to involve discrete losses of energy in the scattered electron, the amplitude and phase of the scattered wave function can only be properly given if the nature of the interaction in the scattering medium is defined. Perhaps as important for the treatment of the problem of image contrast are the coherent scattering effects due to ordering in the atomic lattice of the solid scatterer. The present treatments which are based on a summing of individual atoms assumed to have completely random arrays, or of a crystalline lattice with only the strong Bragg interactions taken into account, do not provide adequate treatments for our understanding of image contrast. Here again, the nature of the inelastic interactions is of utmost importance in a full analysis of the problem.

Recent observations (24, 45a, 52) and analysis of results (21a) have advanced our understanding. Watanabe (52) has constructed an electron optical system which permits imaging with only those electrons which have lost no energy in transmission through the specimen–object or with those electrons which have lost given energies. He has found that specimens of crystalline material such as thin metal foils which show strong coherent scattering phenomena, show these coherent interaction effects not only with the elastically scattered electrons, but that also in images produced by electrons which have suffered inelastic collisions of given energy losses there are coherent interaction among the inelastically scattered electrons.

Haine (15) has used a representational scheme to obtain the change in amplitude and phase of the incident wave function upon transmission through an object to calculate the resultant image contrast based on a wave optical model. While this method may be helpful for illustrative purposes, a quantum mechanical calculation of the wave function obtained upon transmission through the object will be necessary for a satisfactory description of the contrast obtained in the image. Haine's calculation shows that a phase shift of $\pi/4$ is to be expected when the electron wave is scattered from the object. Under conditions of axial illumination, the unscattered or background wave is paraxial while the scattered wave traverses a longer optical path. If the final image is observed at a position where defocusing and spherical aberration also introduce a phase shift of approximately $\pi/4$ in the scattered wave with respect to the unscattered wave, image contrast will be enhanced by the fact that the waves are 180° out of phase and the full amplitude of the scattered wave subtracts from the background wave. Here phase contrast is obtained, but as Lenz (32) has pointed out, the situation is not the same as in the phase-contrast light microscopy of Zernike (56). The Zernike method introduces a phase-retarding plate in the back focal plane of the objective lens which gives contrast in the image that is a linear function of the phase shift in the specimen. Thus the image is observed at true focus and the contrast in the image is a linear function of the optical path length in the specimen and independent of the spatial dimensions of the object being imaged. When the phase shift is obtained by defocusing, the image figure and the contrast also depend on the amount of defocusing. Such phase-contrast relationships are not satisfactory for general observation with the electron microscope.

Attempts have been made to introduce phase-shifting devices in the back focal phase of the objective lens of the electron microscope (*8, 26, 32*). Unfortunately all of these phase-shifting plates introduce diffuse scattering in the electron beam and critical comparative tests must still be made to establish that a real gain in resolution is obtained with such devices. The suggestion has also been made by some workers (*41, 50, 54*) to use lower accelerating voltages. While the ultimate resolution is less with the longer effective wavelengths of the electrons, contrast should be enhanced with the increased scattering at the lower energies. More experimental data on the actual scattering distributions are necessary before the suggested gains with low-energy electrons can be evaluated.

A more complete analysis of the requirements for imaging single atoms would be valuable at this stage of development of the electron microscope. Scherzer (*44*) has made such calculations using approximate expressions for the wave functions of the electrons scattered from single atoms. He has calculated the contrast which could be obtained, taking into account the phase shifts introduced by spherical aberration and defocusing, and concluded that under optimum conditions individual carbon atoms (atomic number 6) could be imaged with 10% contrast by an instrument capable of resolving 2 A.

In our discussion of the limits of resolution we have seen that calculations based on the spherical aberration coefficients of existing objective lenses indicate a theoretical resolution as low as 2–3 A. With the promise of improved lenses using superconducting magnets, it would be very valuable to have an analysis of the requirements on the illumination system, the instrumental stability, and the manner in which the larger angular aperture should be utilized to achieve resolution of individual atoms with adequate contrast.

III. High-Resolution Electron Microscopy

The commercially available electron microscopes are generally engineered to a level where the resolving power of the instrument approaches within a factor of 2–4 of the theoretical limit postulated on the basis of the criteria discussed in Section II. In the hands of a few very skilled workers, instruments have been adjusted to resolve dimensions as small as 4–5 A on selected test specimens. Competent operators can achieve better than 10 A resolution today without great difficulty and working resolutions of only slightly larger dimensions are accepted procedure in several laboratories. There are several critical factors which must be considered in achieving these high levels of instrumental performance and it is not obtained without careful regard for them. An evaluation of the necessary conditions for achieving high resolution will be discussed in this section. While many of the requirements are set by the engineering design of the instrument, the research worker concerned with achieving very high resolution with the electron microscope still must be cognizant of the criteria which set the limits on the observations which he can make. In many instances the final adjustment of the instrument or diagnosis of the factors limiting performance are in the hands of the research worker himself.

With the spherical aberration in the best objective lenses setting a theoretical limit of 2–3 A on the resolution of the instrument, the present limits of observation with the electron microscope are set by instrumental conditions. Of course the preparation of suitable specimens which would permit the utilization of the full resolution of the electron microscope is still a great difficulty. Even suitable specimens for testing resolution are not readily available. While specimen preparation will not be discussed in this chapter, methods will have to be developed for obtaining molecular dispersions without supporting substrates. A promising method, at least for long filamentous molecules such as deoxyribonucleic acid (DNA) and nucleo-proteins, is the technique of Westerberg and Hall (53) (see Fig. 24). At liquid helium temperatures it may also be possible to support monolayers of proteins across very small holes in the substrate film and thus obtain adequate contrast to image the atomic arrangement in these molecules.

In this section, it will be instructive to discuss the instrumental requirements for achieving different levels of resolution. The tolerances in each of several components of the instrument will be evaluated for 10, 5, 2, and 1 A resolution. Table I lists the design parameters for objective lenses which would respectively give these resolutions if spherical aberration were the only limiting factor. Lens B, designed for a resolution limit of 2 A, is very close to the optimum design which can be achieved. Lens D is not practical. Resolution limited by spherical aberration to 10 A requires a weak lens with long focal length and a large chromatic aberration coefficient which would set the limit of resolution. In practice, design B or C would be used, and the resolution limit would be set by instrumental factors other than spherical aberration. Ten angstroms represent a satisfactory limit for most working instruments today; 5A is the present practical engineering level for the best instruments. The conditions for 2A resolution represent the requirements that must be met if an instrument is to be operated at the theoretical limit of presently available objective lenses. Several methods have been suggested for decreasing the spherical aberration of the objective lens (1, 10, 44, 45, 54a), and it is not unreasonable to expect that

TABLE I

MAGNETIC LENSES DESIGNED FOR DIFFERENT LIMITS OF RESOLUTION SET BY SPHERICAL ABERRATION[a]

Lens:	A	B	C	D
d_{min} at:	1 A	2 A	5 A	10 A
Physical parameters				
Bore radius, R (cm):	Cannot be designed on this basis	0.184	0.36	0.586
Gap, S (cm):		0.368	0.72	0.234
S/D:		1	1	0.2
Excitation				
Ampere-turns:	250,000	6,000	3,760	1,940
Magnetic field in gap, H_p (oersteds):	—	20,600	6,520	10,400
Maximum axial magnetic field, H_o (oersteds):	—	17,160	5,430	1,700
$K^2 = 0.022\ H_o^2 R^2/V_r$:	—	2	0.2	0.2
Optical parameters				
Focal length, f (cm):	—	0.147	1.08	3.07
Spherical aberration coefficient, C_s (cm):	0.006	0.092	3.63	58.6
Chromatic aberration coefficient, C_{ch} (cm):	—	0.10	1.08	2.93
$\alpha_{opt} = 1.4\ \lambda^{1/4}/C_s^{1/4}$ (rad):	2.25×10^{-2}	1.13×10^{-2}	4.5×10^{-3}	2.25×10^{-3}

[a] $d_{min} = 0.43\ \lambda^{3/4}\ C_s^{1/4}$; $V = 100$ kv. [Data from Liebmann and Grad (37).]

a lens will be designed and constructed in the near future which will extend the theoretical limit below 2 A. It is therefore interesting to see what demands would be placed upon the instrumental factors of the instrument in its utilization at the 1 A limit even though no practical lens design can be given at this time.

A. Illuminating System

The illuminating system of the electron microscope, consisting of the electron gun and condenser lenses with their apertures, set important limits on the performance of the electron microscope. It was not until the self-biased electron gun with its higher brightness and smaller effective source size was used that important steps such as the correction of asymmetry could be made to improve the resolving power of the electron microscope. The introduction of the double-lens condenser system gave the necessary flexibility to achieve adequate intensities at the very high magnifications required for imaging at the ultimate levels of resolution. Current investigations on the still further reduction of the effective source diameter by point filaments for cathodes are demonstrating the importance of this factor in achieving ultimate resolution contrast with the electron microscope.

1. THE ELECTRON GUN

The electron gun shown schematically in Fig. 27 produces an electron beam of extremely high brightness. The maximum theoretical brightness of a source which can be obtained was given by Langmuir (27):

$$\beta = \frac{i_s}{\pi} \left(\frac{e V_o}{k T} \right) \text{ in amp/cm}^2\text{/steradian} \tag{35}$$

where i_s is the specific electron emission in amp/cm² from the filament, V_o is the potential to which the electrons are accelerated (here the anode voltage with respect to the cathode shield), T is the temperature of the filament, e is the electron charge, and k is Boltzman's constant. With tungsten filaments heated to temperatures of 2700–2800°K, where high emissivities can be attained with reasonable lifetimes of the filaments ($i_s = 3.5$ amp/cm² at 2800°K), the maximum theoretical brightnesses which are given by Eq. (35) for 50 and 100 kv electron energies are 2.3×10^5 and 4.6×10^5 amp/cm²/steradian, respectively. The actual energy flux is small because of the small angular apertures of the system. The coaxial arrangement of the filament tip, cathode-shield aperture, and anode aperture effectively forms an electrostatic aperture lens which produces a beam in which the divergence is the order of 1×10^{-2}

radians. Guns can be designed (47) which will produce smaller divergences or effectively focus the beam, but more flexibility is obtained by
using suitably apertured condenser-lens systems. A most important parameter of the source produced by the electron gun is the effective source
diameter. The smallest source diameter is desired to most closely ap-

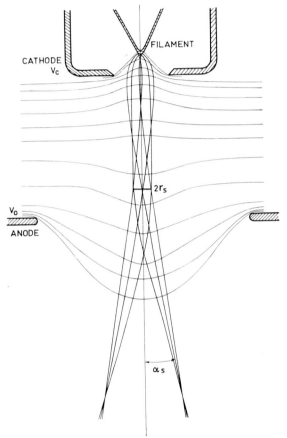

FIG. 27. Electron-gun schematic. The electron beam produced has an effective
source radius, r_g, and angular divergence, α_g.

proximate a point source, the criterion ideally required for complete
coherence in the wave optical model. The angular divergence of the
beam must also be small enough to allow effective imaging by the electron lenses of the condenser system without excessive spherical aberration. In practice, the limiting aperture for the beam is set by an
aperture in the condenser system. The parameters of the gun are
set to produce a beam divergence greater than the desired final

value. The intensity cross section of the beam has a Gaussian
distribution, and a higher brightness will be obtained utilizing only
the central maximum. Alignment of the illuminating system is also
facilitated by having a beam from the gun which diverges more
than the angle defined by the condenser aperture. Very useful
data are provided by Haine and Einstein (*16*) on the performance
of the type of gun generally used in electron microscopy. They give

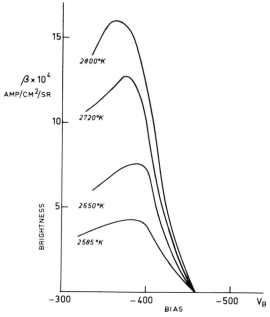

FIG. 28. Brightness as a function of cathode-shield bias voltage for various filament temperatures. Electron-gun configuration as shown in Fig. 27. Cathode-shield
aperture, 0.175 mm diameter; filament to cathode shield, .07 mm; anode voltage, 50 kv.
[From Haine and Einstein (*16*).]

the brightness, effective source diameter, angular divergence, and total
beam currents obtained as a function of gun geometry and bias voltages.
A most important result from their investigation is the conclusion that
close to the theoretical brightness is obtained over a wide range of gun
geometries if the correct bias is used. In Fig. 28, plots of the brightness
as a function of bias voltage (for a given setting of the gun parameters)
are given for different filament temperatures. Similar peak brightness
values can be obtained with different settings of the spacing of the gun
elements if the bias is also changed. Electron microscopes are usually
provided with a fixed-bias resistor which determines the bias voltage at

"saturation" where the gun operates for a given spacing between filament and cathode shield and with a given aperture diameter in the cathode shield. The feedback which gives the saturation effect to the beam current for a given gun geometry occurs because increasing the temperature of the filament and, thus, the emission from the tungsten filament also increases the bias between filament and cathode shield. The increased bias has the effect of limiting the area of filament from which electrons can pass through the shield aperture—an effective narrowing of the aperture in the shield—and at a given beam current the system stabilizes to a "saturation" value. Haine *et al.* (*18*) have given the data for combinations of gun parameters and bias resistances which will produce maximum brightness from the electron gun when operated at "saturation."

Recently investigators (*9, 22, 46, 49*) have shown that the etched-point filaments of the type developed for field-emission-point projection microscopy, may be employed in place of the V-shaped filament now generally used. The point filaments can give an effective source diameter of only 2–10 μ diameter, and with higher specific emission from the points achieve the higher brightness required for high-magnification electron microscopy. The smaller source diameter has the effect of giving a higher degree of coherence to the illuminating beam with the consequent enhancement with which diffraction and phase-contrast effects can be observed in the final image.

2. Condenser System

Two magnetic lenses are now generally used to provide a condenser system of wide flexibility (see Figs. 10 and 11). The first lens is of relatively short focal length and can be used to produce a demagnified image of the effective source. The second lens of longer focal length images this reduced source on, or near, the object plane at about unit magnification. By suitable adjustment of the focal lengths of the lenses, illumination of the object can range from the intense beam in which current densities are the order of a several amp/cm² over areas only a few microns in diameter to the condition in which the beam is spread over an area tenths of a millimeter in diameter but with low current density and very low angular aperture. A limitation inherent in using a single condenser-lens system is the high total energy flux through the specimen at high intensities of illumination. The effective source produced by the gun has a relatively large diameter and when the single condenser lens focuses the effective source produced by the gun on the specimen, a relatively large area of the specimen is irradiated with a beam of high current density. This may cause excessive heating and damage to the specimen.

In the double-lens condenser system, there is approximately the same distance between the gun and specimen so that the first condenser lens of the double system is closer to the effective source of the gun. Thus, a larger solid angle of the beam is subtended for a given size physical aperture, and the intensity of the radiation contained in the beam is increased as the square of the angle subtended. The adjustable focal length of the second lens and its changeable apertures give the wide range of adjustment of illumination on the specimen desired. By using the first lens to demagnify the effective source by $1/10$–$1/15 \times$, an effective source may be obtained with a diameter as small as 1μ with the standard V-filament in the gun, and smaller if a point filament is used. The aperture stop in the second condenser defines the angular aperture of the illuminating beam at the specimen plane when the imaging is in the range of unity. While a large part of the beam is blocked by this physical aperture, the brightness and current density at the specimen will be the same as that which would be produced by a single-lens system apertured to give the same angular aperture. An important advantage over the single-lens system is that the area illuminated will be reduced by the demagnification of the two-lens system and the total energy flux on the specimen will be greatly reduced.

B. Compensation of Asymmetry

The most important factor limiting resolution in practical electron microscopy is undoubtedly the lack of axial symmetry in the electron optical system comprising the objective lens. The behavior of electron lenses described in the earlier section was postulated on the assumption of axial symmetry in the refracting magnetic fields of the lens. When the fields deviate from axial symmetry, the effect on the image produced is equivalent to the addition of a weak cylindrical lens to the imaging system. The focal length of the lens measured in orthogonal planes is different and an image figure such as shown in Fig. 29 is obtained. The difference in focal lengths in directions a and b in Fig. 29 is shown dramatically by the sharp over- and underfocus Fresnel diffraction fringes or "contours" at right angles to each other (17, 23, 29) (see Fig. 30). These sharp Fresnel-diffraction fringes are obtained because all the rays passing through the lens in a given meridional plane (a plane containing the optical axis of the lens) are brought to a focus in a given image plane which varies in position along the optic axis from a maximum to minimum separation from the lens. Since the image is observed in a fixed-image plane, the lens images different object planes in different meridional planes (see Fig. 29), and the image observed is related to the object in varying planes of object space. With an asymmetric lens focused so that the focal length is overfocused (too short) in one direction and underfocused in the orthogonal direction, there is only one meridional plane in which the lens images the plane in which the

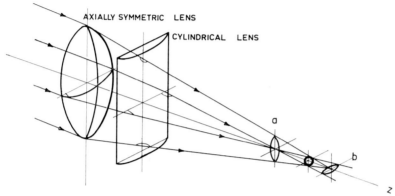

FIG. 29. Image figure produced by asymmetry in a lens illustrated as equivalent to a combined spherical lens and cylindrical lens.

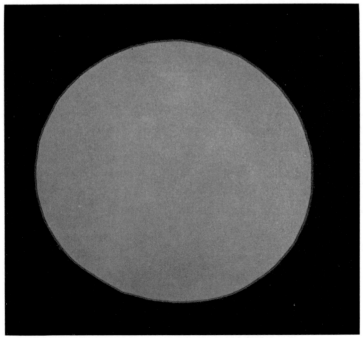

FIG. 30. Overfocus Fresnel fringe produced by an objective lens with about 0.1 μ asymmetry. Magnification: × 150,000.

physical object actually lies. The maximum overfocus direction is imaged in a plane close to the lens, and the Fresnel-diffraction fringe observed is the diffraction pattern observed at this separation below the object, magnified by the instrumental magnification. In the maximum underfocus direction, the virtual diffraction pattern produced above the object is imaged by the optical system.

The mechanical tolerances required to achieve the degree of axial symmetry which will not introduce asymmetries in the image are well beyond the best possible conditions which can be obtained in machining practice (3, 48). Inherent asymmetries will always remain because of the eccentricities in the bore of the pole piece, noncoaxial alignment of top and bottom halves of the pole piece, and inhomogeneities of the iron or asymmetrical fields caused by charges on apertures and specimen holder. These inherent or "basic" asymmetries must be compensated. The practical method of compensating asymmetry, first suggested by Hillier and Ramberg (23), made possible the advance in resolving power of the electron microscope to its present level. Their discussion still provides a valuable evaluation of the problem and the principles involved in its correction. More convenient methods for externally compensating asymmetry have been developed: either electrostatic or magnetic multipole arrangements in which controlled compensating asymmetrical fields can be introduced by varying voltages or currents, or mechanical arrangements in which asymmetrical distributions of soft magnetic materials can be moved into the field at the correct azimuth and axial position to provide compensating cylindrical refraction.

The superposition of a cylindrical refracting field distribution at right angles to the direction of the existing asymmetry in the imaging field of the lens can, in principle, correct the effects of the basic nonaxial symmetry completely. This basic asymmetry can be conveniently designated by a vector, A_b, where the vectorial magnitude, A_b, is a function of the difference in focus in the two extreme directions and vectorial direction, φ_b, is taken as the direction of maximum overfocus or the direction of the meridional plane in which the lens has the shortest focal length. The compensating cylindrical field will introduce a vectorial component of asymmetry of magnitude, A_c, and direction φ_c. The two asymmetries will add vectorially giving a resultant asymmetry of magnitude, A_r, and direction φ_r. If we take the direction φ_b as the angle $0°$ then

$$A_r{}^2 = A_b{}^2 + A_c{}^2 + 2A_bA_c \cos 2\varphi_c \qquad (36)$$

$$\tan 2\varphi_r = \frac{A_c \sin 2\varphi_c}{A_r + A_c \cos 2\varphi_c} \qquad (37)$$

The lens can be compensated completely only with $A_c = A_b$ and $\varphi_c = 90°$. The relations (36) and (37) show the importance of starting with small asymmetries to obtain good corrections. If A_b is small then only a small value of A_c will be needed to compensate the inherent or basic asymmetry of the lens, and the angular setting will not be as critical. When the strength of the correcting "stigmator" is either much smaller or much larger than the basic asymmetry of the lens, Eq. (36) indicates that $\varphi_r \approx 0°$ or $\varphi_r \approx 90°$, respectively. As the strength of the stigmator approaches the strength of the basic asymmetry, i.e., $A_c \approx A_b$, the value of φ_r changes rapidly and it is the rotation of the position of the maximum and minimum separation in Fresnel-diffraction fringes which gives the most sensitive indication for compensating the asymmetry of the lens.

The degree to which compensation is achieved in practice depends on several factors. As Hillier and Ramberg (23) pointed out, the instrumental stability, mechanical and electrical, must be high enough to permit observation of the effects of the asymmetry. The observation of the Fresnel fringes which provide the means of measuring the asymmetry in the imaging system requires a very well-adjusted illuminating system. The smaller the effective source diameter that can be obtained with adequate brightness, the more pronounced will be this diffraction phenomenon, which depends on the degree coherence of the illumination.

The degree of asymmetry in a lens can be measured by the separation between the light and dark Fresnel-diffraction fringes in the orthogonal directions of maximum and minimum separation, Δs_{max} and Δs_{min}, respectively. These differences can in turn be related to the difference in focal length, Δf_A, of the lens in the two directions. This focal length increment, Δf_A, provides a parameter for expressing the aberration figure produced by the asymmetrical lens. The aberration figure conjugate to the Gaussian image plane will have a circle of least confusion with diameter

$$d_A = 2\Delta f_A \alpha_o \qquad (38)$$

The change with focus of the separation Δs, of the maximum and minimum intensities in a Fresnel fringe overfocused pattern can be given to a good approximation ($\sim 25\%$) (17) by

$$\Delta s = \sqrt{\lambda \cdot \Delta f} \qquad (39)$$

From the observed differences in the fringe spacings in the orthogonal directions giving maximum separation Δs_{max} and minimum separation Δs_{min} in an image overfocused in all directions, the value of the asymmetry can be given in terms of the focal difference, Δf_A

$$\Delta f_A = \frac{1}{\lambda} \left[(\Delta s_{max})^2 - (\Delta s_{min})^2 \right] \tag{40}$$

The value for Δf_A obtained from observations using Eq. (40) can be set in Eq. (38) to give the approximate aberration-image figure caused by asymmetry.

The image figure will have a minimum circle of confusion at the midpoint of the separation of the two focal extremes, the Gaussian image plane. In the discussion on the resolution limits set by spherical aberration and diffraction in Section II,B,3, we have seen that the minimum aberration figure was obtained when these factors were adjusted to give an optimum, and was located at the point of "diffraction focus" midway between Gaussian and marginal focus. These are considerations which must again be taken into account in determining the ultimate resolution of an instrument in which the asymmetry of the lens would be adjusted to the limits set by these other factors. However, the limits of resolution in present instruments are set not by the spherical aberration, but by the asymmetry of the lens. It will therefore be of interest to examine the limits of resolution set by the optical system in which the asymmetrical figure in the Gaussian image plane is balanced with the diffraction figure.

Another factor is important in practice with present instruments, the chromatic aberration figure. All present instruments are engineered to have voltage and current stabilization which would be inadequate for the ultimate resolution set by the spherical aberration. Thus, in practice, the asymmetry in the objective-lens system can only be compensated to the limits set by the chromatic aberration produced by the electrical instability of the instrument. The required stabilities in the current and voltage supplies can be related directly to the change in focus, Δf_A, producing the asymmetry through the chromatic aberration coefficient. This subject will be discussed more fully in the next Section III,C. Here it will be sufficient to point out that the change in focal length of the lens may be given in terms of the change in lens current ΔI or accelerating voltage ΔV by

$$\Delta f_{ch} = C_{ch} \frac{2\Delta I}{I}; \qquad f_{ch} = C_{ch} \frac{\Delta V}{V} \tag{41}$$

Then the asymmetry aberration figure may be given in terms of measurable lens parameters as

$$d_A = 2C_{ch}\alpha_o \frac{2\Delta I}{I}$$

$$d_A = 2C_{ch}\alpha_o \frac{\Delta V}{V} \tag{42}$$

and the tolerances in ΔI and ΔV for aberration figures of less than given values can be determined.

The asymmetry in the objective lens does place very severe restrictions on the ultimate resolution of the optical system. In first approximation all aberrations can be neglected, and the figure produced by asymmetry can be compared with the diffraction figure produced by the lens. Then, if we assume the figures add quadratically, from Eqs. (24) and (38)

$$\left(\frac{0.61\lambda}{\alpha}\right)^2 + (2\Delta f_A \alpha)^2 = d_A{}^2(\alpha) \tag{43}$$

Differentiating with respect to α and setting $d(d_A)/d\alpha = 0$ to obtain an optimum value for α, we have

$$\alpha_{opt} = \sqrt{\frac{0.3\lambda}{\Delta f_A}} = 0.55\lambda^{\frac{1}{2}} \Delta f_A{}^{-\frac{1}{2}} \tag{44}$$

Substituting this expression for α_{opt} into Eq. (24) we again have a d_{min}:

$$d_{A\,(min)} = 1.1\lambda^{\frac{1}{2}} \Delta f_A{}^{\frac{1}{2}} \tag{45}$$

The factor 1.1 is quite arbitrary and again depends on the criteria taken for resolution in this case, but Eq. (45) is a relation which sets severe requirements on the compensation of asymmetry. Table II gives

TABLE II

ASYMMETRY TOLERANCES IN TERMS OF Δf_A WHICH SET LIMITING RESOLUTION[a]

Voltage (kv)	Δf_A in μ for different values of d_A			
	1 A	2 A	5 A	10 A
50	0.0015	0.0062	0.039	0.15
100	0.0022	0.009	0.056	0.22

[a] $d_A = 1.1\,\lambda^{\frac{1}{2}} \Delta f_A{}^{\frac{1}{2}}$.

the values of Δf_A which must be achieved to obtain different levels of resolution at 50 kv and 100 kv in this approximation.

As long as the optical system is being limited by the asymmetry of the objective lens and not by the diffraction figure produced by the lens, some improvement in the resolution obtained may be achieved by using a smaller angular aperture of illumination. If $\alpha_c < \alpha_o$, the diffraction figure is poorer by a factor of 1.5, but the asymmetry figure and chromatic aberration figure is improved by a factor of α_c/α_o. Thus, until the instrument can be operated at the limit of resolution set by the diffraction figure and spherical aberration, it would appear to be an advantage to use as small an angular aperture of illumination as possible and still have adequate intensity in the final image.

The discussion of this subject has only been an approximation, and calculations should be made on the manner in which the image figure changes with asymmetry of the lens. Since the asymmetry can be corrected, in theory, to any degree required, it does not present any final theoretical limit to the resolution of the electron microscope as does spherical aberration. However, the tolerances are so stringent at the ultimate limits of resolution that it will be important to know how asymmetry affects resolution in the ultimate limit, since the asymmetry in the optical system will undoubtedly have to be measured independently in the correcting process. To obtain the ultimate limits of resolution of a practical instrument, the wave front at the exit pupil (or aperture) of the objective lens should be calculated taking into account all factors: the spherical aberration which produces a change in wave front given by $-\frac{1}{4} C_s \alpha^4$; the defocusing effect which affects the wave front proportionally to α^2; the asymmetry factor $2\Delta f_A \alpha$, and chromatic aberration figures $C_{ch}(2\Delta I/I)\alpha$ and $C_{ch}(\Delta V/V)\alpha$. The actual distribution of intensity in the image figure as the image plane is moved from the Gaussian image plane toward the lens must be evaluated. These calculations will give the ultimate resolution that can be expected with a given set of electron optical parameters and set the limits within which asymmetry must be corrected and the currents and voltage stabilized.

C. Chromatic Aberration Limits

Electron microscopes should be designed with the high-voltage and lens currents stabilized by electronic circuitry to a level where chromatic effects would not be a limiting factor in the resolving power of the instrument. To attain resolutions below 10 A, difficult requirements are placed on the electronic supplies, and present practice usually sets specifications which would give chromatic aberration figures of about 5 A with the existing pole-piece design for the objective lenses. As we have seen this limit requires very good compensation of asymmetry in the lens to bring the asymmetry aberration figure down to that level, though the limit on resolution set by the spherical aberration in the best lenses used today is 2-3A. It will be of interest to evaluate the voltage and current fluctuations that can be tolerated at these different levels of resolution.

The chromatic aberration figure given by a change in focal length, Δf, has a radius of

$$\Delta r_{ch} = \alpha \Delta f \qquad (46)$$

Figure 31 is a schematic showing how this dependence is obtained by relating the figure in object space to a change in the effective object plane. Thus if the angular aperture of the lens is α, a point moved along the optic axis a distance Δf from the object plane (given by the focal length, f, of the lens) will subtend a disk of diameter $2\Delta r_{ch}$ at the object. The focal length of the lens is proportional to the potential, V, through which the electrons have been accelerated and inversely proportional to the square of the current, I, in the lens coil, producing the

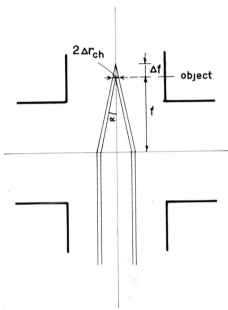

FIG. 31. Chromatic aberration figure (radius Δr_{ch}) produced by an effective change in focal length Δf.

magnetic field. Thus Δf can be related to the changes in these electrical parameters by

$$\Delta f_{ch} = C_{ch} \frac{\Delta V}{V} \tag{47}$$

and

$$\Delta f_{ch} = C_{ch} \frac{2\Delta I}{I} \tag{48}$$

The quadratic addition of these factors gives the resultant Δf

$$\Delta f_{ch} = C_{ch} \sqrt{\left(\frac{\Delta V}{V}\right)^2 + \left(\frac{2\Delta I}{I}\right)^2} \tag{49}$$

The parameter C_{ch} is the chromatic aberration coefficient of the lens and can be obtained for a given pole-piece configuration, S/D, and excitation parameter, K^2, from the data of Liebmann and Grad (*37*). Liebmann (*34*) has calculated the minimum attainable chromatic aberration coefficients $C_{ch(min)}$ as a function of the ratio of pole-piece gap-to-bore diameter, S/D. For $S/D \geqslant 2$, $C_{ch(min)}$ is practically independent of S/D, and $C_{ch(min)} = 5.3$ cm for a value of $K^2 = 1.2$. Values of the chromatic aberration coefficients calculated from Liebmann and Grad (*37*) are also included in Table I. From these data the tolerable fluctuations of voltage and current to put the chromatic aberration figure below a given value can be calculated for a given electron lens. The results are given in Table III.

TABLE III

VOLTAGE AND CURRENT TOLERANCES FOR DIFFERENT LEVELS OF INSTUMENTAL RESOLUTION
SET BY CHROMATIC ABERRATION[a]

d_{ch} at:	1 A	2 A	5 A	10 A
C_{ch} values from Table I				
ΔV in volts:	—	0.9	0.5	0.75
$\Delta I/I$:	—	4.5×10^{-6}	2.5×10^{-6}	4×10^{-6}
Lens B, $C_{ch} = 0.10$ cm				
ΔV in volts:	0.2	0.9	5	22
$\Delta I/I$:	1×10^{-6}	4.5×10^{-6}	2.5×10^{-5}	1×10^{-4}

[a] $d_{ch} = 2 \alpha C_{ch} \Delta V/V$; $d_{ch} = 2 \alpha C_{ch} 2 \Delta I/I$; $V = 100$ kv.

The values required to achieve a 5 A figure are at the limits of the stabilities easily attainable today. To achieve higher stabilities such as 2 parts per 1,000,000 in the high voltage for resolutions at the 1 A level with a lens of the same chromatic aberration coefficient, $C_{ch} = 0.1$, would be a considerable engineering task and would require voltage stability which may be difficult to attain. Since new lenses with lower spherical aberration coefficients must be designed for this task, designing lens configurations with lower chromatic aberration may also be required. Current stability should not be a problem if superconducting lenses are used.

D. Alignment

All previous discussion of the electron optical systems assumed perfect coaxial alignment of the optical components. Considerations of ultimate resolving power based on the limits set by Fraunhofer diffraction and the spherical aberration of the objective lens assume that the pencil of illumination incident on the object plane has a principal ray[4] coin-

---

[4] Principal ray: In a pencil of rays, the central ray. In a divergent pencil all rays make angles with the principal ray which defines the direction of propagation of the radiation.

cident with the optical axis of the objective lens. The total optical
system of the electron microscope usually has two additional lenses
magnifying the image produced by the objective lens and these lenses
also must have their optical axes coincident within given tolerances to
give validity to the evaluations of resolution given previously. Aberrations which have been ignored because they are small in an aligned
system will become important in the image figure obtained as nonaxial
misalignments enter into the optical system.

The most critical element in the alignment of the electron microscope for high resolution is the alignment of the illuminating system.

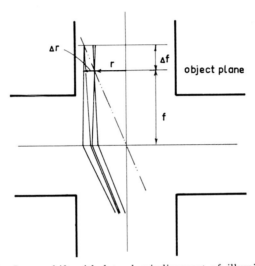

FIG. 32. Image shift with lateral misalignment of illumination.

The direct geometrical effects of misalignment are shown in Figs. 32
and 33. In Fig. 32 the displacement of the illuminating pencil off axis
laterally while still parallel to the optic axis of the objective is illustrated. An object point a distance, r, from the axis will appear to be
displaced a distance Δr as the focal length of the lens is changed an
amount Δf. From simple geometrical considerations

$$\Delta r = \frac{r}{f}\, \Delta f \tag{50}$$

These conditions hold for the high magnification at which the electron microscope is operated, and when $\Delta f << f$ and $\alpha_c < \alpha_o$.

Figure 33 illustrates the effects of a misalignment of the illumination that results when the principal ray of the illuminating pencil makes

an angle θ with the objective lens, though passing through the center of the lens. (A tilting of either the condenser system or objective lens would produce this effect.) The image will appear to center about the object point P at a distance r_p from the true optical center. Then for the small angles of θ found in actual systems

$$r_p = f \tan \theta \simeq f \cdot \theta \qquad (51)$$

As the objective lens is defocused an amount Δf the image will appear

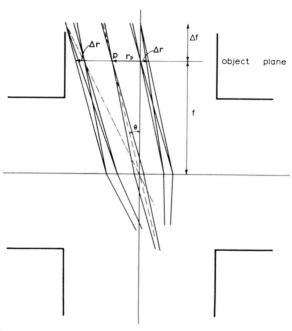

Fig. 33. Image shift with angular misalignment (tilt) of illumination.

to change about the center P. Again the increment of radial changes, Δr, is given by

$$\Delta r = \frac{r_p}{f} \Delta f \qquad (52)$$

and in terms of θ by

$$\Delta r = \theta \cdot \Delta f \qquad (53)$$

With magnetic lenses there is also a rotation of the image. The image point conjugate to r_p will appear as a center of rotation in the image. If the rotation effect is taken into account, Eq. (51) becomes

$$r_p = \varepsilon f \theta \qquad \text{(with } \varepsilon < 1\text{)} \qquad (54)$$

The value of ε can be related to the chromatic aberration coefficient and thus calculated (13). Leisegang (29) has found that for a special lens, $\varepsilon = \frac{1}{3}$, which is in good agreement with the calculated value.

The spherical aberration of the lens will also produce an effect if the illuminating pencil is inclined at an angle to the axis of the objective lens. The rays which have equal optical paths will only be centered about the optic axis if the principal ray of the illuminating pencil is coincident with the optic axis. If the principal ray passes through the center of the lens but at an angle, the pencil of rays of angular aperture α_c, which have equal optical paths through the system will be centered on the caustic of the lens. This effect can be easily observed, as Leisegang (29) pointed out, by examining the image produced by the lens using a large aperture (no physical objective aperture) at low magnification (1000 ×). A specimen such as a film with many small holes used as the object will give an image with strong phase-contrast effect at the edge of the holes. The phase-contrast effect will produce bright fringes at the edges of the holes, and these fringes will be symmetrical around the holes at the point where the rays have equal optical paths through the system. The separation of this center from the true center of the caustic axis and the axis of the lens is given in first approximation by

$$r_c = f\theta \tag{55}$$

from simple geometrical considerations.

Thus we see that two conditions are satisfied if the illuminating pencil is brought into alignment with the optic axis of the objective lens so that $\theta = 0$ and the principal ray is coincident with the optic axis. The axis of rotation with change of focus, r_p, and the caustic axis, r_c, coincide at the center of the image field. Leisegang (29) has shown how these criteria can be used to align the illuminating system of an electron microscope.

The effects of misalignment on the image can be severe. The largest effect will occur in the attendant chromatic aberration as might be expected from Eqs. (50) and (53) and the relation for chromatic aberration $\Delta r_{ch} = \alpha_o \Delta f$, Eq. (46). The angle of misalignment and the ratio of the displacement of the illuminating pencil from the lens center to the focal length, r/f, both must be small compared to α_o if no effects of misalignment are to be introduced.

Approximately the same requirements must hold if the misalignment is not to effect the spherical aberration figure. The misalignment of the illuminating pencil with respect to the objective lens will change the effective angular aperture of the objective, α_o, and thus θ and r_c/f must be small compared to α_o. Alignment tolerances for the lenses defined in

Table I are given in Table IV. The values given in the table are equivalent to the objective aperture, and will cause a deterioration of the chromatic aberration figure and the asymmetry figure by a factor of 2. Alignment of the illumination system with respect to the objective lens should be better than the values listed by a factor of 10 if deterioration of the resolution is to be held to less than 10%.

TABLE IV

ALIGNMENT TOLERANCES SET BY CHROMATIC ABERRATION AND ASYMMETRY

d_{Al} at:	1 A	2 A	5 A	10 A
θ (degrees):	1.3	0.65	0.26	0.13
r (off-axis distance in μ):	—	17	48	69

Glaser (12) has shown that as the angle of the beam is increased, the considerations which allow other aberrations such as coma and astigmatism to be neglected, no longer hold. At an angle $\theta = 1 \times 10^{-2}$ and an objective aperture of $\alpha_o = 5 \times 10^{-3}$, the aberration figures are already $18 \times$ greater than at $\theta = 0$. Since the requirements set by chromatic aberration and spherical aberration are at least as stringent, it is not likely that the other third-order aberrations will become limiting factors in the attainment of very high resolution.

The alignment required between the objective lens and the projector system is less critical. Hillier and Ramberg (23) showed that the axis of the projector lens can be misaligned with respect to the objective lens by a large lateral shift or tilted at a considerable angle before the image figure will deteriorate to the level set by the aberrations inherent in the objective lens. As a first approximation, the projector system can be used misaligned with respect to the objective lens by a factor equivalent to the magnification of the objective lens.

E. External Fields

Transverse external magnetic fields will effect the imaging in the electron microscope. A DC field will bend the optic axis and can usually be corrected by proper alignment of the components of the instrument. But the alternating fields, especially the 60 cycles from power lines, will cause image deterioration and the column of the instrument must be shielded against them. A poorly shielded illuminating system will give an oscillating illuminating pencil and the same criteria apply here as in the alignment of the illuminating system. The illuminating system is relatively easy to shield, but regions between the condensers and the gun, and especially between the condenser and the specimen, are not always adequately shielded for adverse conditions. The region just above and below the specimen is hard to shield because of the mechanical control ports in this region. Fields leaking down into the pole piece from above the specimen may be troublesome.

Leisegang (30) has calculated that a reduction of more than 1/20 the external field must be achieved in the specimen region to bring the effects of a 2–3 milligauss external field down to a level which would not deteriorate the image figure of the objective beyond a level permitting 2 A resolution. The region between objective lens and intermediate lens is less sensitive. But there is a much longer region here over which external fields might act, so this region of the instrument must also be shielded. The region below the projector lens need not be shielded under satisfactory laboratory conditions for operation of the electron microscope.

F. Recording of the Image

The recording of the image in the electron microscope involves the simultaneous observation of a complex variation of intensities incident upon an area a few centimeters square. The physical process by which the energy flux in the image plane is transduced into a pattern which can be observed visually can best be described if we use a particle model for the radiant energy. Bohr's concept of complementarity in contemporary quantum theory states that phenomena can be observed under different aspects, but the different modes cannot be observed simultaneously once the observer enters into the process to record the phenomenon. While it has been useful to describe the imaging process in the electron optical system by considering the wave aspects of the radiation, which provides a satisfactory model for describing the diffraction and aberration effects in the process, the final observation is best described in terms of individual particles interacting with the recording medium at discrete points. Whether our transducing medium is the photographic plate, the fluorescent screen, or some device giving image intensification, the observation will be the electron particle transferring its energy within some limited area in the image surface plane. The discreteness with which this energy transfer can be observed and the statistical fluctuations of the incident electrons within the area representing an image point will be factors in determining the limits of resolution of the system.

The statistical fluctuations in the number of electrons that are incident upon that increment of surface area which represents the resolvable image figure given by the optical system will set an absolute limit upon the resolution of the total system. This limit will depend upon the brightness of the electron source available, upon the efficiency of the available transducer, and the times over which the fluctuations can be integrated in recording the final image. As we shall see, the fluctuation in electron-current density over the periods which are practical within the stability limits of present electron microscopes is not the limiting factor in resolution with the electron microscope, but rather the inefficiency of the recording medium, such as the photographic plate which introduces a granularity in the image that borders on the limits of the resolution required for imaging at 1–2 A.

1. STATISTICAL FLUCTUATIONS

The current density incident on the object area which has the diameter equal to the resolution limit of the electron optical system will determine the statistical fluctuation in the final image area of this object point. The ultimate current density is set by the theoretical brightness limits on the gun which is the source of the electrons, and in practice by the actual brightness obtained and the limiting angular aperture of the condenser system which forms the image of the electron source. As we have seen in Section III, A, 1, a theoretical brightness of 2×10^5 amp/cm^2/sr is the limit set on a gun operating with a tungsten filament at $2800°$K and with an accelerating potential of 50 kv. The angular aperture of the illuminating system most likely will not exceed 1×10^{-2} rad even for the conditions of improved objective lenses in which the spherical aberration sets optimum angular apertures greater than this value. Thus, we have an upper limit of current density of 60 amp/cm^2 for a gun operating at theoretical brightness and imaged with a system which sets the angular aperture at 1×10^{-2} rad. Present instruments and practice set maximum angular apertures for the condenser system of $\sim 2 \times 10^{-3}$ rad. Practical systems may achieve one-half the theoretical brightness, but most likely would be imaged by a condenser system setting a limiting aperture of about 2×10^{-3} rad. The current density of this illumination at the object would be 1 amp/cm^2, a current density which we may take in our discussions as a "practical" value for present electron microscopes.

Table V gives the number of electrons/sec, n_o, incident upon object areas of different diameters for these two incident current densities, an upper theoretical limit of 60 amp/cm^2 and a practical working range of 1 amp/cm^2. The statistical fluctuations in the number of electrons which produce an image point is given approximately by $(n_o)^{1/2}$ and the percentage fluctuations are given by $100/(n_o)^{1/2}$ in Table V. Thus with a perfect transducer, that is one which counted each incident electron, at 1 A resolution a noise of 0.6% would be an ultimate limit for observations integrated over 1 sec, while with the "practical" illuminating system, a noise of some 4.5% in the signal would set the possible limit for 1 A resolution. Presently available transducers are not nearly 100% efficient and it will be the introduction of additional noise by these

TABLE V
ELECTRON FLUX THROUGH VARIOUS OBJECT AREAS

Diameter of object area, d_{min}:	1 A	2 A	5 A	10 A
Practical gun, 1 amp/cm²				
No. of electrons/sec, n_o:	5×10^2	2×10^3	1.25×10^4	5×10^4
% fluctuation, $100/(n_o)^{1/2}$:	4.5	2.2	0.9	0.45
Theoretical gun, 60 amp/cm²				
No. of electrons/sec, n_o:	3×10^4	12×10^4	7.5×10^5	3×10^6
% fluctuation, $100/(n_o)^{1/2}$:	0.6	0.3	0.1	0.06

devices into the final observation of the image which determines the actual limits set by statistical fluctuations.

2. PHOTOGRAPHIC PROCESS

The photographic process will undoubtedly remain the most satisfactory method for the final observation of the image produced by the optical system of the electron microscope. Not only has it the obvious advantages of permanence which provides the desired record for more detailed and leisurely examination, but is so far the best method we have of simultaneously integrating the total optical distribution of energy flux which is characteristic of the complex image produced by an optical system. What we desire is the complete image with its variations and interrelations. The photographic process simultaneously samples each point over the image plane and integrates the process over relatively wide limits of time. The limits in the process are (1) the efficiency with which electrons produce latent image points that can be developed into separate observable silver grains, and (2) the granularity in the photographic plate which sets the noise limits for image areas of given dimensions.

The characteristics of different photographic plates are very similar when exposed to electrons. The wide range of contrasts and sensitivities available in photographic emulsions when exposed to light are not available to electron exposures. The limitations set upon recording the electron image can be adequately discussed in terms of the properties of a commonly used photographic plate, the Kodak Lantern Slide, Medium, plate. This emulsion has fine grain sensitivity that gives satisfactory densities upon exposure of a few seconds to the electron image of the intensities observable on fluorescent screens, and a range of contrasts that can be varied slightly by adjusting developing times. Data is not available which would indicate that other emulsions could be used to give a significantly better resolution limit.

To understand the noise limitations set by the photographic recording of the image, we should first discuss the nature of the photographic image and the requirements it places on the electron optical system. The Kodak Lantern Slide, Medium, plate will have a density, $D = 1$ for exposures of $\sim 6.65 \times 10^{-10}$ coul/cm². ($D = \log (1/T)$ where T is the transmission of the developed photographic plate to light.) In the range of densities of $D \sim 1$ the relationship between density and exposure, Q, which may be taken as number of coul/cm² is given by

$$D = \gamma \log Q + A \qquad (56)$$

where γ, the slope of the plot of density versus $\log Q$ (log of the exposure), is a measure of the contrast in a given film and is approximately constant for a given film under given development over densities in the range of 0.5–2. An average value γ for the Kodak plates under standard development process is 1.6.

A given flux of electrons will be required to produce an image point of satisfactory density. If we take the limit of resolution as an object point of 1 A diameter, we have 3×10^4 electrons/sec incident as an ultimate limit and 5×10^2 electrons/sec with the "practical" illuminating system. The magnification of the electron optical system will set the area in the image which will correspond to the effective object dimension. In the first instance, this magnification can only be of a magnitude which will give the flux densities of electrons which are required to produce satisfactory photographic densities during exposures of the order of a few seconds. The second requirement will be that the area in the photographic plate on which the dimension corresponding to the resolution limit is recorded should be large compared to the grain in the photographic plate. Both these requirements are reasonably satisfied by an electron optical magnification of some 200,000 $\times$. Here the image figure corresponding to an object of 1 A diameter will have a diameter of 20 μ on the photographic plate. A density of $D \sim 1$ will be obtained if 1.3×10^3 electrons are incident on this area, and with 5×10^2 electrons/sec forming this image figure, an exposure of 2.6 sec would be required. A study of granularity in photographic films (21) shows that the Kodak plates have a power spectrum (which describes the granularity of the film) that is characteristic of 2 μ diameter grains. Thus a 20 μ diameter area should provide a satisfactory averaging of the noise produced by the grain. The eye resolves dimensions of 0.2 mm satisfactorily and therefore a 10 $\times$ photographic enlargement of the electron micro-

scope image will provide a satisfactory final presentation of the image at
2,000,000 $\times$ without graininess.

An evaluation of the contrast necessary in the image for observation
at the ultimate limits of dimensions requires that we consider the statistical fluctuations in the number of electrons incident on the photographic plate and how these fluctuations relate to the photographic
process. From the previously cited considerations we have 1.3×10^3 electrons producing the image figure and this number of electrons will
have percentage fluctuations of the order of $100/(n_o)^{1/2} \simeq 2.5\%$. For the
Kodak plate with $\gamma = 1.6$ and in the region of density $D = 1$, these
fluctuations in electron current in the image will produce changes in
transmission in the developed photographic plate of the order of 4%. A
7% change in the electron flux will produce a 12% change in the transmission of the developed photographic plate in this density range, giving
a signal-to-noise of $3 \times$.

Since even at this ultimate limit of 1 A resolution, the photographic
process does not place impractical conditions upon the recording of the
image, larger dimensions of resolution can be recorded photographically
with higher signal-to-noise ratios. At lower resolutions the incident flux
per unit area must be kept the same to give equivalent densities in the
photographic plate and the magnification can remain the same so the
image point is averaged over a correspondingly larger area. Thus for
2 A resolution the corresponding image figure will have a diameter of
40 μ. The fluctuation in the number of electrons on this area is only
1.25% for the "practical" gun and the average fluctuation in density in
the photographic plate will be only some 2%. A change in electron flux
of 7% caused by the interaction of the specimen with the incident electron beam will give the same 12% change in contrast in the plate and a
signal-to-noise of $6 \times$ will be obtained. Of course, material of equivalent
density in the specimen in each case will scatter more over the larger
area, and the actual signal from the 2 A area will be larger than in the
1 A case. In practice, the electron optical magnification is usually
reduced as the resolution requirements are lowered. Then the requirements on the illuminating system are not so stringent and the image
can be recorded at higher levels of intensity, providing easy visual
observation on the fluorescent screen.

The granularity of the photographic plate can be a factor in the
observation of detail in the photographic image, and in an analysis of
the total system this granularity should be taken into account. A useful
method would be similar to the treatment of light optical systems in
which the image detail produced by the optical system is evaluated in
terms of information theory (38). Each element in the system becomes

a filter with a given passband in terms of spatial frequencies and the final result is given by a linear combination of each of the elements. The photographic plate recording the image can also be considered to act upon the image as a filter with a cutoff frequency which corresponds to a spatial frequency given by the grain size in the photographic plate.

3. The Fluorescent Screen

The fluorescent screen provides an efficient transducer of the electron image to a visible light image. The fluorescent screen must provide an image of adequate brightness for observation by the eye. Since the visual acuity of the eye depends both on the brightness and contrast in the object viewed, some criteria must be chosen which will represent reasonable limiting conditions. The brightness which must be available for observation of small differences of contrast are so large that it is not practical to observe small variations of contrast directly on the fluorescent screen. A contrast difference of about 40% on the fluorescent screen is found to be a reasonable lower level to choose for visual observation. Fine variations of contrasts must be left to the photographic record where differences of 5 or 10% in the transmission of the plate can be made observable by viewing the photographic plate under illumination of high brightness. Visual observation on the fluorescent screen is to be used critically only for focusing. Here the high contrast in the light and dark fringes of the Fresnel-diffraction pattern produced at an edge in the specimen will provide an object of adequate contrast, at least in the out-of-focus conditions. The in-focus position can be located by finding the positions at which under- and overfocus can be observed, and by taking a focal series in the intermediate range, or for less critical micrographs choosing an intermediate position where the Fresnel-diffraction fringes lose contrast.

Visual acuity limits the eye to a resolution of objects which have a diameter of at least 200 μ and a contrast of 40% with respect to the background, if the available brightness is 1.0×10^{-3} lamberts. Acuity falls off as the available brightness of illumination decreases so that at 2.5×10^{-5} lamberts only detail of some 500 μ and contrast of 40% can be resolved. Under the conditions of current densities for satisfactory photographic recording of the image as discussed in Section III,F,2, adequate brightness would also be available for observation on the fluorescent screen. The current incident on the specimen was taken as 1 amp/cm^2 for the "practical" gun, and at 200,000 $\times$ magnification this gives a current of 2.5×10^{-11} amp/cm^2 on the fluorescent screen. At 100 kv the incident energy flux is 2.5×10^{-6} watts/cm^2. Thus for a phosphor giving 100 lumens/watt (6) the image would produce 2.5×10^{-4} lumens/cm², or lamberts.

At an electron optical magnification of 200,000 × the image figure of 500 μ diameter coresponds to an object dimension of 25 A, so for visual observation of smaller dimensions additional light optical magnification will have to be provided. Practical magnifiers giving 10–25 × magnification without loss of intensity in the image to the eye can be introduced in the viewing system. Using a microscope of long working distance and with an objective-lens aperture large enough to compensate for the change of intensity with magnification, a magnified image can be provided at the entrance pupil of the eye which has the same intensity as the smaller image on the fluorescent screen observed directly by the eye.

The granularity of the fluorescent screen must be considered. Actually, present screens have a granularity which gives an indicated resolution of 50–100 μ, so under these conditions visual observation with light magnification greater than 10 × would do no more than make viewing somewhat less strenuous. Single-crystal phosphors have been suggested and here 10 μ resolution has been reported (51). The statistical fluctuations which were considered in the photographic recording must now also be considered at this level of visual observations. A direct observation on a nonpersistent phosphor would involve the short integration time of the eye, some 0.1 sec. Again taking 20 μ as the diameter of the image figure, the fluctuations over 0.1 sec will be the order of 14% and a signal-to-noise of about 3 × would obtain for image contrasts of 40%.

4. IMAGE INTENSIFIER

Visual observation at brightness levels of the order of 1×10^{-4} lambert are strenuous and set the observations at limits of low visual acuity. An image intensifier such as described by Haine and co-workers (19) would provide a very helpful device for the visual observation of electron microscope images at comfortable brightness levels and may extend the range of contrast which can be observed directly down to the low levels which are now available only through photographic recording of the electron images. They have developed a scanning system in which the pickup tube is built into the electron microscope and responds directly to the electron image formed by the microscope. The amplified signal is displayed on a cathode-ray tube at high intensity by synchronized scanning and could be adjusted to give high-contrast effects by nonlinear response of the amplifier. The resolution obtained with the image intensifier will be determined by the diameter of the scanning beam in the pickup tube, but the available resolution in the total electron microscope system is still limited by the statistical fluctuations in the imaging beam as set by the current density at the specimen. The limiting values for different resolutions are just those per cent fluctuations given in Table V for integrations of the image over 1-sec intervals. Longer integration could be obtained by using persistent phosphors in the cathode-ray display tube or by recording the final image photographically with long exposures. The advantage of photographing the display tube over present practice would be the much larger flexibility and simplicity in photographic methods available with the photographic material out of the vacuum system.

References

1. Archard, G. D., *Brit. J. Appl. Phys.* **5**, 294 (1954).
2. Archard, G. D., *Brit. J. Appl. Phys.* **7**, 330 (1956).
2a. Bachmann, L., and Siegel, B. M., *Proc. European Reg. Conf. on Electron Microscopy, Delft, 1960* **I**, 157 (1961).
3. Bertein, F. R., *Ann. Radioelec.* **3**, 379 (1948).
4. Black, G., and Linfoot, E. H., *Proc. Roy. Soc.* **A239**, 522 (1957).
5. Born, M., and Wolf, E., "Principals of Optics." Pergamon Press, New York, 1959.
6. Bril, A., and Klasen, H. A., *Philips Res. Rept.* **7**, 401 (1952).
6a. Busch, H., *Ann. Physik* [4] **81**, 974 (1926).
7. Conrady, A. E., *Monthly Notices Roy. Astron. Soc.* June, p. 575 (1919).
7a. de Broglie, L., *Phil. Mag.* [6] **47**, 446 (1924).
8. Faget, J., Fagot, M., Ferré, J., and Fert, C., *Proc. 5th Intern. Conf. on Electron Microscopy, Philadelphia, 1962* **I**, A-7 (1962).
9. Fernandez-Moran, H., Unpublished data, quoted by Lenz (*32*).
10. Glaser, W., *Z. Physik* **116**, 19 (1940).
11. Glaser, W., *Z. Physik* **117**, 285 (1941).
12. Glaser, W., "Grundlagen der Electronenoptik." Springer, Vienna, 1952.
13. Glaser, W., *in* "Handbuch der Physik" (S. Flügge ed.), Vol. 33, p. 123. Springer, Berlin, 1956.
14. Glaser, W., and Schiske, P., *Optik* **11**, 422, 445 (1954).
15. Haine, M. E., *J. Sci. Instr.* **34**, 9 (1957).
16. Haine, M. E., and Einstein, P. A., *Brit. J. Appl. Phys.* **3**, 40 (1952).
17. Haine, M. E., and Mulvey, T., *J. Sci. Instr.* **31**, 326 (1954).
18. Haine, M. E., Einstein, P. A., and Borcherds, P. H., *Brit. J. Appl. Phys.* **9**, 482 (1958).
19. Haine, M. E., Einstein, P. A., and Ennos, A. E., *J. Sci. Instr.* **35**, 466 (1958).
20. Hall, C. E., *J. Appl. Phys.* **22**, 655 (1951).
20a. Hamilton, W. K., *in* "Mathematical Papers of Sir William Rowan Hamilton" (A. S. Conway and J. L. Synge, eds.), Vol. 1, p. 463. Cambridge Univ. Press, London and New York, 1931.
21. Hamlet, R., M. S. Thesis, Cornell University (1963).

21a. Heidenreich, R. D., *J. Appl. Phys.* **34**, 964 (1963).
22. Hibi, T., Yoda, K., and Takahashi, S., *J. Electronmicroscopy (Japan)* **11**, 244 (1962).
23. Hillier, J., and Ramberg, E., *J. Appl. Phys.* **18**, 48 (1947).
24. Howie, A., *Proc. 5th Intern. Conf. on Electron Microscopy, Philadelphia, 1962* **I**, AA-9 (1962).
25. Kamiya, Y., *J. Phys. Soc. Japan* **13**, 1144 (1958).
26. Kanaya, K., Kawakatsu, H., Ito, K., and Yotsumoto, H., *J. Appl. Phys.* **29**, 1046 (1958).
27. Langmuir, D. E., *Proc. I.R.E.* **25**, 977 (1937).
28. Leisegang, S., *Z. Physik* **132**, 183 (1952).
29. Leisegang, S., *Optik* **11**, 397 (1954).
30. Leisegang, S., *in* "Handbuch der Physik" (S. Flügge, ed.), Vol. 33, p. 396. Springer, Berlin, 1956.
31. Lenz, F., *Z. Naturforsch.* **9a**, 185 (1954).
32. Lenz, F., *J. Electronmicroscopy (Japan)* **10**, 205 (1961).
33. Lenz, F., and Scheffels, W., *Z. Naturforsch.* **13a**, 226 (1958).
34. Liebmann, G., *Proc. Phys. Soc. (London)* **65B**, 95, 188 (1952).
35. Liebmann, G., *Proc. Phys. Soc. (London)* **66B**, 448 (1953).
36. Liebmann, G., *Proc. Phys. Soc. (London)* **68B**, 737 (1955).
37. Liebmann, G., and Grad, M. E., *Proc. Phys. Soc. (London)* **54B**, 956 (1951).
38. Linfoot, E. H., *J. Opt. Soc. Am.* **45**, 808 (1954).
39. Linfoot, E. H., "Recent Advances in Optics." Oxford Univ. Press, London and New York, 1955.
40. Lippert, W., *Z. Naturforsch.* **13a**, 1089 (1958).
41. Nixon, W. C., *Proc. 4th Intern. Conf. on Electron Microscopy, Berlin, 1958* **I**, 246 (1960).
42. Pilyankovich, A. N., *Zh. Tekhn. Fiz.* **30**, 226, 232 (1960).
43. Rayleigh, Lord, *Phil. Mag.* [5] **11**, 214 (1881).
44. Scherzer, O., *J. Appl. Phys.* **20**, 20 (1949).
45. Seeliger, R., *Optik* **10**, 29 (1953).
45a. Shaeffer, E., Silcox, J., and Siegel, B. M., to be published.
46. Siegel, B. M., and Specht, R., *Air Force Office of Scientific Research*, TN-60-756 (1960).
47. Steigerwald, K. H., *Optik* **5**, 469 (1949).
48. Sturrock, P. A., *Phil. Trans. Roy. Soc. (London)* **A243**, 387 (1951).
49. Swift, D. W., and Nixon, W. C., *Proc. European Reg. Conf. on Electron Microscopy, Delft, 1960* **I**, 69 (1961).
50. van Dorsten, A. C., and Premsela, H. F., *Proc. European Reg. Conf. on Electron Microscopy, Delft, 1960* **I**, 101 (1961).
51. von Ardenne, M., *Z. Physik* **115**, 339 (1940).
51a. von Borries, B., *in* "Die Übermikroskopie," p. 166. Verlag Editio Cantor, Aulendorf/Württ, 1949.
52. Watanabe, M., *J. Phys. Soc. Japan* **17**, 569 (1962).
53. Westerberg, E., and Hall, C. E., from Westerberg, E. M.S. Thesis, Massachusetts Institute of Technology (1962).
54. Wilska, A. P., *Proc. 5th Intern. Conf. on Electron Microscopy, Philadelphia, 1962* **I**, D-6 (1962).
54a. Wilska, A. P., U. S. Patent 3,100,260 (1963).
55. Zeitler, E., and Bahr, G. F., *Exptl. Cell Res.* **12**, 44 (1957).
56. Zernike, F., *Z. Tech. Physik* **16**, 454 (1935).

Selected Methods and Techniques

CHAPTER 2

Thin Metal Specimens

D. W. PASHLEY

I. Introduction

One of the major advances in specimen-preparation technique made in recent years has been the development of methods to allow the preparation of metal specimens which are sufficiently thin for direct-transmission observation (for applications see Chapter 5). The techniques may be divided into two classes: (*a*) the sectioning of thick metal specimens by mechanical, chemical, or electrochemical methods; (*b*) the growth of thin films by various deposition techniques.

In this chapter, a general account of techniques (*b*) is given, since these techniques are involved in many of the applications discussed in Chapter 5. It was the original intention that techniques (*a*) would be presented largely in support of a chapter on metallurgical applications, but as it has not been possible to include this chapter, a relatively brief summary of these techniques is included here because they are also involved in many of the applications discussed in Chapter 5. Time, however, has not allowed a comprehensive and independent account to be given, and the reader is referred to the reviews given in Kelly and Nutting (*21*), Phillips (*34*), and Thomas (*44*) for further details.

The thickness of specimen required for a transmission micrograph depends upon the energy of the electrons and the atomic number of the constituent atoms of the foil. For 70–100 kv electrons, and light elements (e.g., aluminum), the thickness can be anything below about 5000 A, whereas for heavier elements (e.g., gold) the upper limit is nearer 2000 A. In practice, it is common to work with specimens of about 1000–2000 A in thickness, when the transmission of the electrons and the quality of the image is highly dependent upon the orientation of the specimen. A specimen tilting stage is then most desirable as a means of adjusting the image quality at any particular point in the foil.

II. The Preparation of Thin Foils from Bulk Samples

Various techniques have been investigated for the "sectioning" of bulk material. The final stage of preparation normally requires as its starting material a foil which is certainly no more than 0.004–0.008 inch in thickness, depending upon the metal or alloy. This must be provided either as a mechanically rolled foil or by a suitable procedure which allows a thin slice to be cut from a larger sample. The techniques which are available for the latter purpose include jet machining (21), spark machining (9), and cutting followed by grinding (20). Attention here will be concentrated on the final-stage techniques.

A. Chemical Thinning

The earliest known technique is that of chemical thinning, which was used originally for the purpose of transmission electron diffraction (45). A rolled or beaten foil is floated on the surface of a suitable etching agent until localized areas which are sufficiently thin are produced. This technique was used for both electron diffraction and microscopy by Hirsch et al. (17), who applied it to beaten gold foils; potassium cyanide was used as the etchant. The main disadvantage of the technique is that the metal foils prepared in this way have a small grain size and a complex imperfection structure due to the large amount of cold work present. The technique was subsequently extended to aluminum with annealed rolled foils used as the starting material (18), and this method provided one of the first two examples of specimens exhibiting clear dislocation images on transmission micrographs.

Although the chemical thinning technique has not been very widely used, it is simple, and can be quite effective. More recently the method has been used successfully for the thinning of magnesium oxide (48).

B. Electrochemical Thinning

The method of using electrolysis for the thinning of metal foils was also first applied to the preparation of specimens for electron diffraction (45). The first successful application to electron microscopy was carried out by Heidenreich (*16*), and the first application to dislocation studies was made by Bollmann (*3*) in 1956; since 1956 many variants and developments of the technique have been reported. The technique now provides the most widely used method for the preparation of thinned metal films for the electron microscope.

Although it is relatively easy to find suitable electrolytes to allow a particular metal or alloy film to be dissolved away in a controlled manner, the preparation of specimens with the required properties often requires more specialized techniques. The important requirements are: (*a*) large areas ($>$ 10 μ diameter) of sufficiently thin metal should be produced; (*b*) the surfaces of these areas should be fairly smooth, so that image contrast arising from surface structure does not predominate over contrast from internal structure; (*c*) the surfaces should be substantially free from oxides and other contaminants; and (*d*) in the case of alloys, one component must not be dissolved away preferentially. Many of the baths used for electropolishing of metals are found to satisfy these requirements adequately, but they are not necessarily operated under conditions which lead to the best polish. A common approach used to achieve requirement (*a*) is to allow holes to be formed in the metal foil, when it is possible to find that there are adequately thin regions of the specimen around the holes. There are a number of variations on this approach, stemming from the method first used by Bollmann (*3*). These include techniques in which no special electrode arrangement is employed, and those which rely on special geometry to allow control of the distribution of the electrochemical attack across the specimen. Thus Bollmann used two pointed cathodes placed on each side of the thin foil specimen as anode. The pointed cathodes are first placed close to the specimen, and attack is continued until a hole appears in the center of the foil. The electrodes are then moved apart and further attack leads to the formation of a hole farther away from the center. The attack is continued until the two holes almost meet and it is found that suitably thin regions exist in the material remaining between the two holes.

Fisher (*11*) modified this technique, by taking account of the effect of electrode separation on the current distribution across the specimen anode. With the pointed cathodes close to the specimen there is preferential attack at the center, but with a large separation the rate of attack is faster away from the center. At some intermediate position, a relatively uniform rate of attack takes place, and under these conditions the polishing can be continued until small holes appear. The material around these holes is then often sufficiently thin. Thus use of the method requires a critical setting of the electrode separation. Pashley and Presland have modified the electrode system by using flat-ended cathodes in place of the points. These have similar properties except that the setting of the electrodes for near-uniform attack is less critical.

The techniques which involve no special electrode geometry have been described, for example, by Tomlinson (46), Brandon and Nutting (6), and Nicholson et al. (25). In some cases, control of the position of attack on the specimen is effected by painting a nonconducting varnish over parts of the specimen.

C. Other Thinning Techniques

Bombardment of a metal foil by ions allows very controlled thinning to be accomplished, and the method was first used by Castaing (8) with aluminum alloys. The technique has not been widely used because: (a) the rate of removal of metal is very slow; (b) it is difficult to eliminate fine-scale surface irregularities; and (c) the energetic ions cause damage to the metal structure.

The cutting of metal samples by means of an ultramicrotome has been made possible by the availability of the diamond knife (10). Although many metals and alloys can be sectioned into films of about 1000 A in thickness, the technique has not been widely used, partly because of the difficulties associated with carrying out the technique, but largely because of the way in which the metal is deformed by the cutting process. This deformation, which is mainly intrinsic to the cutting mechanism, makes the technique unsuitable for applications where it is necessary to observe lattice imperfections in the alloy; but it might not matter too seriously in cases where the dispersion of a second phase within a matrix is being studied. A detailed discussion of the technique appears in Phillips (34).

III. Thin-Film Preparation by Deposition Techniques

A. Introduction

A convenient method of preparing metals and other substances in the form of sufficiently thin films is to deposit the material as a surface coating on a suitable substrate. The surface film is then detached by dissolving the substrate in a solution which does not attack the deposit. There are four general ways of carrying out the deposition: (1) by vacuum evaporation; (2) by electrodeposition; (3) by sputtering, and (4) by chemical attack. Method (1) has been widely used, and most attention will be given to this technique. Method (2) has been used to a much more limited extent, and certain special features of this technique are considered in Section III, C. Methods (3) and (4) have so far been used very little for the preparation of electron microscope specimens and will not be considered further.

The advantages of the deposition techniques are that large uniform areas of films of accurately controlled thickness can be prepared, and that the crystal orientation of the films can often be controlled so that single-crystal films are obtained. This arises because in many cases a deposited film has some preferred orientation which is directly related to that of the substrate. A single-crystal substrate can then lead to a single-crystal deposit film. This phenomenon is known as epitaxy, and a review of the examples which have been observed is given in Pashley (30). The deposition techniques, particularly the evaporation one, are applicable to a wide variety of materials.

Although in many respects the structure and properties of deposited films are quite different from those of the bulk material, so that they are not convenient specimens when the main object of an experiment is to study bulk material, they have several important uses. The mechanism of growth and the microstructure of deposited films form a very interesting field of study in itself (see Chapter 5), but our remarks here are confined to the possible uses of deposited films as electron microscope transmission specimens in other kinds of experiments. Because of the control of thickness and orientation which is possible during the preparation of a deposited film, such films are useful as test objects for experiments on the contrast which arises with crystalline objects, particularly those containing lattice defects. Most kinds of lattice defects occur in deposited films. They are also particularly suitable for studies of various electron optical phenomena associated with crystalline objects, such as the formation of moiré patterns with overlapping crystalline films (see Chapter 5). This applies especially when very high resolution is required, since very thin specimens are needed to avoid excessive inelastic scattering which leads to chromatic aberration. An application which is likely to become more important in the future is to use the thin-deposited single-crystal film as a substrate on which to carry out controlled chemical reactions that are studied by high-resolution transmission microscopy (2). This technique promises to provide detailed evidence on the early stages of chemical reactions such as the formation of oxide on the surface of a metal. A wide field of application is in the study of alloys. Although the detailed structure of an alloy prepared by evaporation is in most cases different from the bulk, very valuable fundamental information can be obtained by observations of such specimens. This applies particularly to investigations of phases present in the alloy for any given composition and heat treatment, and to studies on the mechanism of phase changes occurring when the temperature is altered. If proper account is taken of the effect of having a thin-film specimen, the information obtained with the thin film can be usefully interpreted in terms of fundamental phenomena. The special effects associated with using deposited-alloy thin films as specimens are as follows. First, the lattice imperfections present in the film might be abnormal in type or density, and might have some influence on the phase structure. Second, because there is a large surface area close to all points in the specimen, any structure which is formed by diffusion might be modified because of preferential diffusion to the surface. Thus precipitates might form on the surface of the specimen, rather than inside. Third, many transitions from one alloy phase to another give rise to local or long-range strains, and these strains are accommodated in a different manner in a thin film than inside a bulk alloy. In particular, contraction or expansion normal to the plane of the film can occur without giving rise to stress, whereas this is not true for bulk alloy.

Evaporated-alloy films have been used to considerable advantage in a number of investigations including studies on ordered structures and transformations in copper-gold alloy (13, 28, 33), studies on precipitation in aluminum-silver alloys (26), and studies on martensite transformations in iron alloys (35).

Various examples of studies made with evaporated single-crystal films are given in Chapter 5.

B. The Evaporation Technique

Deposition is commonly carried out in a demountable vacuum system with an ultimate vacuum of no better than 10^{-5} mm Hg. At this pressure the rate of bombardment of the substrate surface by the residual gas molecules is comparable with the rate of arrival of the depositing vapor molecules, so that considerable doubts exist about the gaseous content of the deposits. Also, it is possible that the presence of the gas has some effect on the mode of growth, and hence the microstructure of the deposits. Currently, therefore, efforts are being made in a number of laboratories to prepare films in much cleaner vacuum systems, with ultimate pressures as low as 10^{-10} mm Hg. This involves much more careful and prolonged experiments, and it is too early to judge the advantages of these cleaner systems. It is clear that there is a special gain in the case of the readily oxidizable metals, since these deposit as oxides in the poorer vacuum systems. Deposition in a vacuum system of 10^{-5} mm Hg is relatively straightforward and quick to carry out, and leads to good quality films in many cases, so that subsequent remarks are confined to this technique.

Vacuum deposition of thin metal films is now a widely used commercial process, and a considerable amount of information on the technique exists in the literature. A valuable general description has been given by Holland (19). The simplest type of source is a tungsten or molybdenum wire spiral basket which is heated by passing an electric current through the wire. The metal to be evaporated is placed in the spiral basket and heated to a temperature such that its vapor pressure exceeds that of the residual gas pressure. A vapor pressure of the order 10^{-2} mm Hg gives useful rates of deposition on the substrate, which is usually placed 5–15 cm away from the source. If the metal to be deposited readily forms an alloy with tungsten and molybdenum, or if it fails to wet the tungsten or molybdenum wire satisfactorily, then a different type of source must be used. Small crucibles, or ceramic coated wire baskets can be used. A useful discussion of the methods will be found in Holland (19).

The structure of the deposited film is considerably influenced by the temperature at which the substrate is maintained during the deposition. Elevated substrate temperatures lead to films with larger grain size; also, when single-crystal substrates are used oriented growth is more likely to occur at the higher temperatures. The method of heating the substrate is found to be of some importance, particularly for the growth of single-crystal films. It is necessary to ensure that no contamination is formed on the substrate during the heating-up period. Contamination can readily deposit if, for example, low melting-point metals exist as an impurity in a component of the heating device (31).

Few designs of suitable heating devices are given in the literature, although it is clear that many successful types are in use. The simplest type consists of a metal hot plate that can be heated either by a wire-wound heater, or by electron bombardment. The design of a satisfactory heater which is easy to construct is shown in Fig. 1. The metal sheets used in the construction are of high-purity silver, to avoid the possibility of any contamination. Before use it is advisable to bake the hot plate in a vacuum at a temperature above the required operating temperature, in order to clean off any impurities. A power supply of only a few watts is sufficient to produce a temperature of 500°C. The temperature of the hot plate is readily measured by means of a thermocouple embedded in its upper surface, but in determining the true surface temperature of the specimen allowance must be made for any temperature drop occurring across the specimen. For thin specimens this temperature drop will be quite small.

The control of film thickness demands careful attention, but with sufficient care very accurate control can be obtained. There are two

basic methods of control. Either the source is loaded with a limited
and measured amount of material, all of which is evaporated; or the
source contains more than is required, and the amount deposited is
determined by some independent calibration. The difficulty with the
former method is that the efficiency of most sources varies considerably
as a function of direction, as has been clearly shown by Preuss (36). It
is thus not easy to calculate the thickness on a given specimen from the
amount evaporated. A given source can be calibrated by subsidiary

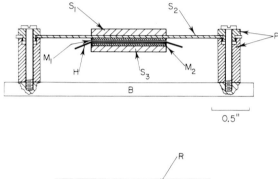

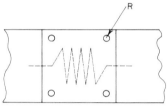

Fig. 1. A simple hot plate used for heating substrates. S_1, S_2, and S_3 are sheets
of pure silver; M_1 and M_2 are sheets of mica; H is the heater element consisting
of 0.005-inch-diameter molybdenum wire; P are porcelain insulators; R are silver
rivets used to clamp the entire hot plate assembly.

experiments, and quite accurate results can be obtained if the source is
so designed that the polar diagram of its efficiency remains fixed. This is
not normally possible with spiral-filament sources, because the polar
diagram depends upon the detailed manner in which the source material
wets the spiral; this occurs as a result of shadowing of the metal vapor
by the wire of the spiral. Possibilities for the latter technique are to
predetermine the rate of deposition under some standard evaporating
condition, and effect control by timing; or to measure the film thickness
during deposition by, for example, resistivity measurements or optical
absorption. An additional technique is to use a rate meter which allows
the rate of deposition to be measured and controlled to a high degree of
accuracy. A rate meter which depends upon measuring the momentum of

the vapor stream has been described by Campbell and Blackburn (7), and one which involves measuring the vapor pressure with an ionization gauge has been described by Schwarz (42).

Various techniques are available for a final measurement of the deposited film thickness, and since they are all quite standard they will not be described. The most common methods are: (1) multiple-beam interferometry; (2) weighing; (3) quantitative chemical analysis; and (4) radioactivity measurements used in conjunction with activated source material. The advantages of (4) are that it is nondestructive and much more sensitive than any of the others. The choice in any particular case depends very much upon circumstances, and all the methods have their limitations. Frequently, thickness measurements are only necessary during the calibration of any particular arrangement.

1. THE CHOICE OF SUBSTRATES

When randomly oriented polycrystalline specimens are required, the choice of substrate is not critical. If a thin supporting film is permissible, then the material can be deposited directly onto a thin film of carbon, which is readily prepared by the technique devised by Bradley (4). Otherwise, soluble substrates such as collodion or rock salt are adequate.

With the growth of single-crystal films by means of epitaxy, the choice of a suitable substrate is much more limited, and is governed by the following desirabilities: (1) its surface must be smooth and clean; (2) the deposit metal must grow on it epitaxially in a convenient orientation; (3) it must be possible to dissolve the substrate without appreciably dissolving the deposit film; and (4) the deposit film should be continuous at the required thickness.

A suitable clean, smooth surface can often be obtained by using a freshly cleaved crystal. Alternatively, polished surfaces can be prepared mechanically, and the worked layer suitably removed. This technique has been used, for example, by Heavens et al. (15). Optically smooth (100), (110), and (111) faces of rock salt were obtained by a suitable polishing technique, and the worked surface layer produced was removed by thermally etching the surface at 350°C in vacuo. Excellently oriented films of copper were formed by deposition onto these surfaces. For metal substrate surfaces, electropolishing has been used successfully, e.g., Brame and Evans (5). Another method which is sometimes possible is to form the substrate itself by evaporation.

There is no method, other than the experimental one, of determining whether a certain deposit will orient on a given substrate. Further, it is not possible to predict with any certainty what relative orientation will occur in a given case. This arises because the phenomenon of epitaxy

is not clearly understood, so that no reliable theory exists. Most
theoretical approaches are based upon the occurrence of relatively small
misfits between the two crystal lattices at the contact plane, but the
experimental evidence is overwhelmingly against this condition as a
criterion for orientation (30). Similarity in structure is a far more reliable
criterion; for example, most face-centered cubic metals can be grown on
each other in parallel orientation, as can most alkali halides with the
rock salt structure. However, good orientation can frequently be obtained
between two quite dissimilar structures (e.g., face-centered cubic silver
on monoclinic mica). In any particular case, previous experience with
some related system can be used as a guide to expected results, but a
direct experimental test of the deposit orientation should be made as
soon as possible, as the only sure means of determining the result. The
effect of substrate temperature should be examined, as this can be very
pronounced.

Unless the substrate used is itself a thin film, it is necessary to remove
the deposit for examination by transmission in the electron microscope.
Except in very special circumstances the deposit cannot be detached
mechanically, the most convenient method being to dissolve the substrate.
This places a severe restriction on the choice of suitable deposit-substrate
combinations, and explains the popularity of the water-soluble alkali
halides, especially rock salt, as substrates. Because the deposit film
contains only a small total amount of material, its solubility in the
substrate solvent must be extremely low.

For most electron microscope applications the deposited film should
ideally be continuous and uniform in thickness. Although this ideal can
be fairly closely approached in many systems, a minimum film thickness
is usually necessary. Thus for gold on rock salt at a substrate temperature
of 300°C, a reasonably uniform continuous film is not formed until the
average deposit thickness reaches 700–800 A (1). The stage at which film
continuity occurs clearly depends upon the ability of the deposit to
spread over the substrate surface, and this in turn is controlled by the
relative values of the interfacial energy between the substrate and
deposit, and the surface energies of the substrate and of the
deposit. Since the interfacial energies involved are generally unknown,
the systems which involve low interfacial energies must be found by
trial and error. General experience is that similarity in structure and
lattice spacing is likely to lead to relatively low interfacial energy, so that
alkali halides with closely similar lattice constants spread well on each
other (41), and thin, continuous, face-centered cubic-metal films can be
prepared by depositing them on other face-centered cubic metals of
similar spacing (32). Again, less obvious cases are found, and it is well

known that gold spreads extremely well on bismuth oxide (*12*). The rate
of deposition also influences the tendency to produce continuous films;
Sennett and Scott (*43*) have shown that fast rates of deposition favor the
formation of continuous films, although the fast rates do not always lead
to the production of well-oriented films.

Double-evaporation techniques are sometimes useful as a means of
overcoming some of the difficulties. Very good single-crystal films of gold
can be prepared by first depositing about 1500 A of silver onto mica or
rock salt, and then depositing the required amount of gold onto the
silver (*32*). The gold films are readily detached by dissolving the silver
in nitric acid. Uniform coherent films of any thickness from about a
100 A upward can be obtained in this way, in (111) or (100) orientation.
Undoubtedly other orientations could be grown by suitable choice of the
initial substrate. Similarly, good thin single-crystal films of nickel have
been grown by first depositing copper on rock salt and then nickel onto
the copper (*15*).

2. ALLOY FILMS

A wide range of alloys can be deposited by the usual evaporation
techniques, but the experimental difficulty is to control the composition.
This arises because the composition of the vapor is generally different
from that of the molten source from which it comes, particularly when
the components of the alloy have widely different melting points. This
leads to one component being enriched in the first layers deposited, and
correspondingly depleted in the molten source, so that there is some
separation of components in the films which are produced. The preparation of homogeneous alloy films must therefore be carried out by more
specialized techniques.

One method of dealing with the difficulty is to use the technique
described by Harris and Siegel (*14*). The powdered alloy is fed slowly
onto a molybdenum boat maintained at a temperature sufficiently high
to cause the alloy particles to evaporate instantaneously. The composition of the deposited alloy film is then closely that of the powder
used, and certainly is constant throughout the film thickness. The rate of
deposition is controlled by the rate of feeding the powder onto the
molybdenum boat.

Another method of controlling the composition of the deposited alloy
film is to use two or more independent sources for the pure metal components of the alloy. The two sources operate simultaneously, and by
previously calibrating these sources, one can control the composition of
the deposited film. Although the method is potentially a very powerful
and flexible one, it is not too easy in practice to obtain sufficient control

of the source to produce accurately predetermined alloy compositions, although fairly well homogenized films are readily obtained. A convenient version of the technique, used for example by Michel (23) and Trillat and Takahashi (47), is to prepare a number of specimens with a wide but continuous variation in composition by having one long substrate, or several separate substrates, as shown in Fig. 2. The composition variations arise from the variations occurring in the source-to-substrate distances. The exact composition at any point must be determined by some independent method, if this needs to be known accurately.

In cases where the interdiffusion of the two component metals occurs at sufficiently low temperatures, an alloy film can be homogenized after deposition. For example, Raether (37) produced films of Cu_3Au by

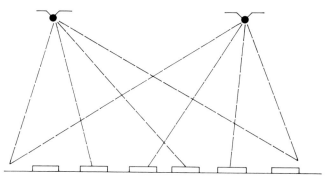

Fig. 2. The arrangement for using two independent sources to prepare a number of specimens of a binary alloy, with a range of compositions.

depositing the alloy directly onto rock salt at 400°C, followed by homogenization at approximately 600°C. The final composition of the deposited film was very close to that of the alloy used; this is a fairly favorable case, however, since the melting points of gold and copper are very close. A variation of the technique is to deposit the components in turn onto a suitable substrate, and then to interdiffuse the two metals. This has been done by Ogawa et al. (28), who deposited the gold onto a rock salt substrate at 400°C, and then, with the substrate at room temperature, added the required amount of copper to produce CuAu. Homogenization was carried out at 350°C. The technique was extended to a ternary alloy system by subsequently adding zinc to the alloy, and homogenizing once again at 350°C (29). If very thin, coherent, and uniform films of one of the components can be prepared, then similar quality films of the alloy can be produced by adding the other component or components to the detached film of the first component. This technique was used by Glossop and Pashley (*13*) to produce uniformly thick films of CuAu less than 500 A in thickness.

The general technique of successive evaporation followed by homogenization is very versatile, and can be extremely successful, but it requires care to control the composition adequately. It is necessary to carry out preliminary experiments in which the amount of material deposited by each source is determined and controlled to the required accuracy. The procedure depends upon the type of source used.

Alloys between metals and nonmetals (e.g., gases) can also be prepared, by first making the metal film which is then heat treated in a suitable atmosphere. Pitsch (*35*) has used the method to prepare iron-nitrogen and iron-carbon alloys. The iron film is prepared by evaporation onto collodion, which is dissolved away before the iron is heated in either a hydrogen-ammonia or a hydrogen-methane gas mixture.

By a suitable choice of substrate, good single-crystal alloy films can be prepared by the evaporation technique. The same general comments apply, as given in Section III, B, 1. Many of the examples quoted above refer to single-crystal films.

C. Electrodeposition

The main reason why electrodeposition is not widely used is because it is limited largely to the deposition of metals upon metals. Since it is not easy, in general, to detach one metal from another by chemical means this represents a very severe restriction. The instances in which the technique has been used have been limited to cases where the detaching of the electrodeposited film is particularly straightforward. In order to produce films of a thickness suitable for electron microscopy, it is necessary to either use rates of deposition which are slow by normal standards or to use very short periods of deposition. This does in some cases lead to experimental difficulties (*24*), but otherwise the method is quite standard and needs no elaboration here. One advantage of the technique is its simplicity; thickness control is particularly straightforward.

Several investigators have made thin films of nickel by electrodeposition onto copper (*22, 27, 38, 39, 40, 49*). The copper is preferentially dissolved in a solution of chromium trioxide in sulphuric acid, as first used by Weil and Read (*49*). Good quality gold films can be prepared by electrodeposition onto silver and these are detached by dissolving the silver in nitric acid. It is possible to produce oriented films by electrodeposition onto single-crystal substrates, and in both examples quoted good quality single-crystal films were obtained.

References

1. Bassett, G. A., and Pashley, D. W., *J. Inst. Metals* **87**, 449 (1958, 1959).
2. Bassett, G. A., Menter, J. W., and Pashley, D. W., *Discussions Faraday Soc.* **28**, 7 (1959).
3. Bollmann, W., *Phys. Rev.* **103**, 1588 (1956).
4. Bradley, D. E., *Brit. J. Appl. Phys.* **5**, 65 (1954).
5. Brame, D. R., and Evans, T., *Phil. Mag.* [8] **3**, 971 (1958).
6. Brandon D. G., and Nutting, J., *Brit. J. Appl. Phys.* **10**, 275 (1959).
7. Campbell, D. S., and Blackburn, H., *Natl. Symp. Vacuum Technol., Trans., 1960* **7**, 313 (1961).
8. Castaing, R., *Rev. Met. (Paris)* **52**, 669 (1955).
9. Cole, M., Bucklow, I. A., and Grigson, C. W. B., *Brit. J. Appl. Phys.* **12**, 296 (1961).
10. Fernandez-Moran, H., *J. Biophys. Biochem. Cytol.* **2**, No. 4, Suppl. 29 (1956).
11. Fisher, R. M., and Szirmae, A., *A.S.T.M. Spec. Tech. Publ.* **262**, 103 (1960).
12. Gillham, E. J., and Preston, J. S., *Proc. Phys. Soc. (London)* **B65**, 649 (1952).
13. Glossop, A. B., and Pashley, D. W., *Proc. Roy. Soc.* **A250**, 132 (1959).
14. Harris, L., and Siegel, B. M., *J. Appl. Phys.* **19**, 739 (1948).
15. Heavens, O. S., Miller, R. F., Moss, G. L., and Anderson, J. C., *Proc. Phys. Soc. (London)* **78**, 33 (1961).
16. Heidenreich, R. D., *J. Appl. Phys.* **20**, 993 (1949).
17. Hirsch, P. B., Kelly, A., and Menter, J. W., *Proc. Phys. Soc. (London)* **B68**, 1132 (1955).
18. Hirsch, P. B., Horne, R. W., and Whelan, M. J., *Phil. Mag.* [8] **1**, 677 (1956).
19. Holland, L., "Vacuum Deposition of Thin Films." Chapman & Hall, London, 1956.
20. Irving, B. A., *Brit. J. Appl. Phys.* **11**, 27 (1960).
21. Kelly, P. M., and Nutting, J., *J. Inst. Metals* **87**, 385 (1959).
22. Lawless, K. R., Garmon, L. B., and Leidheiser, H., *Proc. European Reg. Conf. on Electron Microscopy, Delft, 1960* p. 396 (1961).
23. Michel, P., *Compt. Rend.* **235**, 377 (1952).
24. Newman, R. C., *Proc. Phys. Soc. (London)* **B69**, 432 (1956).
25. Nicholson, R. B., Thomas, G., and Nutting, J., *Brit. J. Appl. Phys.* **9**, 23 (1958).
26. Ogawa, S., and Fukano, Y., *J. Phys. Soc. Japan* **14**, 1671 (1959).
27. Ogawa, S., Mizuno, J., Watanabe, D., and Fujita, F. E., *J. Phys. Soc. Japan* **12**, 999 (1957).
28. Ogawa, S., Watanabe, D., Watanabe, H., and Komoda, T., *Acta Cryst.* **11**, 872 (1958).
29. Ogawa, S., Watanabe, D., Watanabe, H., and Komoda, T., *J. Phys. Soc. Japan* **14**, 936 (1959).
30. Pashley, D. W., *Advan. Phys.* **5**, 173 (1956).
31. Pashley, D. W., *Phil. Mag.* [8] **4**, 316 (1959).
32. Pashley, D. W., *Phil. Mag.* [8] **4**, 324 (1959).
33. Pashley, D. W., and Presland, A. E. B., *J. Inst. Metals* **87**, 419 (1958, 1959).
34. Phillips, R., *in* "Techniques for Electron Microscopy" (D. Kay, ed.), Chapter 10, p. 229. Blackwell, Oxford, 1961.
35. Pitsch, W., *J. Inst. Metals* **87**, 444 (1958, 1959).
36. Preuss, L. E., *J. Appl. Phys.* **24**, 1401 (1953).
37. Raether, H., *Z. Angew. Phys.* **4**, 53 (1952).
38. Reimer, L., *Z. Metallk.* **48**, 390 (1957).

39. Reimer, L., *Z. Physik* **150**, 99 (1958).
40. Reimer, L., and Ficker, J., *Proc. European Reg. Conf. on Electron Microscopy, Delft, 1960* p. 387 (1961).
41. Schulz, L. G., *Acta Cryst.* **5**, 130 (1952).
42. Schwarz, H., *Rev. Sci. Inst.* **32**, 194 (1961).
43. Sennett, R. S., and Scott, G. D., *J. Opt. Soc. Am.* **40**, 203 (1950).
44. Thomas, G., "Transmission Electron Microscopy of Metals." Wiley, New York, 1962.
45. Thomson, G. P., and Cochrane, W., "Theory and Practice of Electron Diffraction." Macmillan, New York, 1939.
46. Tomlinson, H. M., *Phil. Mag.* [8] **3**, 867 (1958).
47. Trillat, J. J., and Takahashi, N., *Compt. rend.* **236**, 790 (1953).
48. Washburn, J., Kelly, A., and Williamson, G. K., *Phil. Mag.* [8] **5**, 192 (1960).
49. Weil, R., and Read, H. J., *J. Appl. Phys.* **21**, 1068 (1950).

CHAPTER 3

Particulate Materials

PAUL KAESBERG

I. Introduction

In dealing with particulate materials, the fundamental problem is to mount the sample on specimen screens in some reproducible way indicative of the original size and shape of the particles, their original concentration, their state of aggregation, or some other characteristic of their nature prior to the manipulations necessary for electron microscopy. We may deal with particles in solution or suspension or it may be essential that the particles remain in the dry state as a powder. As will be seen below, methods for dealing with dry particulates have not lent themselves very readily to quantitative interpretation.

In the case of particles in liquid suspension, it is essential to take into account that their structural properties may change in a very significant way when they are removed from their suspending medium. This may be a manifestation of the differing forces upon particles in

99

the two states or it may be a consequence of the passage of a phase boundary through the specimen as the surrounding liquid is removed. In addition to any structural changes in the particles themselves, there is, of course, a very significant change in their spatial relationship. Thus, the electron microscopist must devise preparative procedures that retain significant information about the properties of the particles as they existed in suspension.

In this chapter we will discuss first some general aspects of preparative procedures, then describe some of the methods which have been developed for preserving the structure of delicate particles, and finally we will indicate how quantitative information about particulate suspensions may be obtained.

II. Preparative Techniques Useful for the Mounting of Particulate Materials

A. Liquid Suspensions

1. THE SINGLE-DROP METHOD

The earliest and perhaps still the most popular procedure for mounting particles in liquid suspension is to place a single drop of the suspension on the specimen screen with the aid of a pipette and allow the material to dry. If the particles were in water or in any other volatile suspending medium only they remain. If the original suspension required a nonvolatile buffer or other nonvolatile constituents the usual procedure is to remove these after the drying has taken place by flushing the specimen screens several times, e.g., with distilled water. It is hoped that the material of interest will remain attached to the specimen film while the smaller, more readily soluble constituents are washed away. Fortunately, most macromolecular materials adhere tenaciously to the film. At the same time, or in a subsequent step, the particles can be stained. The advantage of the single-drop method is its simplicity. Furthermore, the material can be put on the specimen screens at exceedingly low concentration.

Since the drying time for the drop is of the order of minutes there is ample time for unwanted changes to take place in fragile or unstable particles—as a consequence of surface tension, changes in pH, in ionic strength, and in osmotic pressure. For several reasons this procedure does not allow any quantitative determination of the particulate constituents in the suspension. The receding edge of a drying droplet may carry along some particles but leave others. Washing may remove or redistribute some particles preferentially. Optimum dilutions are difficult to obtain because they depend on the size of the drop and upon the film's wetting characteristics, neither of which are readily reproducible.

2. METHODS FOR SPRAYING SMALL DROPLETS

While there had been earlier attempts to spray suspensions of particles onto specimen screens in the form of small, uniform droplets the most far-reaching advances were made by Backus and Williams (3), using a spray gun of their own design. In addition to technical improvements, they introduced several new features which have circumvented some of the deficiencies of the single-drop method.

A modified version (B. Siegel, 1956, unpublished) of the original spray gun of Backus and Williams is shown in Fig. 1. It is a somewhat simpler

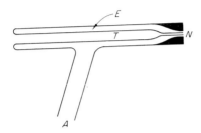

FIG. 1. A spray gun made of Pyrex glass. The air inlet *A* leads into an outer envelope *E* tapered at its open end to an inside diameter of 1.0 mm. The interior tube *T* has an inside diameter of 3.0 mm and tapers to form a nozzle *N* of inside diameter 0.35 mm. A small pipette containing a standard volume of the material to be sprayed is inserted so as to wedge into the tapered end of *T*.

design but retains the essential features of the original gun. It consists of an air inlet *A* into an outer envelope *E* tapered at its open end to an inside diameter of 1.0 mm. The interior tube *T* has an inside diameter of 3.0 mm and tapers to form a nozzle *N* of inside diameter 0.35 mm. The entire unit is made of Pyrex glass. A small pipette containing a standard volume of the particulate suspension is inserted, so as to wedge into the tapered end of the interior tube. When pressure from a compressed-air tank (about 40 lb/inch^2) is applied at *A*, this liquid is ejected through the nozzle of the pipette at high velocity and tiny droplets of exceptionally uniform size are formed. The unit is mounted so as to spray horizontally onto specimen screens which are placed at a distance of about 40 cm from the tip of the spraying nozzle. Best results are obtained when the screens are mounted so as to cause a minimum disturbance to the air stream. This can be accomplished by mounting the screens along the edge of a glass slide with the aid of double-coated cellulose tape. Depending on the parameters of the experiment the mean droplet size can be anywhere from 2 to 20 microns—sufficiently small so that the droplets can be photographed in their entirety at moderate magnification.

The droplets dry in about 0.1 second and the material deposits relatively uniformly within the droplet area except that there is a greater proportion in the periphery of the dried droplet pattern. The extent of dispersal, of course, depends markedly on the hydrophylic nature of the substrate. Backus and Williams have shown, with a series of dilution experiments that, except for statistical variation, the contents of each droplet are representative of the contents of the original suspension so that the relative number of each kind of particle in each droplet is the same and is equal to the relative number of each of the particles in the original suspension. The total number of particles in each droplet is proportional to the droplet size. Thus, as will be discussed later, the number of particles found on the specimen screen has quantitative significance.

It is, of course, essential that the droplets dry and remain undisturbed just as they were deposited. Thus it is not feasible to wash the suspensions free of buffer salts or other nonvolatile material. Backus and Williams solved this difficulty by using solutions containing volatile salts to maintain the desired pH and ionic environment. They suggest solutions containing ammonium acetate, ammonium carbonate, or ammonium benzoate. Of these, only ammonium benzoate is useful for freeze-drying experiments inasmuch as solutions of both ammonium acetate and ammonium carbonate are not frozen in their entirety at temperatures at which a reasonably rapid rate of sublimation is obtainable. It is not known to what extent solutions of these salts (either individually or their mixtures) maintain a particular pH or ionic strength in the tiny sprayed droplets as evaporation proceeds. However, in droplets sufficiently large for feasible pH measurement 0.1 M ammonium acetate approaches a pH of 6.0 during evaporation (6). Presumably ammonium carbonate approaches a pH near 9. Mixtures can be made by trial and error which approach intermediate pH values. Fortunately, the evaporation times are short so that ordinarily these changes need not be considered.

It has been found that a commercial throat-spraying device, the "Vaponefrin Vaporizer" (Vaponefrin Co., Upper Darby, Pa.), can produce uniformly small droplets (12) especially if the delivery tube is modified (19). This unit is shown in Fig. 2. A small volume of the sample is placed in the chamber and is sucked up the capillary C. When a pressure of about 5 lb/inch² above atmospheric pressure is applied at the tube A the liquid is ejected, strikes the baffle B, and is broken into very tiny droplets which diffuse out of the delivery tube *D*. The emerging aerosol consists of rather uniform, tiny droplets, together with a significant number of rather large drops. If the spray gun is mounted so that the aerosol emerges horizontally and then passes through a guide tube that directs it vertically downward onto screens placed just below the end of the tube, almost all of the original large drops are lost on the guide tube wall near the bend.

With this sprayer the droplets hit the specimen screens at a low velocity and hence do not spread out as do the droplets from the high-speed spray gun of Backus and Williams. This difference may be of consequence in freeze-drying applications. In its present form the Vapone-

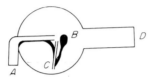

FIG. 2. A spraying device called the "Vaponefrin Vaporizer." A small volume of the sample is placed in the chamber and is sucked up the capillary *C*. When a pressure of about 5 lb/inch² above atmospheric pressure is applied at *A*, the liquid is ejected, strikes the baffle *B* and is broken into very tiny droplets which diffuse out the delivery tube *D*.

frin nebulizer uses a larger volume of material than does the high-speed gun and also it is more difficult to clean. Both of these difficulties could be avoided by simple design changes.

It is clear that these spray-droplet methods and their modifications deserve widespread use and can serve as a standard of comparison for other, more involved, preparative procedures. Particularly significant is that the techniques are standardizable and highly reproducible and that they are readily adaptable to obtaining quantitative counts.

3. DEPOSITION BY MEANS OF CENTRIFUGATION

Sharp (15) has developed a centrifugation technique for depositing particulate material to be examined in the electron microscope. Using a specially designed rotor, he sediments particles onto agar blocks set at the bottom of the centrifuge cells. He has found that the material deposited on the agar block will dry down with the agar imbibing the water and any dissolved salt. The particles on top of the agar can be stripped off by flooding the surface with a dilute collodion or formvar solution and floating off the formed film in much the same manner as replicas are made of solid surfaces.

This method is especially applicable to very dilute suspensions and those which must contain nonvolatile salts. Sharp has found a statistically random distribution of the sedimented particles on the agar surface. Thus, this technique lends itself to quantitative electron microscopy as will be discussed below.

B. Powdered Materials

The preparative procedures for powdered materials and the attendant artifacts depend explicitly on the specimens themselves and are difficult to discuss categorically. However, particle size, shape, size dispersion, and state of aggregation generally are among the characteristics to be determined. The problem is thus to disperse the sample on specimen mounts in such a way as to reveal the characteristics of the bulk materials.

If it is permissible to disperse the powder in water or other volatile medium the procedures already discussed for liquid suspensions apply and similar restrictions hold. It may be desirable to compare several liquids to evaluate the aggregating properties of the liquids themselves. If the particles are dispersible in such liquids as amyl acetate or ethylene dichloride the particles can be mounted within the substrate film, for example, by dispersing them in the collodion or formvar solutions used to make the films. The latter procedure has the advantage that a rather uniform dispersion of particles is obtained, free from the aggregating effects of drying droplets. It is, of course, impractical to use particles much larger than maximum allowable film thickness and this factor limits the procedure to particles less than 2000 A in diameter. On the other hand, particles of low density or very small size are precluded because of low contrast.

If it is essential that the particles of interest remain as a dry powder it may be possible to dust them onto the specimen mount or to let them settle from an air dispersion. Usually powders consist of ultimate particles (frequently small crystals or fibers) which are agglomerated to form larger masses. Depending upon their size, these can be examined in a light microscope or electron microscope, and often from the appearance of their edges a judgment can be made concerning the nature of the ultimate particles. Appropriate procedures, such as chemical treatment, ultrasonic treatment, milling, or grinding may then be applied to fragment the agglomerates for a more detailed examination.

Investigation of colloidal dispersion of solids in air requires special types of precipitators. Simple thermal precipitators (8a) have been used which cause deposition of the particles directly onto substrate-covered specimen screens. Very satisfactory results have been reported using "micropore" filters (10a). The aerosol is pulled through the filter and the particles are deposited in the membrane filter and are mounted on a substrate after dissolving the filter material.

Particle counting in which average values and idealized distribution parameters are the results desired, provide the main application of the electron microscope to observations on dry particulate material. For these applications careful consideration must be given to the method chosen for sampling, and to its statistical evaluation.

III. Effects of Substrates

The appearance of particles in the electron microscope may depend upon the substrate supporting them. The most obvious effects are flattening (as a consequence of surface tension) and aggregation (as a consequence of the adhesive properties of the substrate). Both of these artifacts have been the subject of numerous research papers. In addition, the investigator must take into account that the mass thickness of the substrate influences contrast and that the mechanical stability of the substrate influences image clarity. Furthermore, the type of mounting effects the extent to which contaminating materials present in the microscope specimen chamber deposit onto particles—the contamination rate is found to be very high in the case of particles attached directly to grid wires (i.e., filmless mounts), it is tolerably low in the case of particles mounted on substrates and well away from grid wires, and contamination can be all but ignored in the case of particles mounted within films (where it deposits uniformly on the film rather than upon individual particles).

The common substrate materials are collodion, formvar, and carbon. Each has some advantages. Collodion, the most common substrate material, is easy to prepare as a clean, relatively smooth, thin film. Droplets placed on the film spread sufficiently so that the electron microscopist can find many unaggregated particles. In some instances the wetting properties of collodion have been improved further by including wetting agents (such as serum albumin) in the suspension to be sprayed. Collodion has comparatively little mechanical strength; consequently, frequent film breakage results from the electrostatic charge built up by the electron beam. This is particularly true with unshadowed preparations. In this case, it is essential that the electron beam be kept sufficiently large in cross section at the specimen so that it always strikes the specimen-screen metal.

Formvar films are relatively stable in the electron beam. However, formvar is less hydrophilic than is collodion and as a result aggregation of particulate materials occurs readily; this defect has served to restrict its usefulness in many laboratories that deal primarily with particulates in water suspension.

Carbon films are strong and stable and when made thicker than 100 A are virtually unbreakable in the electron beam. The preparation of carbon films is more laborious and requires the use of an evaporating unit. Most commonly, carbon films are made by evaporating the carbon as a thin layer onto collodion or formvar that has already been mounted on specimen screens. Alternatively, it may be evaporated onto mica, glass, or other smooth material and removed by floating onto water and subsequently mounted on specimen screens. While carbon is an ideal substrate material from the point of view of stability, it has the undesirable characteristic that it is exceedingly hydrophobic so that particulates drying from water droplets are almost invariably aggregated. The smoothness of carbon films has as yet not been tested critically. However, it seems clear that carbon films prepared by evaporation onto collodion or formvar are no smoother than the collodion and formvar films on which they are made. In instances where stability is of great concern but the hydrophobic properties of carbon are to be avoided it may be desirable to ion-bombard the carbon or to mount specimens on the collodion rather than the carbon side of collodion-carbon films. Sometimes it may be possible to evaporate the carbon after the particles and the shadowing metal have been applied to the original collodion substrate. Whether or not this is practical depends on the particle dimensions as compared with the thickness of the carbon film and upon the particle orientation. For example, elongated particles standing on end would be coated with carbon and, in consequence, would be distorted in appearance; but if they were lying flat the depositing carbon would cover them and their substrate as a rather uniform, almost invisible film.

Another mounting scheme may be used when highest resolving power is desired to the exclusion of other considerations. This may be accomplished by mounting the sample on a fenestrated carbon film so that a continuous check on astigmatism can be made by focusing on the edges of the holes. Huxley and Zubay (10) find a considerable gain in contrast by using exceptionally thin carbon films which they mount on the thicker fenestrated film.

Hall has used freshly cleaved mica as a substrate material. (See Chapter 8 for a more extensive discussion.) Since mica cannot be cleaved sufficiently thin to be transparent in the electron microscope, a replica procedure is necessary. In addition to being very smooth, mica surfaces are exceedingly hydrophilic, thus aggregation effects are virtually eliminated. Because of the extensive spreading of the droplets, moderately high concentrations of particles may be applied, thus making possible better comparison with other physical measurements which may require high particle concentration. A further advantage is that some nonvolatile material (e.g., salts for maintaining ionic strength or pH) can be tolerated without adversely affecting the visibility of the particulates. However, the droplet patterns are now so large and their edges are so ill-defined that an entire droplet pattern cannot be included in a single micrograph and particle counting is impractical. Mica is sufficiently smooth so that it does not limit the smallness of the particles that can be recognized, rather, the limitations now reside in the smoothness and the geographical distribution of the shadowing metal.

IV. Effects of Shadow-Casting

The vacuum deposition of a metal film obliquely onto a specimen may greatly enhance the contrast of the image of particles observed in the electron microscope. This shadow-casting technique has become a standard part of electron microscopy procedure, both for study of particulate materials and replication of surfaces. A variety of metals has been used. The desired characteristic is a high-density material which condenses as a uniform film.

It may be shown, however, that the shadowing metal, whatever it may be, has a considerable structure. When a small amount of metal is evaporated it appears on the specimen film in the form of very small isolated particles. When deposited somewhat more heavily the metal forms a surface with a distinctly pebbly appearance. Furthermore, its appearance can be altered in the electron beam, with the resultant formation of globules of metal larger in dimension than the original irregularities. Clearly, these artifacts adversely affect resolution. Bradley (5) has suggested that the evaporation of mixtures of platinum and carbon results in films which are exceedingly smooth. However, such a mixture must have a low average density, and thus it is required that relatively thick layers be deposited on the specimen. A more promising approach is that reported by Bachmann (2) using iridium, which has a high density and apparently nucleates in extremely small crystallites. Platinum together with paladium (in the ratio 4:1) has been used frequently for high-resolution shadowing.

Apart from considerations of the particle size of the shadowing material, there is considerable evidence that the evaporated metal, before it comes to rest, may be able to wander a few angstroms on the surface it strikes (18). Thus, one finds metal on the leeward side of shadowed particles and in the area of the umbra. It seems clear also that the thickness of the metal coat on shadowed particles is frequently under-estimated and, in consequence, many research workers have neglected this effect in measurements of particle size. Hall, Nisonoff, and Slayter (9) have studied this artifact and have concluded from careful measure-ments of shadowed and unshadowed particles that the metal itself, con-tributed significantly to particle dimensions even under experimental conditions in which the amount of shadowed metal was minimal.

V. Methods Designed to Preserve the Structure of Fragile Particles

A. Freeze-Drying Methods

In addition to the effects of high salt concentration, osmotic pressure, and the rearrangement of particles in the drying process, there is also the distortional effect due to surface tension as the drying of the drop-lets containing the sample proceeds. Most of this distortion takes place in the last stages of drying as the water surface, in maintaining a mini-mum area, pushes all particles tightly against the substrate film and flattens those which are not sufficiently staunch. These distortional effects can be minimized by freezing the droplets as (or before) they land on the substrate and subsequently removing the water by sublimation at low temperatures. Williams (19) has defined conditions for adequate freeze drying and has applied these methods with considerable success. Since the time of his original freeze-drying experiments there have been modifications (13) which provide adequate freeze drying. However, for the purposes of this chapter only Williams' method will be described in detail, inasmuch as it was the first adequate method and also remains as the method that adheres most closely to many of the theoretical cri-teria of adequate freeze drying.

Williams' freeze-drying apparatus is shown schematically in Fig. 3. It is a glass system made up of a sublimation chamber and a cold trap attached to a vacuum system. The freeze-drying experiment proceeds as follows: Collodion film is prepared on the smooth upper surface of a copper support, which is placed in the bottom of the sublimation tube and is anchored there with vacuum grease which also serves as a thermal conductor. The sublimation chamber is then sealed and a vacuum is drawn for a short time while the chamber and its contents are cooled by means of a liquid nitrogen or a dry-ice-alcohol bath. At the same time, the cold trap is kept at liquid nitrogen temperature. In about 20 minutes, when the copper support has come to an equilibrium tem-perature, dry air is admitted to the chamber and its cover is removed.

A spraying tube is inserted (so as to minimize the amount of moisture that will eventually remain in the chamber) and a few hundredths of a milliliter of the suspension are sprayed onto the collodion surface. The spraying tube is withdrawn, the system is closed and evacuated. The bath surrounding the sublimation chamber is then replaced with one at a temperature appropriate to the sublimation to be carried out. With delicate specimens, in which it may be essential for the sublimation to proceed slowly, the operating temperature may be maintained as low as —65° C. A more common sublimation temperature is —50° C. When the sublimation is complete, the chamber and the block are warmed slightly above room temperature to avoid condensation, and air is admitted. The specimen and its support are removed and shadowed in

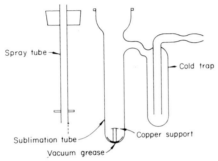

Fig. 3. Drawing of Williams' apparatus in which spray droplets are frozen upon impingement and are then sublimed under vacuum. The spray tube is inserted into the sublimation chamber during the spraying operation. The copper support is prefilmed with collodion (Williams, *19*).

the conventional manner. After shadowing, the collodion film is removed from the copper surface with the aid of cellulose tape which has had several holes punched in it slightly larger than the diameter of the specimen grids. The areas of the collodion film covering these holes are then easily mounted onto a specimen grid. In instances where the initial, very rapid freezing of the droplet suspension is not essential, this time-consuming extra mounting step may be avoided by placing collodion-covered screens directly on the copper block.

The results of freeze-drying experiments are markedly different from those of air drying. On the larger scale of dimensions, the appearance of frozen-dried specimens depends on the size and shape of the particulates and how they are able to aggregate or to attach to the substrate while the sublimation takes place. In place of the usual droplet pattern of an air-dried spray droplet, one finds a mass of aggregated particles surrounded by many individual particles attached to the substrate. Unless the original particle concentration was very high, no evidence of a droplet edge is apparent. In a successful experiment the particles within the aggregate are clearly distinguishable from each other and the individual particles attached to the substrate will be oriented in a

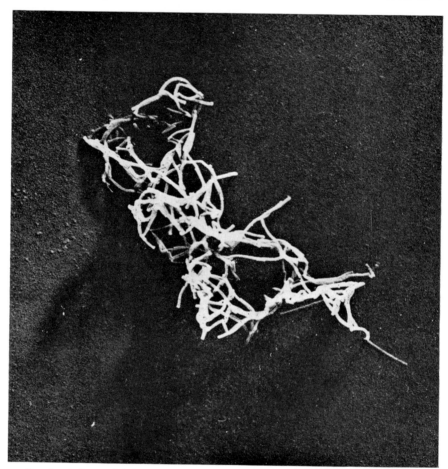

FIG. 4. A frozen-dried preparation of tobacco mosaic virus magnified 46,800 times. The rods of the virus are formed into a network, which extends a considerable distance from the substrate film. (Note the long and detailed shadow cast by the network.) The individual rods which make up the network are easily distinguishable, indicating that the freeze-drying procedure was successful.

variety of positions. Aggregates of asymmetric particles like nucleic acid and rodlike viruses appear like very fragile three-dimensional networks and are easily collapsed or otherwise distorted in the electron beam. Figure 4 shows such an aggregate of frozen-dried tobacco mosaic virus.

Individual frozen-dried particles show none of the flattening effects frequently encountered in air-dried preparations.

Ordinarily, a considerable fraction of the sample is lost in the vacuum system as the sublimation proceeds. In fact, only those particles which attach to the substrate or to something which is attached, would be expected to remain. The proportion which are retained depends on concentration, droplet size, and on several other factors. A further technical problem is that of specimen contamination in the electron microscope specimen chamber. Contamination is omnipresent in frozen-dried preparations which are apt to extend a considerable distance from the substrate. It is thus essential that pictures of frozen-dried objects be taken quickly and under conditions of minimal contamination.

B. The Critical-Point Method

Anderson (1) has devised a method of reducing distortion in delicate specimens by making use of properties of fluids near their critical temperature. He reasoned that since a major distorting force on small, fragile particles was the passage of the phase boundary through the specimen as the ambient fluid was removed, this distortion could be avoided if the passage of the phase boundary were eliminated. This can be accomplished if, at constant pressure, the liquid is changed into a gas by raising its temperature above its critical point. Unfortunately, water, the usual ambient liquid, has the rather high critical temperature of 374° C. Thus, it is desirable to replace water with some other liquid having a more tractable critical temperature. Anderson has concluded that liquid carbon dioxide, with a critical temperature of 31° C is a most suitable liquid. However, since water is not miscible with carbon dioxide, the specimen must be passed through a series of intermediate liquids, each of which is miscible with its neighbor. Thus, water is replaced by alcohol-water mixtures and these are replaced successively by absolute alcohol, by amyl acetate, and finally by liquid carbon dioxide. The final substitution must be made at high pressure, in a bomb, so that the carbon dioxide is in the liquid state at room temperature. A more precise listing of a typical set of miscible liquids is given in Table I. Since the specimen passes through several liquids, any of which may dissolve a portion of it, the specimen is usually fixed prior to the start of the manipulation, most commonly with osmic acid. Also, since the specimen must remain in place during the manipulations, yet complete exchange of liquids is essential, its mounting is distinctive. The specimen grid coated with formvar is placed on a screen or on a perforated plate. Droplets containing the specimen are placed on the grid,

TABLE I

SUBSTITUTION SERIES OF MISCIBLE LIQUIDS LEADING FROM WATER TO CARBON DIOXIDE

Liquid mixture	Time allowed for substitution (min)
10% Ethyl alcohol in water	2
40% Ethyl alcohol in water	2
70% Ethyl alcohol in water	2
100% Ethyl alcohol	10
10% Amyl acetate in ethyl alcohol	2
40% Amyl acetate in ethyl alcohol	2
70% Amyl acetate in ethyl alcohol	2
100% Amyl acetate	10
Liquid carbon dioxide at 25°C or lower	10

and then a cellulose acetate film is placed over the top so that the droplet is sandwiched between the two films. The series of substitutions of the liquids can then take place readily. The bomb required for the final step in which liquid carbon dioxide replaces amyl acetate is shown in Fig. 5. The entire assembly, immersed in amyl acetate, is placed in the bomb vessel, which is then closed and attached to a tank containing liquid carbon

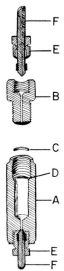

FIG. 5. A drawing of a pressure vessel used for the critical-point method. The body of the vessel A and its stopper B are made of 1-inch hexagonal stainless steel stock. They are threaded together and sealed with a copper washer C which fits in a shoulder in the body D. By means of threaded "super pressure" connectors E they are sealed to 1/4-inch "super pressure" tubing F leading to the pressure tank and to the escape valve (Anderson, 1).

dioxide. The liquid carbon dioxide is allowed to enter the vessel and gradually replace the amyl acetate. These manipulations must take place below the critical temperature of 31° C—commonly at a temperature of about 25° C. The closed vessel is then brought to a temperature of about 45° C, the valves are opened and the gaseous carbon dioxide is slowly released into the atmosphere. The specimens are available then for viewing in the electron microscope.

Thus far, the critical-point method has been used by only a comparatively few research workers. Nevertheless, the results of some of the experiments have been spectacular. Fragile specimens such as red blood cell ghosts, bacteria, and viruses appear to be exceedingly well preserved. Since the critical-point procedure is very much different from freeze-drying in its effect on the sample, it would be useful to compare results obtained by the two procedures. So far this has not been done extensively. It may be stated, however, that insofar as these results have overlapped, the conclusions have been virtually identical.

C. Heavy-Metal Embedding

In this technique the basic requirement is to produce a uniformly thin sheet of an electron-dense material in which the particles of interest are embedded. The particles will be evident as transparent regions, inasmuch as they are less dense than their surroundings. Brenner and Horne (8) have described some of the practical considerations involved in embedding with phosphotungstate, and they and their collaborators and others have obtained excellent pictures of a variety of biological materials whose structure had been seen hitherto with far less clarity in shadowed preparations. In their recipe, a 1% solution of phosphotungstic acid is brought to a pH near neutrality, this is mixed with a suspension of the specimen, and is sprayed onto carbon-coated specimen grids. Areas are sought in which contrast conditions are optimal. For different materials, it may be desirable to try several concentrations of both the embedding material and the specimen inasmuch as their relative thickness is an important consideration and this depends both on the specimen dimensions and on the character of the film on which the deposits take place. Huxley and Zubay (10) have modified the embedding procedure by applying the particulate suspension by means of a small pipette directly onto a carbon film. The solution spreads as a thin, uniform sheet and the excess is removed by applying a fine glass capillary to the edge of the grid. They find that highest contrast and improved clarity is obtained where the phosphotungstate dries as a thin sheet across holes in the carbon film. A further important modification for some experiments is the use of a fixative prior to the staining procedure. The remarkable detail made evident by the heavy-metal embedding technique is illustrated in Fig. 6 which shows *Helix pomatia* hemocyanin embedded in a uranium-EDTA complex.

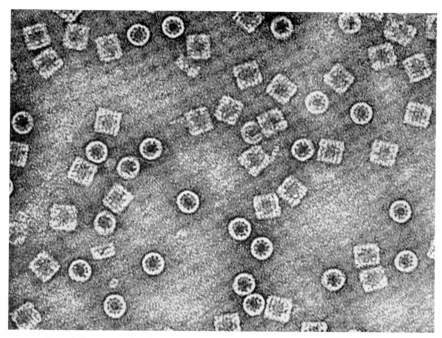

Fig. 6. *Helix pomatia* hemocyanin molecules embedded in a uranium-EDTA complex magnified 194,000 times (Van Bruggen *et al.*, *17*).

VI. Quantitative Methods

A. Direct Particle Counting

The development of spraying procedures which provide droplets sufficiently small to be seen in their entirety has made it possible to use the electron microscope to count the number of particles in a given volume of a suspension (*20*). This number may be intrinsically useful and also it may lead directly to such other useful parameters as biological titer and molecular weight.

The procedure is elegantly simple in principle. The suspension is quantitatively mixed with a suspension of indicator particles whose number concentration is determined independently. The resultant suspension is sprayed onto specimen screens to form small droplet patterns. The numbers of both types of particles are counted and thereby the particle concentration in the original suspension is established. It is necessary only that the particles be sufficiently large and discrete so that they may be readily identified and counted and that an appropriate suspension of indicator particles be available—in practice, the latter is a limitation of considerable severity.

Backus and Williams employed polystyrene latex particles of exceptionally uniform size (Dow PSL Lot 580G) in water suspension. They determined the number concentration of the PSL particles by measuring (a) the volume average of the latex spheres, (b) the density of dry latex, and (c) the dry weight of the PSL particles in a known volume of the suspension. The volumes were obtained from electron microscopic measurements of the diameters of the latex particles, and since the value as measured must be cubed to obtain volume, this measurement was an important source of uncertainty. Thus far, the Dow Latex PSL 580G particles (whose size and size distribution have been investigated extensively) have been the only ones used as indicator particles. Unfortunately their supply is now apparently exhausted. Other latex particles of rather uniform size have been described (4) and undoubtedly will now be used.

A study by Luria, Williams, and Backus (11) provides an interesting example of the use of direct particle counts to determine the numerical relationship between numbers of virus particles and infectious titer. They counted numbers of particles of the bacterial viruses T2, T4, and T6 by the method described above and assayed for infectivity by plaque counts on the sensitive host *Escherichia coli* B. Their results showed a close correspondence between activity titers and numbers of characteristic virus particles—the ratios of the two quantities being very nearly unity. Thus they were able to conclude that nearly all of the viruslike entities were indeed infectious and, furthermore, that the titration method was almost 100% efficient.

For absolute determinations of particle titer, it is necessary to have independent knowledge of the number of latex particles per milliliter of solution. However, if only relative titers are desired, the particle counting procedures are particularly simple as illustrated by a study of Rochow, Ross, and Siegel (14). In their experiments, they showed a proportional relationship between numbers of particles presumed to be virus and infectivity. The essential point is that the infectivity assay required a period of days or weeks whereas the electron microscopy assay took a matter of hours.

Ideally, the ratio of numbers of indicator particles to sample particles should be near unity, although experimentally this is not always achievable. Breese and Trautman (7) have made a careful experimental and statistical study in an attempt to determine what ratios are tolerable. They present a protocol for deciding whether groups of droplet patterns involving large ratios should be discarded and show experimentally that it is possible to draw meaningful conclusions from data in which the ratio of indicator particles to sample particles is as high as 30.

B. Determination of Particle Weight

As has been discussed above, the particle counting procedure yields particle concentration. Particle concentration combined with a dry-weight determination immediately gives particle weight. Thus we have a method of particle-weight determination by means of electron micros-copy independent of the necessity of making accurate measurements of the dimensions of the particles. Since the method depends only on recog-nizing each particle, it is possible, in principle, to obtain the molecular weight of even the smallest protein molecules.

C. Counting of Sedimented Particles

Sharp's (15, 16) method of deposition of particles by centrifugation, described earlier, has been found to give random deposition of particles onto specimen films and thus can be used for quantitative electron mi-croscopy.

After deposition of all the particles in a given volume of a suspen-sion to be assayed, a count of the particles in the electron microscope image is directly related to the concentration in the original sus-pension. Here no indicator particles of known concentration are needed, and the statistical error of the sampling can be reduced to any desired level by counting an adequately large number of particles.

The method is especially valuable for low particle concentrations. Sharp has obtained reliable assays with as few as 10^5 particles per milli-liter. Some care must be taken to assure that all particles have stuck to the agar and subsequently have been removed in the stripping process.

VII. Summary

In this chapter we have discussed the problem of mounting particu-late specimens for electron microscopy in such a way as to obtain infor-mation about their structure and their spatial relationship as it existed in suspension or as a powder. Both with powders and with suspensions, adequate sampling is essential. In the case of liquid suspensions there is the additional consideration that extensive structural alteration may occur in removing the suspending liquid. Several methods, notably freeze drying, critical-point drying, and heavy-metal embedding have been developed to preserve the structure of fragile particles.

REFERENCES

1. Anderson, T. F., *in* "Physical Techniques in Biological Research" (G. Oster, A. W. Pollister, eds.), Vol. 3, p. 177. Academic Press, New York (1956).
2. Bachmann, L., *Naturwissenschaften* **49**, 153 (1962).
3. Backus, R. C., and Williams, R. C., *J. Appl. Phys.* **21**, 11 (1950).
4. Bradford, E. B., and Vanderhoff, J. W., *J. Appl. Phys.* **26**, 864 (1955).
5. Bradley, D., *Proc. 4th Intern. Conf. on Electron Microscopy, Berlin, 1958* p. 428 (1960).
6. Bradley, D. G., *Virology* **15**, 203 (1961).
7. Breese, S. S., Jr., and Trautman, R., *Virology* **10**, 57 (1960).
8. Brenner, S., and Horne, R. W., *Biochim. et Biophys. Acta* **34**, 103 (1959).
8a. Drummond, D. G., *J. Roy. Microscop. Soc.* **70**, 45 (1950).
9. Hall, C. E., Nisonoff, A., and Slayter, H. S., *J. Biophys. Biochem. Cytol.* **6**, 407 (1959).
10. Huxley, H. E., and Zubay, G., *J. Mol. Biol.* **2**, 19 (1960).
10a. Kalmus, E. H., *J. Appl. Phys.* **25**, 87 (1954).
11. Luria, S. E., Williams, R. C., and Backus, R. C., *J. Bacteriol.* **61**, 179 (1951).
12. Palmer, F., and Kingsbury, S. S., *Am. J. Pharm.* **124**, 112 (1952).
13. Rice, R. V., Kaesberg, P., and Stahmann, M. A., *Arch. Biochem. Biophys.* **59**, 332 (1955).
14. Rochow, W. F., Ross, A. F., and Siegel, B. M., *Virology* **1**, 28 (1955).
15. Sharp, D. G., *Proc. Soc. Exptl. Biol. Med.* **70**, 54 (1949).
16. Sharp, D. G., *Proc. 4th Intern. Conf. on Electron Microscopy, Berlin, 1958* p. 542 (1960).
17. Van Bruggen, E. F. J., Wiebenga, E. H., and Gruber, M., *J. Mol. Biol.* **4**, 1 (1962).
18. Williams, R. C., *Biochim. et Biophys. Acta* **8**, 227 (1952).
19. Williams, R. C., *Exptl. Cell Research* **4**, 188 (1953).
20. Williams, R. C., and Backus, R. C., *J. Am. Chem. Soc.* **71**, 4052 (1949).

CHAPTER 4

Ultramicrotomy

KEITH R. PORTER

I. Introduction

In the preparation of certain materials (biological and mineral) for electron microscopy, it was recognized early that there would be no substitute for thin sections. Parts of a structured object might be separated or fragmented to render them small enough or thin enough for electron-beam penetration, but their relationship to the whole and to other parts would be revealed only in sections of the whole. Because of the special properties of the electron beam and the resolution it provided, the problems involved in providing thin sections for electron microscopy were in most respects unique. Attention had to be given to: (*a*) preserving the natural form against subsequent dehydrations; (*b*) replacement of water with a solid or semi-solid matrix which could be sectioned; (*c*) finding an edge of adequate sharpness and hardness to cut the sections; and (*d*) developing microtomes of sufficient precision and reliability to cut sections as thin as 25 to 50 mμ, and possibly thinner. On the basis of previous experience with microtomy for light microscopy, these requirements were recognized as very substantial and not satisfied by any of the procedures and devices available in 1940–1950 when the possibilities inherent in the electron microscope first became evident. However, in the decade since the birth of this realization these various problems have been overcome at least to the point where without great compromise the information made available can be regarded as valuable.

At the present time, the techniques involved in preparing thin sections are both predictable and controllable. A variety of embedding matrices are in use, each with virtues which outweigh the drawbacks. It is possible to displace the water in biological specimens with water-soluble methacrylates and to preserve enzymic activity for subsequent localization in the embedded material. Diamond cutting edges are gaining in popularity over glass edges. When really sharp, the diamond knife possesses a number of important advantages, not the least of which is its capacity to cut sections without noticeable distortion of the embedding matrix. A number of useful cutting machines are available. These vary in the principles of advancement, but all succeed in cutting successive sections of uniform thinness in the range of 25–500 mμ. It is now common practice following sectioning, to "stain" the sections with high atomic number elements to enhance the contrast of the images. Of these so-called "stains," some are selective in their reactions with tissue components (especially after aldehyde fixation) and so become valuable in the identification of certain components of the section.

The image of the section provided by the electron microscope is believed to be a close representation of the material in the section— which, in turn, can be shown to be faithful to the morphology of the native, living material. Phenomena associated with beam impingement on the specimen are, in part, understood and can be evaluated.

This, in brief, is the picture of the current status of specimen preparation involving thin sectioning of biological materials. Those acquainted with the procedures and problems are cognizant of important areas for improvement. Nonetheless, the available techniques are largely successful in yielding predictable results, and can be applied to relatively large volumes of experimental material. This fact represents the sum total of progress over the situation 10 years ago when isolated successes were recorded, but when the unpredictability of the procedures forbade their application to materials from experimental studies. In this chapter, various aspects of thin sectioning will be discussed in so far as they are currently understood. The purpose is not so much to provide details of procedure as it is to evaluate the worth of available techniques and instruments and to define problems.

II. Microtomes

The development of special microtomes for thin sectioning began about 20 years ago with the attempt of O'Brien and McKinley (21) to produce a microtome that would drive the cutting edge through the specimen at speeds of 3.3×10^6 cm/second (see also Fullam and Gessler, 10). Their idea was to produce with such velocities a thinner compression wave in advance of the knife which would more readily cleave the embedding matrix and yield a thinner section. This seemed an excellent plan in theory, but in practice the hazards and difficulties involved in harvesting the sections made the procedure impractical. It would be correct to say that in sectioning, the block was in a flash transformed into a cloud of sections.

In its subsequent history, microtomy followed a more conservative development. First, conventional microtomes were modified to advance the block in smaller increments (22), the principle of thermal advancement was introduced (20), and the "single pass" or "bypass" mechanism for avoiding the troublesome pickup of the section on the return stroke was included in microtome design (3, 12). Finally, in place of the thermal advance, which at best is difficult to control, an effective mechanical feed was designed and constructed (23). Gettner and Ornstein (12), in an excellent review, have recorded these various stages in the early development of thin sectioning and have thus relieved the author of the same task. For interested readers, a complete list of published reports on "new" microtomes is included at the end of this chapter (refs. 1-28).

Out of these various experimental models, there gradually emerged a few usable instruments which are now manufactured on a commercial basis, and are used for cutting the major part of the thin sections for electron microscopy. Each was designed independently and each is manufactured in a different part of the world.

A. Sources of Instrumental Error in "Ultramicrotomes"

That microtomes have been and can be created which will advance a specimen to a knife edge as little as 250 A and hold it rigidly enough to permit thin sectioning is in many ways remarkable. When, in fact, this sectioning is accomplished by an instrument with a mechanical advance of variable magnitude within an error of ± 100 A, the achievement is something of a miracle. One can only assume in the face of demonstrable performance that through repeated cutting cycles of uniform length, all the stresses, thermal fluctuations, frictions, and soft bearings, which introduce errors into the system, remain uniform in their effect on the increment of advance. The instrument may be said to operate with its various faults in dynamic equilibrium; it may be thought of as a machine which set in motion, and not subjected to any changes in conditions effecting that motion, essentially floats through the work of cutting thin sections.

The sources of error which contribute to uncertainty in microtome operation are not difficult to recognize. If the advance is mechanical, all the components are subject to environmental temperature changes, drafts, etc. Obviously such instruments should be used under conditions which exclude thermal fluctuations. Then also, in operation, all parts of a microtome are placed under stress as the forces required to cut sections are distributed. These strains introduce distortions which relax in time and to a predictable degree in a period of time. This is one reason why rhythmic motions of operator and microtome are essential for successful sectioning and why motor driven microtomes usually give more uniform serial sections. The sponginess of metal to metal contacts is another expression of stress distortion which can also be expected to have a reproducible effect on section thickness if the forces applied are not altered by changes in rate of sectioning. Oil films, it is agreed, are to be avoided in microtome construction except where fluctuations are transmitted to the actual feed through the small ratio of a large mechanical advantage as in the spindle drive on Sorvall (Porter-Blum) or Cambridge (Huxley) microtomes. Moreover, such oiled bearings are ordinarily spring-loaded and under conditions of steady operation establish a uniform relation to one another. Where motion is intermittent, static friction in the bearings plays a role which at very small increments may be detrimental to uniform advance. This possible source of error is readily eliminated by making even the smallest advance of the cutting arm dependent on a circumferential rotation of several millimeters in the spindle. Finally, in any system where the cutting arm is heated to achieve specimen advance, the problems of uniform sectioning are multiplied, unless other structural features are greatly simplified. It is, of course, to be recognized that only a part of this thermally controlled advance is linear, and that this particular part of the heating cycle has to be used where sections of uniform thickness are required.

Fortunately in the face of all these uncertainties in microtome operation, precision sectioning is not needed for many of the observations made by electron microscopy. Most investigations require for any one period of microscopy, a few "silver" or "silver-gold" sections. What is not displayed to full advantage in one section because of excessive thickness will probably be shown to better advantage in other grids which, for reasons of variation inherent in biological material, should be examined in any case.

Therefore, though full of potential variations and fluctuations, the microtome with demonstrable capacity to cut thin sections provides for the average needs, and even for more demanding precision sectioning.

B. Useful Models of Microtomes

As mentioned previously a few microtomes have proved, through reliable performance, to be practical laboratory instruments. These differ somewhat in basic design, and each has certain performance characteristics which set it apart from the others. They will be discussed in the order in which they were introduced.

The earliest was described in 1953 and came to be manufactured by Ivan Sorvall, Inc. It is known as the Sorvall MT-1 or the Porter-Blum microtome. The prototype model consisted only of a horizontal bar with a collet-type chuck on one end to hold the embedded object and two sets of pivots (constituting a gimbal) at the other end to hold the bar and provide for its universal motion (23). In operation, the specimen end of the bar was guided over the knife on the cutting stroke and past the knife on the return stroke within the limits of a frame in the shape of a parallelogram. The feed of the specimen to the knife was achieved by heating the long cantilever bar. Less significant features contributed to the general usefulness and simplicity of operation.

A later improved model (Fig. 1), which is also now available commercially, advances the specimen mechanically at regular increments of 25 mμ. For this purpose the gimbal at the back end of the cutting bar is suspended in a fork which, in turn, is supported by pivots placed a fraction of a millimeter above those of the gimbal. Thus, as the fork swings forward, the cutting arm moves 1/200 as much in the same direction. The motion of the fork is governed by a spindle which revolves a controlled amount with each cutting motion of the microtome. The cantilever bar and advancing mechanism are housed in a case which protects them somewhat from the thermal changes in the environment.

This microtome, if properly used, produces sections of uniform thickness in extended series. It is quick and easy to operate. The movable parts, pivots, advancing spindle, and associated elements, wear well and require little adjustment. The most important bearings are in the gimbal and its suspension. These are line bearings—resulting from the ball-in-a-conical-socket arrangement. They are under spring tension to maintain uniform contact at all times.

More recently, the manufacturers of the MT-1 produced a second and improved model referred to as the MT-2 (Fig. 2). This has a few operational advantages over the hand driven earlier microtomes. The

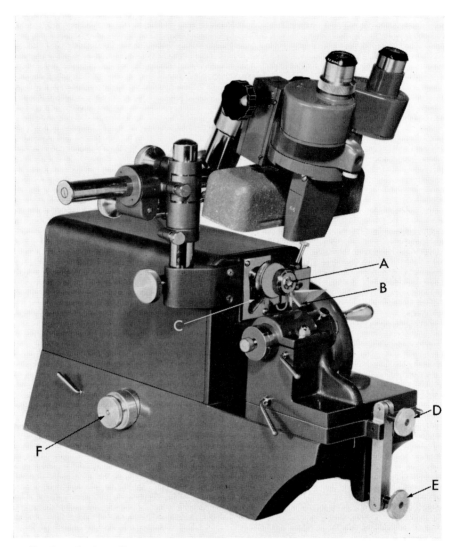

Fig. 1. The Sorvall MT–1 or "Porter-Blum" microtome. The specimen is held by a collet type chuck at (A) and is moved vertically past a glass, or diamond knife, held at (B). On the return stroke of the cutting arm, the specimen holder is guided in a bypass by the parallelogram-shaped opening (C). The knife may be advanced toward the block for trimming and thick sectioning by coarse and fine advancing screws (D) and (E). For cutting thin sections, the block is advanced to the knife by a mechanical device controlled by knob (F). With this, section thickness may be varied from 25–500 mμ, and thicker, if one uses repeated bypass without sectioning.

suspension and feed mechanism are similar, but all the bearings are spring-loaded knife edges rather than pivots. A motor drive provides a rhythmic motion of variable speed. The range of section thickness is broad (100 to 4000 A) and permits the operator to shift readily from thin to thick sections. The obvious conveniences incorporated in the new design contribute greatly to the efficiency of sectioning as well as to the quality of the sections.

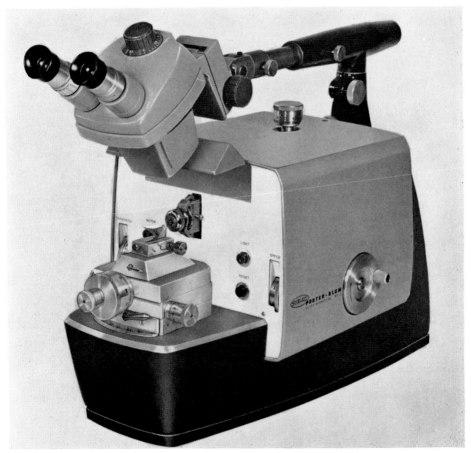

FIG. 2. Photograph of Sorvall microtome MT-2. The entire mechanism is contained in one compact unit. Section thickness, which can be varied from 100 A to 4 μ, is determined by two controls. The one on the left-hand side of the panel controls the excursion of the rachet by which the spindle is rotated, and the knob on the top can be used to vary the ratio of long to short arms in the lever of the advance mechanism. The knife stage provides for controlled, universal motion of the knife and permits precision trimming of the block in preparation for thin sectioning. These and several other conveniences make this a very effective microtome.

A fairly recent addition to the list of available microtomes is manufactured by LKB—Producter AB, Stockholm, and is referred to as the
"Ultratome" (14) (Fig. 3). It includes a number of important features
designed as far as possible to eliminate fluctuations in section thickness
and operational inconveniences. A cantilever arm is used as in other

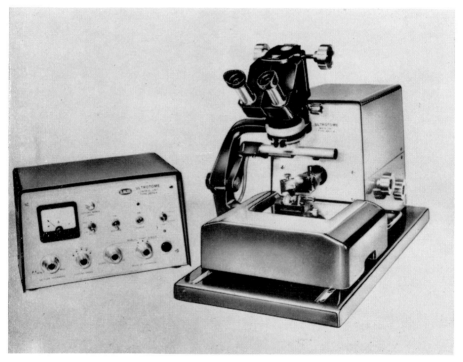

FIG. 3. Photograph of "Ultratome"—manufactured by LKB-Produkter Fabrik-
saktiebolag, Stockholm, Sweden. A thermal advance microtome of uniquely simple
design and construction. A magnet under the stage platform is activated during the
return stroke of the specimen arm, and flexes the whole stage downward, thus tilting
the knife away from the specimen block 20–30 μ and permitting the free bypass of
the cutting surface.

models as the principal moving part. One end of this bar supports the
specimen block; the other end is attached to a leaf spring which, in turn,
is attached to the base and frame of the microtome. This spring is flexed
in operation and provides for the up and down motion of the bar, the
only motion it has. Except for the small chance of buckling in such
spring suspensions, this effectively eliminates the sponginess inherent in
metal to metal contacts as in bearings. There is, in fact, little excuse
for each motion of the block not to repeat exactly the preceding one

as long as temperature is held constant. Advance of the block to the knife is achieved by controlled heating of the cutting arm. The force for the cutting stroke is gravitational, but the motion is rate controlled by a motor which also lifts the arm on the return stroke. The bypass of cutting surface and knife edge on the return stroke is achieved by flexing the base under the knife holder with an electromagnetic force applied only during the return phase of the motion. This pulls the knife back from its cutting position a distance of 20–30 μ. Problems of residual

Fig. 4. The Huxley Ultramicrotome, shown with draft shield removed, is an instrument with mechanical advance and double-leaf spring suspension throughout. The cutting force is gravitational, and the rate of fall of the cutting arm is controlled by an oil-filled dashpot (A). The long arm of a lever system (B) (ratio 250 to 1) is moved by a spindle (C) which is rotated by a rachet mechanism each time the cutting arm is lifted by handle (D). The specimen is mounted in a chuck at (E), and the knife in holder at (F). This is an excellent precision microtome.

magnetism and hysteresis are not significant in regular rhythmic cutting which is provided by the automatic control of motor, magnets, etc. The added advantages of a well-designed specimen holder and general availability of boat and microscope and manipulation areas contribute greatly to the value of this microtome.

A third microtome to achieve popularity with users was designed a few years ago by A. F. Huxley, and is now manufactured by the Cambridge Instrument Co., Ltd., London (17) (Fig. 4). It is unique in several minor respects, but is like the others in having a horizontal bar hinged by leaf springs at one end and supporting the specimen at the other. All of the flexing joints in the system involved in specimen motion and the mechanical advance system are of the same type: double-leaf spring. A micrometer screw, which is turned with each return stroke, moves the long arm of a lever upon which the cutting bar is suspended. The reduction is 250 to 1. The specimen bar is allowed to fall in response to gravity on the cutting stroke, but the speed of the motion is controlled by an oil-filled dashpot. The knife holder is sturdy and supplied with multiple controls essential for positioning. For precision cutting, the microtome is unexcelled. It is not so responsive to manipulation by the operator as the other models and so takes more of the operator's time.

C. Cutting Edges

The earliest thin sections for electron microscopy were cut with steel razor blades which had been especially sharpened (46). In general, these edges had a relatively short life. Special knives made of selected hard steel have been reported as superior to razor blades (31), especially when lapped to a sharp edge and subsequently polished on an abrasive free surface of glass. Such edges are, however, quickly oxidized by the water in the boat and for this reason, if none other, are of limited usefulness.

Of all cutting edges, glass is the most popular. A glass knife, properly prepared, can ordinarily be used to cut a few sections and then be discarded for another without great expense. That glass might be used for this purpose was first reported by Latta and Hartmann (39) in 1950. The great value of this contribution to electron microscopy is evident from the fact that a very large part of the sectioning since 1950 has been done with glass edges. At the outset, these authors obtained their knives from commercial sources and so employed the services of professional glaziers. Subsequently, microtomists have manufactured their own, and a number of techniques have been described for this purpose.

Since the difference between success and failure in obtaining good thin sections is ultimately dependent on a good knife edge, reliable techniques for breaking plate glass deserve attention. It is, for example, important for the front face of the knife to be as smooth as possible— i.e., free of the small irregular fracture lines introduced by the glazier's glass cutter. If long strips of glass are prepared by a glazier or with the usual cutter, these fracture lines are inevitable, and one of them will almost certainly intersect the edge destined to be the cutting edge of the knife. What may therefore be regarded as a superior procedure for preparing long glass strips with smooth back edges was described by

Cameron (30) some years ago. It essentially results in a long, more or less straight, free break, and provides two strips with smooth edges from which knives can be prepared in the usual manner (see below).

A technique of manufacture that is currently popular because of its effectiveness is described herewith in some detail.[1]

Ordinarily, 3/16-inch plate glass is used for making knives and an 8 × 8 inch initial square is a convenient size with which to start. While thicker or larger pieces of glass may be used, it becomes more difficult to control breaks under these conditions.

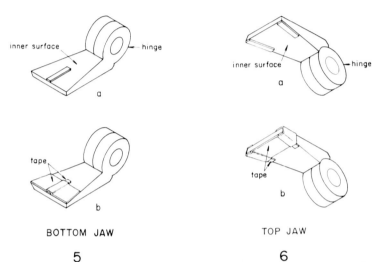

BOTTOM JAW   TOP JAW

5   6

Figs. 5 and 6. The drawings illustrate the position of tape placed on glaziers pliers to transform them into an instrument for making glass knives. The central strip in Fig. 5a creates the fulcrum over which the glass is broken. The additional tape, the position of which is illustrated in Fig. 5b, holds the central strip in place and provides a covering cushion. In Figs. 6a and b, the apposing jaw of the pliers is illustrated with tape in place. The marginal strips in Fig. 6a obviously create pressure points which make the central strip in Fig. 5a effective. The overlying tape in Fig. 6b secures the lateral strips.

The 8 × 8 inch plate should be scrubbed vigorously in a detergent and thoroughly rinsed in hot water. The glass is then propped at an angle and allowed to dry in a dust-free area. If one tries to dry the glass with a paper or cloth towel, electrostatic charges accumulate on the glass and, as a result, particles of lint and dust may be attracted to clean surfaces.

A clean sheet of hard-surfaced paper can be used to cover the working surface of the bench where the glass is to be broken. It may be necessary to change the paper from time to time when small chips and slivers of glass contaminate the surface. Implements and materials required during the procedure include: a pair of

---

1 The author is pleased to acknowledge the help of Dr. Charles W. Philpott in the preparation of the following description.

glass-breaking pliers (wide parallel jaws are preferable); a sharp glass cutter (wheel type); a plastic ruler; masking tape; and applicator sticks. The jaws of the pliers are taped according to Weiner's directions (50) as shown in Figs. 5 and 6.

A slight irregularity in sticking the tape to the proper positions on the jaws of the pliers may cause an uneven distribution of forces when the jaws are clamped against the glass. This is a potential cause of crooked breaks. Small chips of glass, which sometimes adhere to the jaws following their use, should be removed likewise to avoid irregular results. Obviously, the jaws must be retaped from time to time.

There are several operational rules that one must keep in mind in attempting to break plate glass for predictable results. (1) A slow, even break will produce much

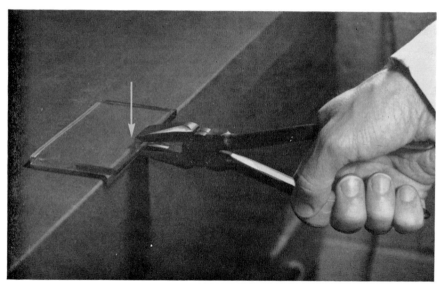

Fig. 7. This photograph illustrates the method of using the taped pliers. The central strip on the lower jaw should be placed directly beneath the score mark (position indicated by arrow). Pressure is then applied as indicated with the purpose of producing a slow, even break.

smoother surfaces than a fast break or a slow, uneven break. (2) Scoring an 8×8 inch sheet of glass along its whole length with a wheel cutter introduces surface stresses that result in striations and waves along the two new surfaces which are produced. (3) To avoid these irregular surfaces, it is best to make an initial short score mark at 90° to the bottom edge of the plate and then encourage the fracture to continue along an unscored surface. For the break to continue in a straight line, two conditions must be met. Equal pressures must be applied at equal distances on either side of a fulcrum centered beneath the initial score mark (Fig. 7). The initial score mark should be no longer than $1/2$ inch and should be centered so that a continuation of this line will exactly bisect the piece of glass (Fig. 8).

In practice, as mentioned earlier, one should start with a clean 8×8 inch sheet of plate glass. A $1/2$-inch score mark is made with a sharp cutter which is centered and at right angles to the base of the glass plate. The scored edge of the plate is positioned so that it will overlap the edge of the working surface by about 1/4 inch. The edge of the glass should be parallel to the edge of the table. With the jaws of the breaking pliers open and the central piece of masking tape centered beneath the score mark on the glass, the face of the bottom jaw is pushed flush against the edge of the table (Fig. 7). When the pliers are gently squeezed, the pressure of the lateral tape strips is equally distributed on either side of the score. Additional pressure

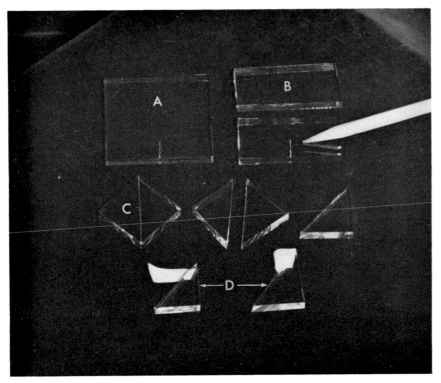

FIG. 8.   This shows the final successive stages in the manufacture of the glass knives. A 2 × 2 inch piece is shown at (A). It has been broken at (B) and is reoriented for the final square break. Each resulting square should have 2 corners created by the meeting of 2 smooth edges. One of these corners is chosen, because of the flatness or smoothness of the edges, as best for the origin of the cutting edge. A diagonal score mark is started 1 or 2 mm from this corner and extended to the opposite one as in (C). The break is made with the pliers, and one knife only is selected from the pair. A boat is constructed on it with masking tape as at (D).

produces a slow, even and straight break, and the two new surfaces will be smooth and free of artifacts except for the short line where the initial score was made. The smooth edges thus produced are potential knife faces, and should be protected from fingerprints, dust, and chipping. By convention, the 4 × 8 inch pieces of glass are turned 90° so that the smooth edges are away from the table edge. One piece of glass is scored in the center of the old, long edge and the procedure is repeated to produce two 4 × 4 inch plates. The apical corner having two new edges is turned away from the table edge. This prevents an accidental score mark on a good edge and, too, the smooth edges are removed from the scoring area where small fragments of glass are apt to contaminate one of the good edges.

The glass plates are bisected repeatedly until 1 × 1 inch squares are produced that have at least two smooth edges that meet at a 90° angle. The final 1-inch high knives will be broken from these squares (Fig. 8). Obviously, if knives with longer edges are desired, one must start with an initial glass plate having appropriate dimensions, i.e., a 12 × 12 inch plate produces 1½-inch knives.

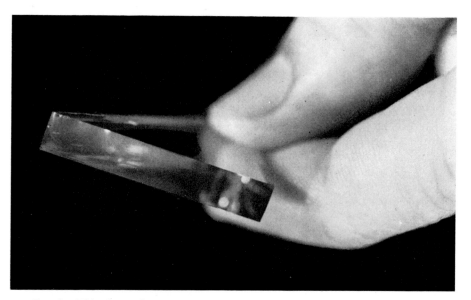

Fig. 9. This shows the appearance of the front surface of a "good" glass knife. It should be absolutely flat. Only the other (back) surface should show a pattern of irregularities associated with breaking (see Fig. 10).

Although it requires greater skill, the final squares can also be made by using a split applicator stick as a fulcrum. The splinter is placed beneath and in line with the short score mark and equal pressures are applied with the thumbs at opposite corners on the bottom edge of the glass plate.

Before making the final break (Fig. 8C), one should examine the edges of the 1 × 1 inch square and then choose the best adjacent edges. Potentially, either of these edges could be the front face of the knife. A diagonal score is then started within a millimeter or so from the apex of the angle where these two smooth faces meet and is extended to bisect the opposite corner. The pliers are carefully centered about halfway along this line and pressure is gradually applied. Only one triangular knife is produced by this break; the opposite side is discarded. The cutting edge should be even and straight, and the front surface absolutely flat (Fig. 9). Viewed from above, the back face of the knife will show either a right- or left-handed configuration (Fig. 10). The arc formed by the curved stress mark on the upper (back) surface of the knife, may be used to determine the best side of the knife for thin sectioning.

That part of the knife edge nearest the top of the arc is the best. A spike may be present on the opposite side of the cutting edge (Fig. 11).

If the diagonal score nearly bisects the two 90° angles of the 1 × 1 inch square, there will be no spike (Fig. 11a). If, however, this score is misplaced, the spike becomes larger, as shown in Fig. 11c. The quality and amount of cutting edge decreases as the size of the spike increases.

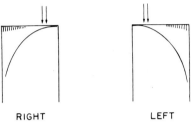

RIGHT   LEFT

Fig. 10. Diagrams illustrating the two configurations one may see on the back face of the glass knife, i.e., either a right-handed or left-handed turn of the stress line. Where this approaches the cutting edge, the properties of the latter will be best for thin sectioning (arrows). The opposite end shows "feathers" which intersect the cutting edge and give it a saw-tooth character.

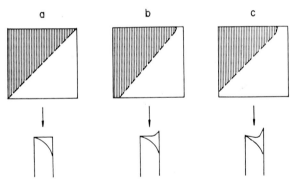

Fig. 11. This diagram illustrates the result of varying the position of the final diagonal score mark with respect to the true diagonal of the glass square. The aim should be to create as straight an edge as possible, so care should be taken to make the score mark a true diagonal.

A good 45°-angle knife made as described previously is usually suitable for cutting tissue embedded in methacrylates, polyesters, and epoxies of average hardness. However, the knife edge deteriorates rapidly with use, and the number of high-quality sections available from a given zone of a knife edge depends on the hardness of the block, the size of the block face, and section thickness. While it may be desirable to increase the knife angle for sectioning harder blocks, and decrease the knife angle for softer blocks, these knives are more difficult to break. With practice, however, one can produce knife angles of a few degrees greater or less than 45° by bisecting diamond-shaped pieces of glass, as shown in Fig. 12. The diamond-shaped pieces are obtained by saving and bisecting larger pieces of glass having curved edges that may have resulted from irregular breaks.

The edge of a knife as seen from above may be arbitrarily divided into three zones as shown in Fig. 13. The zone labeled poor is never used; the fair zone is used for trimming or facing the block; the good zone is used for thin sectioning.

Ordinarily, knives are broken a short time before sectioning and are protected from dust in a covered petri dish or in other suitable dust-free containers.

Troughs made of metal or masking tape are attached to the final knife by beeswax. One must be careful, however, to avoid contaminating the knife edge with wax during attachment of the trough. Metal troughs are usually larger than boats made of tape and offer greater working areas. The disadvantage here is that the large working area is more difficult to keep clean. Important, also, where metal boats are used over and over, is the practice of carefully cleaning them each time before use. Greater

Fig. 12.   Knives with angles greater (β) or smaller (α) than 45° may be created by cutting diamond-shaped pieces as illustrated here.

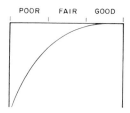

Fig. 13.   The average glass knife shows varying cutting properties along its length. The location and quality of these, with respect to the curved line, is indicated.

care must be exercised in working from metal troughs than from tape troughs since the former are more easily dislodged to produce a leak.

Finally, the breakability of a particular sheet of plate glass and its suitability for making good knife edges are variable. Plate glass obtained from different vendors usually varies in hardness, brittleness, and inherent stresses resulting from different techniques of breaking and polishing. While this has been recognized for some time, there is no available basis on which to recommend a particular type of plate glass for knife making. Usually, one tries several types and then procures a large stock of a "good" one.

D. Diamond Knives

In discussing the fragility and relatively short life of the average glass knife, Latta and Hartmann (39) mentioned the possibility of making suitable knives from industrial diamonds or artificial sapphires. The practical testing of the idea was, however, left to Fernandez-Moran (32, 33) who reported its achievement in 1953. Since then, progress in the manufacture of diamond knives has been tediously slow, doubtless reflecting the problems inherent in the process.

Currently, diamond knives of fairly satisfactory quality can be obtained from at least three sources.[2] The cutting properties are, however, variable, and there is still not complete assurance that a really good knife will be obtained.

The advantages of a good diamond knife are obvious. It can be used over and over again, thus obviating the necessity of making glass knives. It can be used to cut extraordinarily hard objects (bone, wood, insect cuticles) as well as soft ones. For some materials, there is no substitute. Even though the initial expense is great (of the order of 200 to 300 dollars) the saving in time and the success achieved more than compensate for the investment.

The major problem is to get a good knife. The experience of the writer and the people in his laboratory has been fairly extensive. One knife, obtained from Caracas in 1961, has proved exceptional. Although used constantly by two people to cut anything and everything, it has shown no change. It is, in other words, as good now, after 2 years of use, as when received. It will cut smooth sections in the gray-silver range. At least one other knife of equal quality has been obtained from the same source within the last 3 years and a few others of adequate quality have come from Caracas and from Ge-Fe-Ri in Italy. One feature common to all these diamond knives of unusual quality is that they have been polished in a direction parallel to the cutting edge.

The complaint is frequently voiced that diamond knives are hydrophobic and that one, therefore, has difficulties getting a satisfactory meniscus for receiving the section. This property may be evident when the knife is first obtained, but gradually the surface changes and becomes almost as hydrophilic as glass. Saliva on the small applicator stick used to "clean" the knife edge seems to hasten the acquisition of these desirable wetting properties.

It seems also to be the impression that a diamond knife wears out and needs to be resharpened. This may be true for some knives and may result from the relationship of the polished facets of the knife to the crystal planes of the diamond. That it need not be true is proved by our own experience. We can say categorically that diamond knives can be produced which are truly remarkable in cutting properties and durability. It is reasonable to expect that eventually some manufacturer

2 E. I. Du Pont de Nemours & Co., 101 Beech St., Wilmington 98, Delaware; Ge-Fe-Ri, Via Marittima 1, Frosinone, Italy; and Instituto Venezolano de Investigaciones Cientificas, Apartado 1827, Caracas, Venezuela.

will learn all the tricks and make a consistently good product. In the meantime, it is well worth the time and expense to persist in the ordering and replacing of knives until one gets a real gem.

III. Embedding Media

It was entirely natural that early attempts at sectioning for electron microscopy should have been made with materials embedded in the matrices then used for relatively thick sectioning. Discovering the inadequacies of paraffins and even the harder carbowaxes did not, however, take long. Pease and Baker (22) achieved an early though modest success with double-embedding Parlodion and a carnauba wax mixture. Upon removing the wax, and before putting the sections in the microscope, the fine structure collapsed with an exaggeration of the already ample artifact. Only a little later, Newman *et al.* (20) examined the properties of an amorphous embedding material, *n*-butyl polymethacrylate, and demonstrated its substantial worth for the purpose. It permitted the cutting of extremely thin sections, beginning at about 20 mμ. It was easy to handle and penetrated the tissue well; and toward the end of its period of popularity it yielded uniform embeddings when all influential conditions were controlled (43). The chief faults were found in the somewhat unpredictable hardness of the blocks, the general shrinkage of the embedding, and the polymerization damage resulting from localized acceleration of the polymerization and monomer migration. Also of significance was its sensitivity to thermal effects of the beam. Despite these recognizable shortcomings, polymethacrylate enjoyed great popularity and contributed enormously to the study of tissue and cell fine structure. It was of such recognized worth that one prophet had this to say of it as recently as 1960 (44): "It is clear that in the foreseeable future, most ultrathin sectioning will continue to be done with methacrylate-embedded material." These impressions notwithstanding, the shift to other matrices in the last 2 years has been so rapid and complete that it is scarcely worthwhile to discuss polymethacrylate now as especially useful for electron microscopy.

If more were known about the physics of cutting very thin sections, it would be valuable to consider some of the properties of embedding substances—properties which might influence the quality of the sections. Obviously, for example, the matrix should not be so soft as to flow over the cutting edge and probably be melted or otherwise permanently distorted by the heat generated in sectioning. On the other hand, the block should not be so brittle that as the wedge, which is the knife edge, moves through the matrix, it produces extensive fracture planes. Actually the hardness and brittleness of polymethacrylates is quite temperature-dependent, and so in the sense that these can be controlled, methacrylate blocks are good. It is the consensus that events in the zone of compression which precedes the knife edge in sectioning lead to good or bad sections. If the matrix is very soft, it will lack the elasticity to recover after distortion of compression; if, on the other hand, it is very hard and brittle, the fracture surfaces which develop in the compression zone will extend way beyond the knife edge and bear a less than desirable relation to it. There are obviously many complex considerations involved in selecting or developing a good embedding material—some less well known than others (12). To a greater degree in recent years than ever before these have been met by the introduction of epoxy and polyester resins which will now be briefly discussed.

A. Epoxy Resins

The several faults of methacrylate as an embedding material for biological objects and thin sectioning have, of course, stimulated the search for something better. Out of these efforts, especially by microbiologists who encountered unusual difficulties with methacrylate, there have developed two compounds of value: epoxy resins (one trade name: Araldite) and a polyester, Vestopal W. They both cure or harden without significant shrinkage, they show none of the localized swellings (or "explosions") or uneven polymerizations which were troublesome in methacrylates, they section well, and the resulting sections are remarkably stable under the electron beam even without a supporting film. The first of these was introduced in 1956 by Maaløe and Birch-Anderson (42) and by Glauert et al. (38). Some problems were initially encountered with the relatively high viscosity of the resin and, related to this, with its penetration into biological materials. These were somewhat overcome by using a hardening agent of higher molecular weight [an aliphatic anhydride (37)] and by introducing propylene oxide into the procedure as a reactive diluent for the liquid resins. The availability of Araldite to the many interested investigators, particularly in the western Atlantic community, remained uncertain and this led to trials of other epoxy resins. One of these, Epon 812 (Shell Oil Corp.), was introduced to the task by Finck (34) and by Luft (41), and has developed into a satisfactory substitute with, indeed, some real advantages over Araldite. As a result, it is now the most widely used embedding agent for thin sectioning and electron microscopy.

Epon 812 is described as a glycerol-based aliphatic epoxy resin. Its viscosity is low compared with Araldite, it penetrates quite rapidly, and sets into blocks, the hardness of which can be varied to suit various sectioning conditions and whims of individual investigators. Luft (41) has provided one of the best descriptions of the compound and its use.

Currently in the laboratory of the author, tissues fixed in any of several ways are dehydrated in cold ethanol and are finally brought to absolute alcohol. They are then taken through 3 changes of propylene oxide (5 minutes in each) and then into a 1:1 mixture of propylene oxide and the resin mixture (for 1–3 hours). This latter mixture consists usually of equal parts of two solutions (Epon and setting agent) recommended by Luft[3] plus accelerator (1.5% v/v of DMP-30 (2, 4, 6-dimethylaminomethyl phenol)]. The tissue blocks are then transferred to gelatin capsules containing the same mixture of resin, hardener, and accelerator, and placed in a vacuum oven at 60°C. Under these conditions the residual or excess propylene oxide is evaporated off and the blocks set in 24–36 hours. The hardness of the final embedding can be varied by changing the proportions of solutions A and B in the final mixture; more of A for softer blocks and more of B for harder ones. The firmness of the set will increase to some extent with time at 60°C.

Sections cut from such blocks are remarkably robust. The image shows distinctly better contrast than with Araldite and shows no apparent evidence of beam damage that used to be a problem with methacrylate. It is not, therefore, important to blanket the sections (49). Staining both for electron microscopy and light microscopy (1 μ sections) presents no serious problems though the resin is apparently less permeable to the effective ions than are methacrylates.

B. Vestopal W

Investigations arising from this same dissatisfaction with methacrylate led to the discovery of yet another embedding material: Vestopal W. This is a polyester produced by the esterification of malic anhydride with glycerol or some other polyhydric alcohol. Polymerization is induced by including in the Vestopal 1% tertiary butyl benzoate as the initiator and 0.5% cobalt naphthenate as the activator. Both these compounds, though kept cold and in the dark, must be restocked every few months.

When the tissue is destined for Vestopal embedding, it is dehydrated with acetone (at least in the final stages) and taken through increasing concentrations of the polyester in acetone. Finally, it is placed in

---

[3] Solution A: Epon 812, 62 ml and DDSA (dodecenyl succinic anhydride), 100 ml. Solution B: Epon 812, 100 ml and MNA (methyl nadic anhydride), 89 ml.

capsules in the presence of the embedding mixture alone. Hardening is achieved in 12 hours at 60°C. Vestopal has the important advantage of rapid penetration and polymerization, and in this respect is like methacrylate, but without the faults of this latter polymer. It is apparently important to remove all the acetone from the system at the end, so polymerization in a vacuum oven may be desirable. The resulting blocks are hard, and several references to sectioning problems are recorded in the literature. The advantages of Vestopal W over Epon 812 are not sufficiently impressive to recommend its use unless it is found in some places to be more readily available or, for some reason peculiar to the biological specimen, it is found to have advantages for infiltration or sectioning or both.

C. Maraglas

Another epoxy resin under the trade name of Maraglas 655 has recently been introduced by Freeman and Spurlock (35). These authors claim that it sections more easily than Epon 812, and they stress that relatively large area sections can be cut without evidence of "chatter" artifact. It is further said that the "granularity" inherent in Epon 812 preparations is not evident in Maraglas embedments.

This epoxy is described as yielding, when used alone, extremely hard blocks which are not easily shaped for sectioning. Thus for greater ease in handling, it is recommended that a mono-epoxide diluent called Cardolite NC-513 be used in variable amounts to reduce hardness and brittleness. Twenty to forty per cent v/v of Cardolite in Maraglas is suggested, the higher concentrations giving the softer blocks. Several curing agents may be used but the tertiary amine, benzyl dimethylamine, is recommended in concentrations of 1–15 parts per hundred of resin. In the event that it is desired to vary the cutting properties further by softening the block, dibutyl phthalate may be added in quantities totaling 5–15% v/v of resin.[4]

Tissue samples for Maraglas embedding are dehydrated in alcohol, taken through propylene oxide-resin mixtures toward the pure resin

---

[4] In their most recent publication Spurlock et al. (47) give the following formula for Maraglas embedding:

Reagent	Milliliters
Maraglas 655	68
Cardolite NC-513	20
Dibutyl phthalate	10
Benzyl dimethylamine (curing agent)	2

mixture. The blocks in gelatin capsules harden in 48–72 hours at 60°C, and increase in hardness with age. Sections may be stained by the usual methods with lead hydroxide, uranyl acetate, etc. Shrinkage of up to 15% in volume during setting is reported. Also, while sections are described as fairly stable under the beam, supporting membranes are indicated. The most significant advantage of the new matrix would seem to reside in its superior sectioning properties.

D. Water-Soluble Embedding Materials

One of the most interesting and potentially useful innovations of the past few years stems from a report of Gibbons (36) that a water-soluble fraction of Epon 812 could be prepared by relatively simple means and dehydrated. Biological specimens, following fixation with formalin or other reagents, were dehydrated directly with this Epon extract (known as Aquon) which was then cured with a suitable hardener (dodecenyl succinic anhydride) and accelerator (benzyl dimethylamine) to a solid resin. Thin sections, which were cut by conventional methods, showed some evidence of swelling in H_2O but did not dissolve. (See Fig. 14.)

Subsequent to these findings of Gibbons, other water-soluble resins were described (29). Of these, glycol methacrylate has come into perhaps greatest use.

While it cannot be claimed that all the "bugs" have been eliminated from these procedures, enough has been done with them to indicate their potential usefulness. Glycol methacrylate, which is readily available commercially,[5] is a colorless liquid, completely miscible with H_2O, ethanol, and ether. The water in tissues fixed or frozen may be replaced by increasing concentrations until a concentration of better than 90% is achieved. Polymerization is induced by adding 0.5–1% ammonium persulphate. The lower the water content of the mixture the harder the resulting blocks. Sections are insoluble in H_2O but do swell to some extent. This and the tendency of the sections to expand, perhaps soften, under the beam, result in the appearance of morphologically significant artifacts (40).

With sections cut from glycol methacrylate blocks, Leduc and Bernhard (40) have demonstrated selective enzyme digestion with pepsin, trypsin, and nucleases of parts of formalin-fixed tissue cells. The results were variable and not always as reasonably expected, and in some instances indicated that a reaction had taken place between the methac-

---

[5] Rohm & Haas, Philadelphia, Pennsylvania.

rylate and tissue components. Nonetheless the evidence presented is suggestive that histochemical localization of cell components, including enzymes, will be possible within the plastic-embedded section once the best water-miscible resin is found.

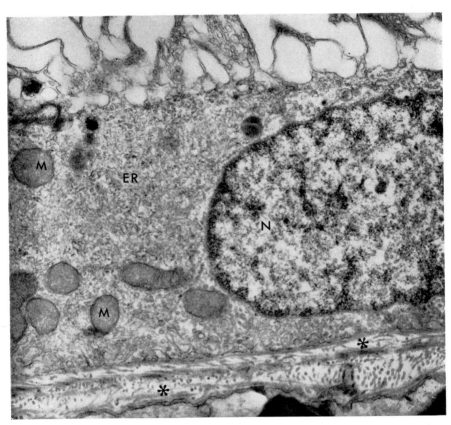

FIG. 14. This electron micrograph shows part of a cell from the pigment epithelium of the rat's retina. The tissue was fixed in osmium, and then dehydrated and embedded with Aquon—a water-soluble derivative of Epon. (Preparation made and photographed by Ian Gibbons.) The nucleus is at (N), mitochondria at (M), and the cytoplasm is filled with profiles of a complex, smooth-surfaced endoplasmic reticulum (ER). The basement membrane and underlying connective tissue (lamina basalis) are indicated by asterisks. Magnification: × 19,840.

IV. Sectioning

Success in preparing thin sections for electron microscopy depends on attention to a number of individual steps. The microtome, the cutting edge, and the embedding material are of paramount importance, but not to be neglected are such lesser aspects of the procedure as preparation of the cutting face and the adjustment of the cutting speed.

Before a block is ready to be put in the microtome, it must be trimmed down so that the embedded material available at the cutting face is as small an area as is consistent with the purpose of the study. Tools for this are readily available. The harder and tougher epoxy resins require the use of fine files and jeweler's saws, but the final finish should be made with new and sharp razor blades. These latter, before use, should be washed in acetone or chloroform to clean them of any oil. The final shape of the block may be that of a right angle, truncated pyramid, with short vertical sides only leading up to the cutting edge. The pyramidal shape lends support to the cutting face and perhaps minimizes distortion of the block during cutting.

The cutting face may be square, but the preference of experienced microtomists runs to an asymmetry with the longer axis oriented normal to the cutting edges. The upper and lower edges should, of course, be parallel, and sophistication in the art of sectioning recommends that the lower edge be slightly longer than the upper. Thus, the final shape is trapezoidal.

Occasionally the sections are required to bear some particular relation to tissue structure, and so the block must be precisely oriented with respect to the plane of sectioning. This is best achieved by shaping the block appropriately with saw and file and then sticking it (with liquid epoxy) on the face of a second block. Some adjustment can finally be achieved by changing the orientation of the microtome chuck, but the performance of the Sorvall microtome (at least) is not improved by having the axis of the chuck far off the longitudinal axis of the cutting arm.

When placed in the chuck, the prepared block should be firmly held by the front edges of the jaws, and should not extend beyond this level more than a few (3–4) millimeters. This may require the operator to remove several millimeters of empty resin from the other end of the block. A long block, projecting 5–10 mm beyond the chuck, introduces a long and flexible element into the sectioning complex which only multiplies the problems.

Facing the block in preparation for sectioning should be done with the block in the microtome. The less valuable part of the cutting edge may be used for this purpose. When this trimming is completed, the best part of the cutting edge is moved into position for thin sectioning.

With respect to sectioning, a few recommendations seem important. The actual sectioning should be performed slowly. In other words, a second or two may be consumed in moving the cutting edge through the embedded material. Then also, if sections of uniform thickness are required, it is essential to observe some rhythm in the motions involved. The microtome and block, no matter how steady in appearance, constitute on elastic body which is distorted by the act of sectioning. This distortion will relax or change between each section, but the degree of relaxation will vary with time. Hence the time between sections should be kept constant or nearly so. Finally the clearance angle should be as small as possible, i.e., $\alpha = 2$–$5°$ (Fig. 15).

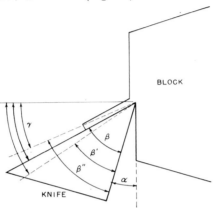

Fig. 15. This figure indicates the various angles which influence the quality of sectioning. Of these, the clearance angle and knife angle are of greatest significance. α = Clearance angle; β = knife angle of 45°; β' = knife angle of less than 45°; β'' = knife angle of greater than 45°; and γ = sheer angle.

Probably everyone experienced in microtomy has encountered in his sections very narrow, regularly spaced, thick and thin bands. This is evidence of "chatter," and if the spacing is small (less than 1 μ) it may be extremely troublesome. For the most part it is a reflection of a vibration set up in the block or microtome arm while the block passes the knife. Occasionally it may reflect, as well, vibration in the knife edge, especially when the clearance angle of the knife is so large that the knife scrapes the section off the block rather than cutting it. Not all the causes of chatter have been determined, but it most often results from a rapid up and down motion of the cutting face along the axis of sectioning. It may be relieved or lessened by changing one or more of several aspects of the operation. The face of the block can be reduced in size or changed in shape. The rate of cutting should be retarded. A change may be made to a knife with a smaller contained angle, β, at the cutting edge (Fig. 15). The temperature of the room and block may be lowered to make the block harder. All these and other devices may be tried to overcome this problem.

The "art" of thin sectioning includes a number of notions and substantial equipment, the real value of which has never been scientifically examined. It does not seem important to record many of them here. However, one which has impressed us as significant is the use of a plutonium strip near the block to eliminate the charge on the face of the block. In this manner, one controls the tendency otherwise shown for the water in the boat to wet the cutting surface.

It can be said that all matrices currently in use show some tendency to compress during sectioning, especially when the sheer angle is small. This is not so serious with the epoxy resins as it was with the methacrylates, but it remains significant. To some extent it was corrected in methacrylate sections by vapors of xylene or toluene or any agent that would soften the sections (45). Agents with similar properties for Epon are not so numerous but at least one, trichloroethylene, is effective. An applicator stick, or matchstick soaked in the compound, serves to bring vapors close to the sections.

Finally, mention should be made of the value of thick sections cut adjacent to the thin. One or two micron sections from Epon or methacrylate, stained in any of several ways (48), are superb preparations for light microscopy. In addition, they can be examined to advantage by phase contrast for purposes of orientation and for finding the best field and areas in the block or section for electron microscopy. The best routine practice is to cut thick sections both before and after each series of thin sections.

REFERENCES

Microtome Design

1. Buck, R. C., and Jarvis, C. E., *Stain Technol.* **34**, 109 (1959).
2. Claesson, S., and Svensson, A. A., *Exptl. Cell Research* **11**, 105 (1956).
3. Claude, A., *Harvey Lectures* **43**, 121 (1947–1948).
4. Cocks, G. G., and Schwartz, C. M., *Rev. Sci. Instr.* **23**, 615 (1952).
5. Danon, D., and Kellenberger, E., *Arch. sci. (Geneve)* **3**, 169 (1950).
6. Eaves, G., and Flewett, T. H., *Exptl. Cell Research* **6**, 155 (1954).
7. Ekholm, R., and Zelander, T., *Experientia* **12**, 195 (1956).
8. Farrant, J. L., and Powell, S. E., *Proc. Reg. Conf. Electron-Microscopy Asia Oceania, 1st, Tokyo, 1956,* p. 147 (1957).
9. Fernandez-Moran, H., *Ind. Diamond Rev.* **16**, 128 (1956).
10. Fullam, E. F., and Gessler, A. E., *Rev. Sci. Instr.* **17**, 23 (1946).
11. Geren, B. B., and McCulloch, D., *Exptl. Cell Research* **2**, 97 (1951).
12. Gettner, M. E., and Ornstein, L., *in* "Physical Techniques in Biological Research" (G. Oster and A. W. Pollister, eds.), Vol. 3, p. 627. Academic Press, New York, 1955.
13. Haanstra, H. B., *Philips Tech. Rev.* **17**, 178 (1955).
14. Hellstrom, B., *Sci. Tools* **7**, 10 (1960).
15. Hillier, J., and Gettner, M. E., *J. Appl. Phys.* **21**, 889 (1950).

16. Hodge, A. J., Huxley, H. E., and Spiro, D., *J. Histochem. and Cytochem.* 2, 54 (1954).

17. Huxley, A. F., Cambridge Instrument Co. Technical Brochure (1959).

18. Huxley, H. E., *Proc. Intern. Conf. Electron Microscopy, 3rd, London, 1954*, p. 112 (1956).

19. Kellenberger, E., *Experientia* 12, 282 (1956).

20. Newman, S. B., Borysko, E., and Swerdlow, M., *J. Research Natl. Bur. Standards* 43, 183 (1949).

21. O'Brien, H. C., and McKinley, G. M., *Science* 98, 455 (1943).

22. Pease, D. C., and Baker, R. F., *Proc. Soc. Exptl. Biol. Med.* 67, 470 (1948).

23. Porter, K. R., and Blum, J., *Anat. Record* 117, 685 (1953).

24. Sitte, H., *Naturwissenschaften* 42, 367 (1955).

25. Sjöstrand, F., *Experientia* 9, 114 (1953).

26. von Ardenne, M., *Z. wiss. Mikroskop.* 56, 8 (1939).

27. von Borries, B., and Huppertz, J., *Z. wiss. Mikroskop.* 63, 484-494 (1956–1958).

28. Watson, M. L., *Biochim. et Biophys. Acta* 10, 1 (1953).

General

29. Bartl, P., Rosenberg, M., and Lesko, J., *Proc. European Regional Conf. Electron Microscopy Delft, 1960*, p. 619 (1961).

30. Cameron, D. A., *J. Biophys. Biochem. Cytol.* 2, Suppl., 57 (1956).

31. Ekholm, R., Hallen, O., and Zelander, T., *Experientia* 11, 361 (1955).

32. Fernandez-Moran, H., *Exptl. Cell Research* 5, 255 (1953).

33. Fernandez-Moran, H., *J. Biophys. Biochem. Cytol.* 2, Suppl., 9 (1956).

34. Finck, H., *J. Biophys. Biochem. Cytol.* 7, 27 (1960).

35. Freeman, J. A., and Spurlock, B. O., *J. Cell Biol.* 13, 437 (1962).

36. Gibbons, I. R., *Nature* 184, 375 (1959).

37. Glauert, A. M., and Glauert, R. H., *J. Biophys. Biochem. Cytol.* 4, 191 (1958).

38. Glauert, A. M., Rogers, G. E., and Glauert, R. H., *Nature* 178, 803 (1956).

39. Latta, H., and Hartmann, J. F., *Proc. Soc. Exptl. Biol. Med.* 74, 436 (1950).

40. Leduc, E. H., and Bernhard, W., *in* "The Interpretation of Ultrastructure," Symposia of the International Society of Cell Biology (R. J. C. Harris, ed.), Vol. 1, p. 21. Academic Press, New York, 1962.

41. Luft, J. H., *J. Biophys. Biochem. Cytol.* 9, 409 (1961).

42. Maaløe, O., and Birch-Andersen, A., *in* "Bacterial Anatomy, 6th Symposium of the Society for General Microbiology," p. 261. Cambridge Univ. Press, London and New York, 1956.

43. Moore, D. H., and Grimley, P. M., *J. Biophys. Biochem. Cytol.* 3, 255 (1957).

44. Pease, D. C., *in* "Histological Techniques for Electron Microscopy." Academic Press, New York, 1960.

45. Satir, P. G., and Peachey, L. D., *J. Biophys. Biochem. Cytol.* 4, 345 (1958).

46. Sjöstrand, F. S., *J. Cellular Comp. Physiol.* 42, 15 (1953).

47. Spurlock, B. O., Kattine, V. C., and Freeman, J. A., *J. Cell Biol.* 17, 203 (1963).

48. Trump, B., Smuckler, E., and Benditt, E., *J. Ultrastructure Research* 5, 343 (1961).

49. Watson, M. L., *J. Biophys. Biochem. Cytol.* 3, 1017 (1957).

50. Weiner, S., *J. Biophys. Biochem. Cytol.* 5, 175 (1959).

Selected Applications of the Electron Microscope

CHAPTER 5

In Physics

D. W. PASHLEY

I. Introduction

Before 1955, almost all electron microscope observations on crystalline materials involved the use of the surface-replica technique. Powerful though this technique is, it provides no information on the structure inside the crystalline material, except that which can be deduced from the surface structure. The difficulties associated with the direct observation of the internal structure, since it must involve transmitting the electrons through the specimen, arise from the fact that the limited

149

penetrating power of the electrons restricts the thickness of the specimen
to a few 1000 A for 50–100 kv electrons; the exact value of this thickness
depends considerably upon the scattering power of the particular crystalline material involved. There are various possibilities for producing such
thin specimens, and even in 1949 Heidenreich (52) had prepared sufficiently thin films of aluminum by electrochemically thinning aluminum
foil, but this advance seems to have been largely ignored for several
years. This arose, in part, because Heidenreich was concerned mainly
with the dynamical theory interpretation of the various diffraction effects
which were present on his micrographs; very little was deduced on the
internal structure of the metal.

   Although Castaing (27) produced some thinned films of aluminum
alloys by an ion-bombardment technique, no substantial progress was
made until Hirsch *et al.* (54) and Bollmann (19) independently and
simultaneously studied thinned metals in which they could unambiguously recognize certain features of the internal structure. Hirsch *et al.*
used aluminum thinned chemically, while Bollmann developed an electrothinning technique for stainless steel. In both experiments, the authors observed certain lines on the images, and they interpreted these
as dislocation lines in the metal. The geometrical arrangements of the
lines were consistent with them being dislocations, and the interpretation was completely confirmed by the observation by Hirsch *et al.* that
the lines could be made to move by use of an intense localized illuminating electron beam in the Siemens Elmiskop I. Thus the most common
mode of plastic deformation of a crystal, namely slip, could be observed
directly at near atomic detail as dislocations moved along their slip
plane. These new observations represented an important advance in
experimental technique, and since 1955 a considerable volume of work
on transmission electron microscopy of thin metal films has been
reported.

   At about the same time as these developments were taking place,
a different but complementary technique was demonstrated. The first
high-resolution electron microscopes became generally available in
1955, and because their resolving power (better than 10 A) was close
to atomic dimensions they opened up the possibility of looking directly
at the atomic structure of crystalline materials. The first direct observation of the periodic structure of a crystal was made by Menter (73), who
studied the metal organic compounds copper and platinum phthalocyanine. These were chosen because their molecular lattices have convenient spacings, and Menter was able to obtain high quality micrographs showing the projection of the $(20\bar{1})$ planes which have spacings
of approximately 10 A and 12 A respectively. This technique also allows

lattice imperfections such as dislocations to be observed directly, since one is able to see the actual rearrangements in the crystal lattice associated with the imperfections. Although the resolving power of the modern electron microscope is still inadequate to allow this technique to be applied directly to more simple crystals such as metals, a further development has allowed an indirect-resolution method to be used. This is based upon the formation of moiré patterns with overlapping crystals, and it was shown independently by Hashimoto and Uyeda (45) and Pashley et al. (85) that moiré patterns can be used for studying dislocation in crystals.

The combination of the techniques described previously, together with selected area diffraction and dark-field techniques, has provided a completely new approach to the study of the microstructure of crystals, particularly metals, and the electron microscope is now one of the major instruments for structural studies on lattice imperfections. Since the first observations mentioned previously, considerable success has been achieved with the development of techniques for thinning specimens for electron microscopy. In addition, techniques for growing sufficiently thin films (e.g. by vacuum evaporation) have been developed. The two methods, which are described in Chapter 2, have allowed many observations to be made on thin crystalline specimens. As a result, many varied features have been observed on electron micrographs, and this has led to problems in understanding and interpreting the contrast effects which appear. For example, the contrast effects with nonperiodic images are controlled largely by local variations in the intensities of the diffracted beams (Bragg reflections), so that a new theory of so-called "diffraction contrast" has had to be developed. Although this theory is still very much in its infancy, it has already provided a reasonable understanding of the more important contrast effects.

The purpose of this chapter is to outline the contrast mechanisms involved in the various types of images, and to review the application of the thin-film technique to crystal physics, particularly metal physics. There is no sharp dividing line between the metal physics applications and the more general metallurgical applications of the thin-film technique, so that a number of topics are more strictly metallurgical. Since metallurgical applications will not be discussed fully in this volume, the treatment of the more metallurgical applications is by no means comprehensive. In particular, it is regretted that there is an absence of any discussion of precipitation in alloys, despite the considerable volume of electron microscopy carried out on this topic during recent years.

Since most of the major advances of electron microscopy in the crystal physics' field in the last few years have been with the direct-transmission technique, this chapter deals exclusively with transmission through crystals. Replica techniques are not considered.

II. Images of Crystals (Thin Films)

A. General Mechanisms of Contrast

When a thin crystalline specimen is examined in the electron microscope, the contrast seen in the image is controlled largely by the way in which the electrons are diffracted in the film. Most treatments of the contrast consider only the elastic scattering of the electrons, on the implicit assumption that inelastic scattering does no more than cause electrons to contribute to a continuous diffuse background which reduces

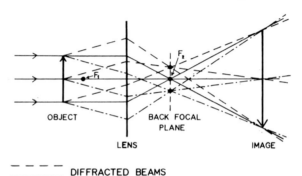

——————   DIFFRACTED BEAMS
—·—·—·—·—

FIG. 1.   Ray path diagram for the objective lens.

the level of contrast produced by the purely elastic scattering. We suppose, initially, that this assumption is valid.

Figure 1 shows the ray-path diagram for the objective lens of the electron microscope, with diffracted beams included. Since all beams leaving the specimen in a particular direction pass through the same point in the back focal plane of the lens, it follows that a focused electron-diffraction pattern is formed in the back focal plane. Modern microscopes have an adjustable aperture in the back focal plane, so that the beams which are allowed to pass into the remaining lenses can be selected as desired. There are two distinct modes of operation. First, only the undeviated electron beam is allowed to pass through the objective aperture, so that none of the diffracted beams is used in forming the image. Then, for points in the object which are diffracting strongly, the transmitted beam is weakened, so that the corresponding image point is darkened. Any contrast obtained in this way is due to variation in the intensity of the diffracted beams from one point of the specimen to another, and is therefore termed "diffraction contrast." Second, one or more diffracted beams is allowed to pass through the objective aperture, in addition to the undeviated beam. The contrast in the image is then controlled by the manner in which these beams are combined (or interfere) in the image plane, since the beams are coherent with each other. This technique gives rise to "periodic contrast" in the image, which can be related to the periodic structure in the specimen.

A variation on these two modes of operation is to use the dark-field technique, and form the image with diffracted beams only. The mechanism of contrast for the dark-field images is fundamentally the same as that for one or the other of the two cases just discussed, depending upon whether one or more diffracted beams are used. The mechanisms of contrast are now considered in more detail.

1. CONTRAST WITHOUT LATTICE RESOLUTION (DIFFRACTION CONTRAST)

We first consider the case of crystals which contain no lattice defects. Diffraction contrast then arises in the image as a result of variations in one or more of the following: (a) the composition or crystal structure of the specimen; (b) the orientation of the crystalline material; or (c) the thickness of the specimen.

It is first necessary to consider the effect of these variables on the intensity of the diffracted beams. Three different approaches may be made to this problem. First, one may apply Bragg's law, that $2d \sin \theta = n\lambda$ (θ is the glancing angle of incidence of the electron beam on the planes, λ is the electron wavelength and n is an integer) for a strong reflection to occur from a set of crystal planes of spacing d. Although this approach can be used to obtain qualitative results for some problems, it is not easy to apply in general. Second, the contrast may be considered in terms of kinematical diffraction theory, which leads to the concept of the reciprocal lattice. This is a geometrical construction which allows the directions of the diffracted beams to be determined. The treatment embraces the concept of Bragg's law, but is of wider application. Its main disadvantage is that it is liable to give incorrect values for the relative intensities of the diffracted beams. This arises because kinematical theory is based upon the false assumption that the scattering of electrons by atoms is weak. To overcome this difficulty the third approach, that of the dynamical theory, is required. This treats the propagation of the electron waves through the crystal in terms of wave mechanics, proper attention being paid to the boundary conditions.

Although these different treatments have been successfully applied to the determination of diffraction patterns, certain difficulties arise when they are used to explain image contrast. The nature of the problem follows from a consideration of the elementary kinematical theory.

According to this theory, each atom in the crystal acts as a scattering center for the incident electron wave, and the scattered wavelets in any direction are all added together, due account being taken of the phase differences, to give the amplitude of the diffracted beam in that direction. However, the wavelets scattered in the same direction from all the atoms can be combined only at infinity, because the wavelets in a particular direction from any two atoms R and Q (Fig. 2) will not meet, except at infinity, unless RQ happens to be parallel to the chosen direction. Thus the kinematical theory, as normally used for calculating

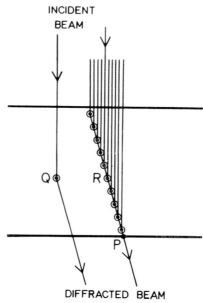

INCIDENT BEAM

DIFFRACTED BEAM

FIG. 2.   The overlapping of scattered wavelets from individual atoms in the crystal.

diffraction patterns, gives the diffraction pattern at infinity. It gives no direct information on how the intensity of a given diffracted beam varies across the lower surface of the crystal. But it is precisely this variation which is required, because the image detail is controlled by it, and it can be effectively assumed, as a first approximation, that the objective is normally focused onto the lower surface of the specimen.

Hirsch *et al.* (56) have, however, supposed that the kinematical theory can be used to calculate the variation in the diffracted beams across the lower surface of the crystal, implicitly assuming that all effective interference has occurred by the time the wavelets have passed through the lower surface. An immediate consequence of this assumption is that the diffracted beam at a point P can be contributed to only by the wavelets emanating from the column of atoms along the line RP (Fig. 2), where RP is along the direction of the diffracted beam. This introduces the concept of the column approach, and simplifies the problem a great deal, because the specimen can be divided into a large number of such parallel columns, and each column is then treated separately. The difficulty is that if this treatment is applied strictly, it does not predict the diffraction pattern correctly, because it does not take into account the interference between wavelets scattered from neighboring columns, which on conventional kinematical theory occurs as the wavelets travel away from the specimen. The approach is therefore much oversimplified, and its limits of applicability are difficult to deduce. Its application has, however, been highly successful in predicting many qualitative and semiquantitative features of the contrast due to imperfections (dislocations, stacking faults, etc.). It seems likely that the approach is reasonably valid provided the atomic displacments associated with the strain field of an imperfection are such that they lead mainly to relative phase shifts of the wavelets scattered from within one column element, rather than relative phase shifts of wavelets from neighboring columns. Further, it is generally recognized that dynamical theory provides the more correct formal approach to the problem; and this theory is based upon interference which takes place entirely within the crystal. Thus to this extent the column approach seems to represent a modification of kinematical theory which takes it a little closer to dynamical theory. The detailed application of the column approach by Hirsch *et al.* (*56*) is discussed later (see Section II, B, 1).

The dynamical theory, originally developed by Bethe (*18*), is concerned with treating the passage of an incident electron wave through a medium with a periodic potential distribution (the specimen) by means of wave mechanics. Although relatively simple to formulate, the problem is generally difficult to solve because an infinite set of waves (diffracted beams) is produced inside the crystal, and approximations are necessary in order to arrive at any usable solutions. Many calculations are carried out by means of the two-beam approximation, which is based upon the assumption that only two beams, the zero-order and one diffracted beam, are strong. The main difficulty in any application is to justify all approximations which are made.

We now consider the effect of (*a*), (*b*), and (*c*) mentioned previously. If any two parts of a thin-film specimen are composed of crystals with different compositions or crystal structures, the two regions will appear in contrast against each other, because the diffracted beams are different, leading to a difference in the intensity of the local undeviated beams. Thus a region of hexagonal cobalt within a matrix of fcc cobalt will be

Fig. 3. Prominent extinction contours in a buckled single-crystal gold film. Magnification × 110,000. Micrograph from reference (87).

readily observed. Similarly, any discrete change in orientation will give observable contrast effects, so that, for example, twinned regions of a crystal appear in good contrast on an image (e.g., Figs. 46 and 68). Local bending is sufficient to give very pronounced effects. The Bragg angles for diffraction are very small, and bends of just a few degrees are ample to sweep the crystal through the Bragg position for a number of different reflections. The image of a bent crystal (Fig. 3) contains a fringe pattern, each fringe representing the locus of points which reflect strongly into a particular diffracted beam, i.e., the locus of points for which the reflecting planes are equally inclined to the incident electron beam. The fringes are known as extinction contours due to bending. If the extinction

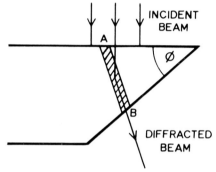

FIG. 4. Diffraction from a wedge-shaped crystal.

contours are indexed, as can be done, for example, by means of selected area diffraction, the geometry of the extinction contour pattern can be used for determining the detailed shape (i.e., buckling) of the film.

Variations in thickness of the specimen lead to changes in contrast, and this is most readily demonstrated by reference to the column treatment used by Hirsch *et al.* (*56*). Consider a wedge-shaped crystal (Fig. 4), and divide it into column elements such as *AB*, chosen to be along the direction of the strong diffracted beam (i.e., for the two-beam case). We can plot an amplitude phase diagram (Fig. 5) to allow all the wavelets due to scattering by atoms in the column *AB* to be added together. Figure 5 applies to the case when the crystal is set slightly off the optimum position for a Bragg reflection, i.e., it applies when the element *AB* lies near the edge of an extinction contour, but not when *AB* is at its center. There is then a small phase difference between the waves scattered from successive atoms in the column *AB*, so that the amplitude phase diagram is a part of a regular polygon, each element of the polygon representing the scattered wavelet from a single atom in the column. The origin *O* corresponds to the midpoint of the column *AB*, and the resultant diffracted beam is represented by the vector **PP'**. The longer the column AB becomes, the nearer P' approaches P; when P' and P coincide there is no diffracted beam. As AB is further increased, P' and P travel around the same polygon again, and **PP'** increases. Thus the amplitude of the diffracted beam varies periodically with the film thickness of the specimen, between the limits of zero and that given by the "diameter" of the polygon. Clearly, the transmitted undeviated beam varies with the same period in antiphase with the diffracted beam. This leads to the observation of fringes from a wedge-shaped crystal (Fig. 6). These wedge fringes occur also when the crystal is set accurately at the Bragg angle, but a dynamical theory treatment is required to

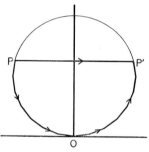

Fig. 5. Amplitude phase diagram from a column AB in a wedge-shaped crystal (see Fig. 4).

explain them in this case. The periodic variation in the amplitude of the diffracted beam, and hence the increase in crystal thickness corresponding to the spacing between adjacent fringes, is then known as the extinction distance t_0 for the reflection operating. When there is a deviation from the Bragg setting, the equivalent increase in thickness, or equivalent extinction distance t'_0 is given by $t_0/(1 + x^2)^{1/2}$ where x is given approximately by $t_0 s$. The symbol s is the distance of the appropriate reciprocal lattice point from the reflecting sphere, measured in a direction normal to the specimen plane (see, for example, reference *117*). The general result is that the spacing of the wedge fringes decreases as the deviation from the Bragg angle is increased. The spacing is given by $t'_0 \cot \phi$ (see Fig. 4).

2. Contrast with Lattice Resolution

   a. Direct Lattice Resolution. When one or more diffracted beams is allowed to contribute to the image formation, in addition to the undeviated beam, periodic structure can occur in the image. The beams required for this type of image are selected by suitable positioning of an

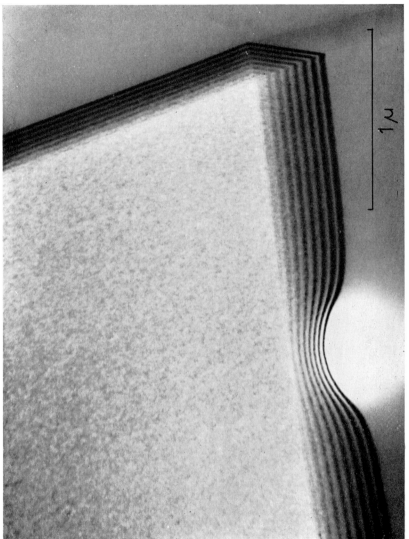

FIG. 6.   Wedge fringes at grain boundary in stainless steel. Magnification × 48,000.

objective aperture of adequate size in the back focal plane of the objective lens (see Fig. 1). The mechanism by which the image contrast appears follows closely that of the formation of images of periodic objects such as line gratings, in the optical microscope. This is covered by the Abbe theory (1) of image formation, which leads to the rule that a periodic image of a line grating will appear only if at least one diffracted beam from that grating is included in the image. The meaning of this rule can be illustrated by analogy with the technique of structure analysis by x-ray (or electron) diffraction. The structure analysis involves measuring the intensities of a large number of diffracted beams from a single crystal specimen, and an analytical procedure based upon Fourier transforms is applied to convert the intensity measurements to an electron-density map for the crystal. The larger the number of diffracted beams included, the more correctly detailed is the final answer. The use of a very small number of diffracted beams is liable to give false detail. In the limit, when no diffracted beams are included, no periodic detail of the structure can appear, even if the intensity of the undeviated beam is measured, because the information that periodicity exists is contained in the diffracted beams, by means of their intensity and phase relationships with the incident beam and each other. The structure which is determined may be considered as a Fourier synthesis of the various beams which are measured. In the electron microscope the lenses effectively carry out the Fourier synthesis automatically, but for reasons discussed later the number of diffracted beams which can be used is severely limited, so that the periodic images of crystals obtained with an electron microscope represent a very incomplete projection of the structure.

A simple approach is to regard the periodic image obtained in the electron microscope as a pattern formed by the interference between the undeviated beam and the various diffracted beams which contribute to the image. If there is only one diffracted beam at an angle α to the main beam, elementary interference theory shows that it will produce a fringe pattern of spacing $s = \lambda/\alpha$, where λ is the wavelength. Since the diffracted beam (Bragg reflection) from a set of crystal planes of spacing d makes an angle of λ/d with the undeviated beam (i.e., $\alpha = \lambda/d$), it follows that $s = d$, so that the fringe spacing is equal to the spacing of the set of crystal planes giving rise to the diffracted beam. It is therefore concluded that the necessary diffracted beam for forming a periodic image of the projection of a set of crystal planes is the Bragg reflection from that set of planes. This was first discussed by Menter (73), who was able to verify the rule experimentally, with specimens of platinum and copper phthalocyanine.

It means that when a buckled specimen exhibiting well-defined ex-

tinction contours is used, the periodic image of a set of crystal planes
will appear only in the extinction contour corresponding to diffraction
from that set of planes, and then only if the particular diffracted beam
is allowed through the objective aperture.

A fine example of the periodic image of the $(20\bar{1})$ planes in platinum
phthalocyanine is shown in Fig. 7. Since the Bragg angles involved are
very small ($<$ one degree), the $(20\bar{1})$ planes are very nearly parallel to

FIG. 7. The image of the $(20\bar{1})$ planes in platinum phthalocyanine. Magnification
$\times$ 870,000. Micrograph from reference (73).

the electron beam, so that the image can effectively be regarded as the
projection of the $(20\bar{1})$ planes. When more than one diffracted beam is
involved in the image formation, a two-dimensional periodic structure
is formed. These are more difficult to analyze in detail than a simple
one-dimensional fringe pattern, but the periodicity in any direction
should be directly related to that of the crystal planes perpendicular to
that direction. This point is discussed further in relation to moiré patterns (see Section II, A, 2, b).

Because of objective lens aberrations, only those diffracted beams
which are sufficiently near to the objective axis can be usefully utilized

in forming periodic images; this sets a lower limit to the spacing of a set of crystal planes which can be resolved in this way. Since the factors controlling the resolution limit for periodic objects are effective in a manner somewhat different from the normal situation (see Chapter 1), the resolution limit is discussed in Section II, A, 2, c. The general conclusion is that with the best microscopes available at present the practical limit is around 5 A. This means that relatively simple crystal structures, such as those of the elements and simple inorganic compounds, cannot be studied by this technique. For this reason, indirect lattice resolution techniques (see Section II, A, 2, b) have been developed, so that periodic information can be obtained with crystal spacings well below 5 A.

The mechanism of contrast from periodic objects has so far been discussed in terms of the kinematical theory of electron diffraction, according to which all effective interference occurs outside the crystalline specimen. This is adequate for many purposes. However, as with the diffraction contrast discussed in Section II, A, 1, the more correct approach, and the approach which lends itself to more detailed interpretation of the images, is via the dynamical theory. According to the dynamical theory, interaction between the various diffracted beams occurs inside the crystal, and one important result is that the intensity of the diffracted beams varies periodically with crystal thickness. These extinction effects, as considered by Niehrs (77), modify the contrast of the image, and have an effect on whether the actual positions of projection of the planes of atoms are dark or light on the image. In effect, the image intensity at any point changes periodically with specimen thickness, the period corresponding to one extinction distance. Thus, in general, the projection of the planes of atoms coincides with neither the light nor the dark fringe on the image, but it can coincide with either at the appropriate specimen thickness. This effect leads to steps in the resolved lattice image from edges of crystals which are wedge-shaped (74). A detailed discussion of the application of dynamical theory to the interpretation of periodic images has been given by Hashimoto et al. (48) and Cowley (30).

b. Indirect Lattice Resolution—Moiré Patterns. The well-known optical technique of overlapping two line gratings to produce a coarser grating, or moiré pattern, can be applied directly to the electron microscopy of crystals. The optical analogues of Fig. 8 illustrate the two principal modes of formation of moiré patterns. Either two gratings of different spacing are superposed in parallel orientation to produce "parallel" moiré patterns (Fig. 8a), or two equally spaced gratings are superposed with a small relative twist to produce "rotation" moiré patterns (Fig. 8b). The two effects can be combined by superposing two gratings of different spacing with a small relative twist. In the electron microscope, similar effects are produced by suitably superposing two thin crystals, so that two sets of crystal planes either have different spacings, or are rotated with respect to each other. In this way, moiré patterns were obtained quite fortuitously by a number of workers (*33, 52, 75, 106, 107*), but Pashley *et al.* (*85*) deliberately superposed single-crystal films to produce the moiré patterns as a means of indirect lattice resolution. Since the moiré pattern has a larger spacing than either of the two component gratings, it is possible for the electron microscope

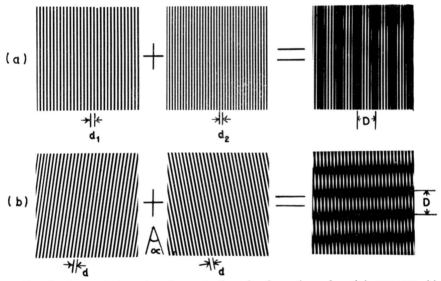

FIG. 8. An optical analog demonstrating the formation of moiré patterns: (a) parallel moiré patterns; (b) rotation moiré patterns.

to resolve the moiré pattern even though the crystal spacings in the two overlapping films are below the resolution limit.

The spacing of the parallel moiré pattern is given by

$$D = d_1 d_2/(d_1 - d_2)$$

where d_1 and d_2 are the spacings of the parallel sets of crystal planes involved. If $(d_1 - d_2) \ll d_1$ or d_2, then $D \gg d_1$ or d_2 and we get a big magnification effect. We can define a "moiré magnification" M, such that $D = M d_2$, and $M = d_1/(d_1 - d_2)$. Thus the planes of spacing d_2 are imaged with a spacing $M d_2$ by using the parallel moiré patterns formed with the spacing d_1. The rotation moiré patterns have a spacing given by

$$D = d/(2 \sin \alpha/2)$$

which for small α becomes

$$D = d/\alpha$$

where each grating has a spacing d, and their relative rotation is α. The moiré magnification in this case is then $1/\alpha$. When a rotation occurs with parallel moiré patterns the spacing is given by

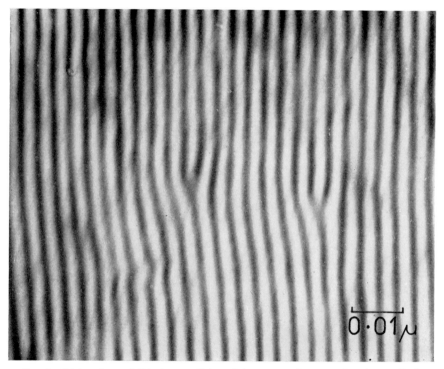

FIG. 9. Dislocations visible in parallel moiré patterns from overlapping palladium and gold layers in (111) orientation. Magnification $\times$ 1,300,000. Micrograph from reference (85).

$$D = d_1 d_2 / \sqrt{(d_1{}^2 + d_2{}^2 - 2d_1 d_2 \cos \alpha)}$$

which, for small values of α, becomes

$$D = d_1 d_2 / \sqrt{(d_1 - d_2)^2 + \alpha^2 d_1 d_2}$$

Examples of moiré patterns obtained by superposing two metal films (9) are given in Figs. 9 and 10.

The origin of fringe patterns obtained with overlapping crystals was not fully understood by those who first observed them. The two types of explanations put forward were that they are either moiré patterns, as defined by Fig. 8, or that they are due to a double diffraction effect. This ambiguity was resolved by Dowell *et al.* (*32, 33*) who showed that double diffraction is necessary for any contrast to occur on moiré pat-

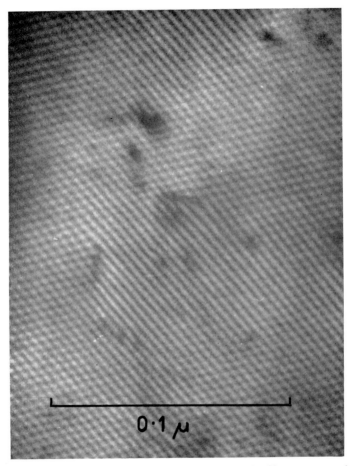

Fig. 10. Rotation moiré patterns from two (111) gold films superposed with a relative twist of about 2°. Magnification × 640,000. Micrograph from reference (*9*).

terns. As discussed in Section II, A, 2, a, it is necessary for at least one diffracted beam to contribute to a periodic image, and Dowell *et al.* showed that the necessary beam is one which has been diffracted once by each of the two overlapping crystals. This is demonstrated, for the case of parallel moiré patterns, by reference to Fig. 11. The large open and closed circles (Fig. 11a) represent the primary diffraction spots from two superposed parallel face-centered cubic crystals in (111) orientation. For a diffraction constant K, $OP = K/d_1$ and $OQ = K/d_2$, where d_1 and d_2 are the respective $(2\bar{2}0)$ spacings in the crystals. If crystal 1 is uppermost, then part of the $(2\bar{2}0)$ beam from this crystal passes undeviated through crystal 2 to form the spot P. However, an appreciable part of this beam may be diffracted again by the $(\bar{2}20)$ planes in crystal 2 to produce a double-diffracted beam at S, where $PS = K/d_2$. It follows that

$$OS = PS - OP = K(d_1 - d_2)/d_1 d_2$$

so that the position of S corresponds to the diffracted spot from a grating of spacing $d_1 d_2/(d_1 - d_2)$, i.e., the spacing of the parallel moiré

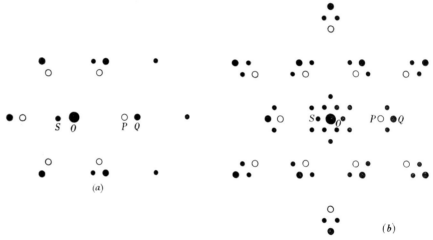

Fɪɢ. 11.   Double diffraction from two overlapping parallel crystals in (111) orientation (see reference 9).

pattern. The same general result applies to rotation patterns. When all possible double diffraction combinations are considered, the diffraction pattern appears as in Fig. 11b, and an example of such a pattern for nickel deposited in parallel orientation on gold is given in Fig. 12. Thus, the moiré patterns are formed by the combination of the doubly diffracted beams surrounding the undeviated beam with the undeviated beam itself, these doubly diffracted beams having a direction corresponding to a Bragg reflection from the moiré pattern spacing.

In order that the required doubly diffracted beam be formed, it is necessary that the diffraction conditions for both the initial primary diffraction and the subsequent secondary diffraction be satisfied simultaneously. This is readily shown to be possible for small spacing differences with parallel moiré patterns, and for small angles of twist with rotation moiré patterns. Figure 13 illustrates the former case. CO is the incident beam and O is the origin of the two reciprocal lattices. P and P' are reciprocal lattice points for crystal 1 and Q and Q' are the corresponding points for crystal 2. CP represents the strong reflected beam

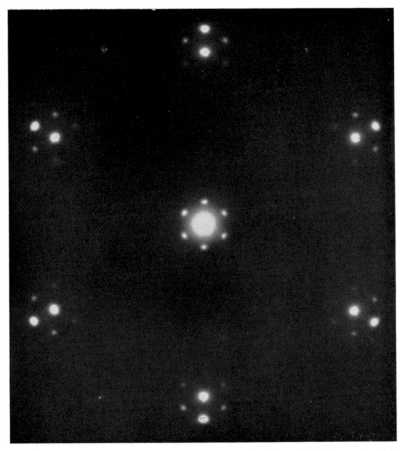

Fig. 12. Diffraction pattern from parallel overlapping (111) films of gold and nickel (see reference 9).

in crystal 1, so that CP is the beam which is to be diffracted by crystal 2. If we translate the reciprocal lattice of crystal 2, without any rotation, so that its origin coincides with P, the sphere of reflection remains as before. Q' is shifted to Q'', and is almost exactly on the sphere of reflection, since it is very close to O. Thus a very slight relaxation of the third Laue condition ensures that the double-diffracted beam CQ'' will appear, so that if the condition for the primary diffraction is satisfied the condition for the double diffraction required for a moiré pattern is automatically satisfied almost exactly.

The planes which appear resolved indirectly by means of moiré patterns therefore depend upon the local diffraction conditions in the specimen. This can be clearly demonstrated (9) by the appearance of periodicities in different directions in the various extinction contours. When two or more sets of planes diffract simultaneously, a two-dimensional moiré pattern is formed. The exact form of this depends very much on the detailed diffracting conditions; in appropriate circumstances a two-dimensional array of dots is formed (Fig. 14), and these may be regarded

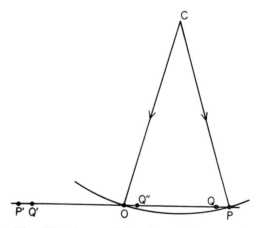

FIG. 13.   The diffracting conditions for moiré pattern formation.

as the projection of lines of atoms in the crystal, magnified additionally by the moiré magnification.

Again, the dynamical theory should be applied to the more detailed interpretation of moiré patterns, and this has been done by Hashimoto *et al.* (48).

c. The Resolution Limit for Periodic Structures. Since the range of application of the study of periodic structures depends considerably upon the magnitude of the spacings which can be resolved, it is appropriate to discuss the resolution limit here.

The resolution limit for periodic structures is basically different from that of other types of image because the periodic image is produced, in its simplest one-dimensional form, by two relatively narrow beams. This means, as was pointed out by Menter (73), that only two small areas of the objective lens aperture are used, instead of the complete area defined by the objective aperture, so that the effect of spherical aberration is much reduced. Chromatic aberration is similarly reduced.

The spherical aberration limitation is considered as follows. If a ray makes an angle α with the optic axis on the object side of the lens, spherical aberration gives rise to a phase delay of $\pi C_s \alpha^4 / 2\lambda$, where C_s is the spherical aberration coefficient of the lens, and λ is the wavelength. If this phase delay were constant over the diffracted beam wave front,

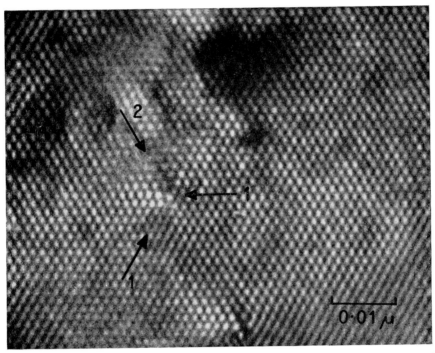

FIG. 14. A two-dimensional parallel moiré pattern from overlapping copper and gold layers in (111) orientation. A dislocation gives 2, 1, and 1 extra half-lines in the images of the three {220} planes shown. Magnification $\times$ 1,800,000. Micrograph from reference (9).

it would not limit resolution, since the delay could be corrected by a suitable change in objective lens current. What matters is the variation in phase delay across the wave front, since any such variation will produce a blurring of the image, by causing a continuous range of relative image displacements. The image shift for a phase change of ϕ is $\phi/2\pi$ spacings of the fringe pattern on the image. The criterion for the resolution limit is taken by allowing a maximum phase variation of $\pi/2$ across the wave front. This is to some extent arbitrary, but clearly a phase variation of π would lead to a very low image contrast. In practice, the precise limit would depend upon such factors as the photographic plate contrast.

The width of the diffracted beam wave front is controlled by its divergence $\Delta\alpha$, so that by differentiation of the expression for the phase delay given above, the phase delay across the diffracted beam wave front becomes $2\pi C_s \alpha^3 \Delta\alpha/\lambda$. By putting this value equal to a maximum value of $\pi/2$ we obtain for the resolution limit, as controlled by spherical aberration alone

$$d_{\min} = \sqrt[3]{4C_s\lambda^2\Delta\alpha}$$

$d_{\min}$ is the smallest periodic spacing which can be resolved according to this criterion. In practice, $\Delta\alpha$ is controlled by the divergence of the incident beam and by the width of the diffracting region of the crystal, since small crystals give divergent diffracted beams. Thus

$$d_{\min} = \sqrt[3]{4C_s\lambda^2(\delta + \lambda/W)}$$

where δ is the divergence of the incident beam and W is the width of the diffracting region of the crystal in the direction normal to the reflecting planes. For W sufficiently large (say 1000 A) and the best available electron microscopes this value of $d_{\min}$ can be 3 A or less.

In a similar way, the effect due to chromatic aberration leads to a resolution limit given by

$$d_{\min} = \sqrt{4C_c\lambda\Delta V/V}$$

for a variation of ΔV in the accelerating voltage V. C_c is the chromatic aberration coefficient of the objective lens. This value of d_{min} appropriate to the best available electron microscopes is about 4 A, with a corresponding value of 4 A due to variations in objective lens current.

In practice, these three effects have to be combined, together with effects due to mechanical instability in the instrument (e.g. specimen drift). It is possible for one effect to partly cancel another; for example, the effect due to a drift in V can be canceled by a drift of the appropriate magnitude and direction in the objective lens current. This is consistent with the experience that the practical resolution limit for periodic structures is about 5 A, and that at this level of resolution the performance is somewhat erratic, because fortuitous good performance can occur if the effect of one aberration happens, by chance, to cancel that of another. An example of a moiré pattern with a spacing of 5.8 A clearly resolved is shown in Fig. 15.

A gain in resolving power for periodic objects should be possible by tilting the illuminating system of the electron microscope so that the undeviated and diffracted beams are symmetrical with respect to the optic axis of the objective lens. This leads to the spherical aberration being reduced so that d_{min} is 0.63 times the value given previously. Further, what seems to be more important is that the effect of chromatic aberration should be eliminated since the phase delay on one of the beams due, for example, to a fluctuation in V is compensated by an equal phase delay on the other beam, and no image shift occurs. No serious

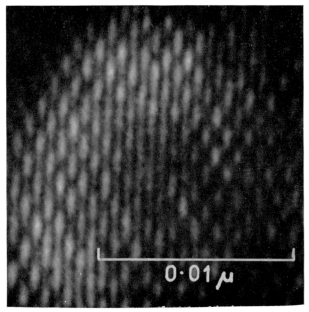

FIG. 15.   Parallel moiré pattern of $(4\overline{2}\overline{2})$ planes from a nickel layer deposited onto a (111) gold film. A moiré spacing of 5.8 A is clearly resolved. Magnification $\times$ 5,200,000. Micrograph from reference (9).

attempt to benefit by this technique seems to have been made so far, but it would seem to offer some hope of a resolution of perhaps 3 A or a little less with existing microscopes.

3. DARK-FIELD IMAGES

An important aspect of the examination of crystalline specimens in the electron microscope is that electron-diffraction patterns can be obtained from the same area of the specimen as used for the micrograph. This is normally carried out by placing an aperture of suitable size in the image plane of the objective lens. This aperture is positioned while the image is under observation, and the lens between the objective and projector lens (the intermediate lens) is changed in strength until the back focal plane of the objective, and hence the diffraction pattern, is in focus. Care is needed to ensure that the specimen area is correctly selected, and in addition the spherical aberration of the objective lens leads to limitations on the accuracy of the technique (2, 92, 102), for selected areas below about 1 μ in diameter. However, within this limitation the technique is most powerful since it allows direct and detailed correlation between the image and the diffraction pattern. This allows information concerning the structure and orientation of the specimen to be obtained on a fine scale, and also provides information which is vital to a proper understanding of the image contrast (cf. Section II, A, 1 and 2).

A complementary technique to that of selected area diffraction is the dark-field technique. Instead of the image being formed by the directly transmitted electron beam, which is the normal case, a diffracted beam is used for the purpose. This beam is selected by suitable positioning of the objective aperture. The dark-field image thus reveals the way in which the intensity of the diffracted beam varies across the specimen. Provided the region of the specimen under examination is suitably oriented, the dark-field image gives contrast similar to that of the bright-field image, except that it can be complementary in character. The advantages of the dark-field image are that (a) the operating reflecting plane is automatically determined; and (b) the contrast of the image is often improved. The disadvantage of the technique described previously, is that spherical aberration causes the image to have poor resolution, because the diffracted beam is not parallel to the objective axis. This can be overcome by tilting the illuminating system until the required diffracted beam is parallel to the objective axis (see, for example, references 43 and 86). If this operation is carried out, the resolution of the image is as good as that for bright-field images, and periodic images of spacings as low as 7 A have been obtained recently by the author using this technique.

The contrast of the dark-field image is determined in exactly the same way as outlined for the bright-field image, since it depends upon the diffracting conditions in the specimen. One of the complications arising in the interpretation of bright-field images occurs when two or more strong diffracted beams are formed in the same area of the specimen. There are then at least two components to the contrast. It would seem at first sight that the dark-field image from that area would be simpler and contain just one component of the contrast. This is not necessarily the case, since if the specimen orientation is favorable for two strong reflections to occur, then it is also favorable for double diffraction to occur. This means that electrons diffracted into the beam used for dark-field can be subsequently diffracted again into the second diffracted beam. Two different reflections will therefore contribute to the contrast of the dark-field image.

A common use of the dark-field technique is to employ it to distinguish between various components of a multiple system. Thus (see Fig. 47) if a crystal contains twins, a dark-field image formed by a diffracted beam arising from the twin orientation will show up the twins brightly on a dark background.

B. Contrast Due to Imperfections in Crystals

1. CONTRAST WITHOUT LATTICE RESOLUTION (DIFFRACTION CONTRAST)

The diffraction contrast arising from lattice imperfections is considered mainly in terms of the column approach in kinematical theory, as developed in detail by Hirsch et al. (56). The technique consists of using the amplitude phase diagram as illustrated in Fig. 5 to calculate the diffracted beam intensity at all points on the lower surface of the crystal. The strain field associated with the imperfection must be known, so that the positions of the atoms within all the columns is known.

a. Planar Faults—Stacking Faults. Consider that AB (Fig. 16) represents a stacking fault in a fcc crystal. The two parts of the crystal separated by the fault are displaced relative to each other by the vector $\mathbf{R} = \frac{1}{6}[2\bar{1}\bar{1}]$, lying in the (111) fault plane. If $\mathbf{g}$ is the reflection vector for the (hkl) diffracted beam, the phase difference between the diffracted beams from the two sides of the fault is given by $2\pi\mathbf{g}\cdot\mathbf{R} = \pi/3$ $(2h\text{-}k\text{-}l)$. The possible values of this phase difference, depending upon the reflection (khl) (h, k, l, must always be either all even or all odd for fcc. crystal) are zero or $\pm120°$. The amplitude phase diagram for the column shown in Fig. 16 is given in Fig. 17, for the case of a phase difference of $-120°$, which occurs at Q, where the stacking fault passes through the column. PP'' represents the resultant diffracted beam, instead of PP' which would apply to an unfaulted crystal. In general, for a film whch is several extinction distances in thickness, the amplitude phase diagram includes several completed circuits of one or both of the circles of Fig. 17. It can be deduced readily from a series of these diagrams that the contrast of the fault is in the form of a set of fringes parallel to the line of intersection of the fault with the specimen surface, with a spacing represented by a change in depth of the fault of t'_o, the equivalent extinction distance; i.e., the spacing is given by $t'_o \cot \phi$ (see Fig. 16). Examples of this fringe contrast are shown in Fig. 41.

Whelan and Hirsch (117, 118) have calculated the contrast of oblique stacking faults by means of the two-beam dynamical theory. The column approach is not used in this treatment; the fault is taken into account by suitable matching of the waves inside the crystal at the fault plane *AB*. The results outlined above are in good agreement with this more rigorous treatment, for the case when the crystal is not set exactly at

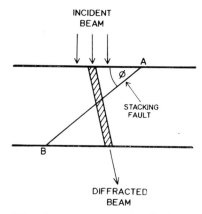

Fig. 16.   The diffraction contrast associated with a stacking fault.

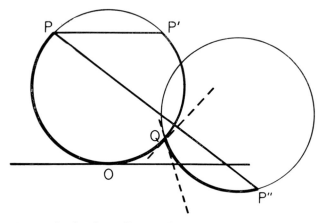

Fig. 17.   The amplitude phase diagram for a column traversing a stacking fault (see Fig. 16).

the reflecting position. The dynamical theory predicts that the spacing of the fringes is halved when the crystal is set exactly at the Bragg angle, and this is confirmed by observation (*118*). The dynamical treatment allows the detailed intensity profiles of the fringes to be calculated for all cases.

Other kinds of planar faults can be treated by the same technique as described previously. In Section VI, the application to the contrast due to antiphase boundaries in ordered alloys is discussed.

b. Line Imperfections—Dislocations. The contrast due to a dislocation line is more difficult to calculate than that of a planar fault because the atomic displacements (i.e. the strain field) extend throughout a volume, rather than just over one surface, and vary in magnitude and direction from one atom to its neighbor. A simple consideration illustrates one feature of the contrast. Figure 18 shows the kind of strain field associated with an edge dislocation, visualized in this case as a line lying in a foil parallel to the foil surface. To a first approximation the

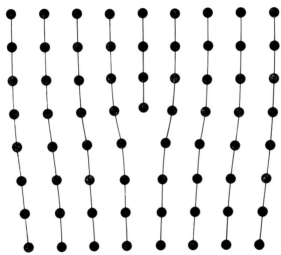

FIG. 18.   The atomic displacements around an edge dislocation.

atomic strain field can be considered in terms of local lattice rotations, which are seen to be in opposite directions on the two sides of the dislocation line. If we consider the case where the crystal is set slightly off the Bragg angle for a given reflection, then the planes on one side are rotated closer to the Bragg angle, and those on the other side are rotated away from the Bragg angle. This leads to a one-sided type of contrast of the dislocation, so that the image of a dislocation line appears to one side of the actual projected position of the line.

The column approach in kinematical theory is applied as follows: Figure 19 shows a slab of crystal containing a screw dislocation *AB*. *CD* represents a column which applies to a perfect crystal. *EF* is a similar column in the dislocated crystal, the distortion of the column representing the local strain field of the dislocation. The amplitude phase diagram for such a column is no longer a circle, because the phase difference between wavelets from successive atoms down the column is no longer constant. The kind of diagram for the case of *EF* close to the dislocation line is shown in Fig. 20, the diffracted beam at the bottom of the column being given by a vector such as **PP'**. The positions of *P* and *P'* move

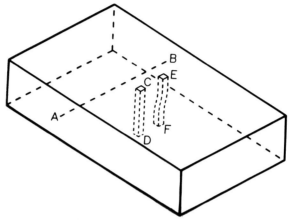

FIG. 19. The column (*EF*) used in calculating the diffraction contrast due to a screw dislocation *AB*.

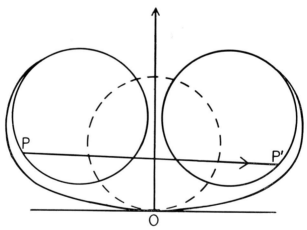

FIG. 20. The amplitude phase diagram for the column *EF* (see Fig. 19), when *EF* is near to the dislocation *AB*.

round the spirals as the crystal thickness is changed. By considering how the value of **PP'** varies with the distance of the column *EF* from the dislocation line *AB* (Fig. 19), Hirsch *et al.* (*56*) determined the intensity profile of the image of the dislocation line. Examples of such intensity profiles are given in Fig. 21. The main results which follow from the calculations are: (1) the image is a line given by the projection of the dislocation on the image, but displaced by approximately 100–200 A from the exact position (see Fig. 21); (2) the width of the image is normally 100–200 A for low-order reflections; (3) the contrast vanishes when $\mathbf{g} \cdot \mathbf{b} = 0$, where $\mathbf{g}$ is the reflection vector and $\mathbf{b}$ is the Burgers vector of the dislocation. This latter result means that a dislocation image vanishes when the reflecting plane is parallel to the Burgers vector of the dislocation. An important consequence of this is that if a specimen is tilted until a dislocation goes out of contrast, the indices of the reflec-

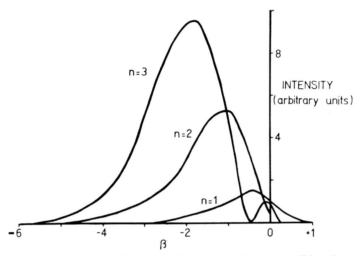

FIG. 21. The intensity profile across the image of a screw dislocation which is parallel to the film plane; $n = \mathbf{g} \cdot \mathbf{b}$ and β is referred to the real position of the dislocation as origin.

tion operating can be used to determine the Burgers vector of the dislocation (see Section III, A, 1, a). Since the magnitude and direction of the displacement of the dislocation image depends upon the reflection operating, it follows that two separate images can be formed if two reflections operate simultaneously (e.g. Fig. 29b).

c. *Effects Involving Dynamical Theory and Absorption.* As pointed out previously, the kinematical theory is not adequate for a detailed analysis of contrast effects, and extensions or modifications of the kinematical calculations have already started to take into account inelastic scattering (absorption), and to use the dynamical theory. Hashimoto *et al.* (47, 49) have considered inelastic scattering by applying dynamical theory equations to a crystal with a complex lattice potential. The imaginary part of the lattice potential gives rise to absorption. This mathematical technique cannot be justified at present, especially in view of the results of Kamiya and Uyeda (*64*) discussed later, but it seems to lead to several correct predictions. The first application has been to the contrast due to a stacking fault. The absorption leads to modifications in the intensity profile of the fringes, and in particular leads to differences between the profiles for bright- and dark-field images. These predictions are confirmed by observation.

Howie and Whelan (*57, 59*) have used a similar technique to study the contrast of a dislocation, but they still retain the column approach. In addition to confirming the general results obtained by kinematical

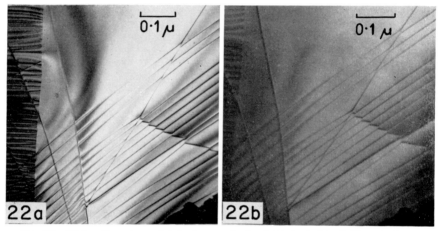

FIG. 22. Dislocations in molybdenite as obtained (*a*) in bright-field and (*b*) dark-field on diffusely scattered electrons surrounding the main beam. Magnification × 100,000. Micrographs from reference (*64*).

theory, this treatment explains some of the details of the contrast which have defied explanation by kinematical theory. For example, it explains the occurrence of a typical broken-line contrast sometimes obtained with dislocations (see Fig. 29b). In addition, it makes the interesting prediction that with thick specimens the bright- and dark-field images are not necessarily complementary, as would have been expected in the absence of absorption, but are sometimes similar. The occurrence of this effect has also been confirmed by observation.

Although the inelastically scattered electrons have been assumed to make no contribution to the image contrast in the theories discussed previously, Kamiya and Uyeda (*64*) have shown that the inelastically scattered electrons do give rise to observable contrast. A small objective aperture has been used, and this has been displaced so as to allow the image to be formed only by the diffusely scattered electrons surrounding the incident electron beam. Figures 22a and b show such an image of dislocations in molybdenite, together with the corresponding bright-field image. The dislocation structure is clearly visible in Fig. 22b, and although the sharpness is poorer than that of the bright-field image, this difference is not very great for thick specimens. Similar diffraction contrast is obtained if the image is formed by the diffusely scattered electrons surrounding one of the diffracted beams.

These results are of importance because they show that the inelastically scattered electrons do contribute to the diffraction contrast of the image. Since many diffusely scattered electrons normally pass through the objective aperture, and contribute to normal bright-field and dark-field images, one must consider the effect which the diffusely scattered electrons have on normal images. It is clearly insufficient to suppose that only the elastically scattered electrons are important, although it remains to be determined how much of this new effect results from scattering by the specimen contamination. Qualitatively one can see that electrons which suffer inelastic collisions after an initial elastic scattering will show diffraction-contrast effects. The diffusely scattered electrons around the incident beam will be more intense from the regions of the specimen for which there is a strong incident beam. Thus the intensity variation of these diffusely scattered electrons across the specimen will tend to follow that of the incident beam, and hence lead to the same diffraction contrast. Clearly, the diffraction-contrast theories outlined in Section II, B will have to be modified to take these effects into account.

2. CONTRAST WITH LATTICE RESOLUTION

a. Dislocations. As a first approach to considering the effect of various kinds of lattice imperfections on resolved images of lattices, the image may effectively be regarded as a two-dimensional projection of the lattice in the direction of the incident beam. Lateral displacement of this projected image, particularly if it undergoes a sharp discrete change, is the main conclusive observable effect. Consider first a dislocation line *AB* passing from top to bottom of the specimen (Fig. 23), for the case where the (*hkl*) planes are resolved in the image. The projection *A'B'* of the dislocation line will lie in the projection of the slip plane. The dislocation is introduced into the otherwise perfect lattice by slipping the crystal to the right of the slip plane by an amount [uvw] relative to the crystal on the left-hand side, where [uvw] is the Burgers vector of the dislocation. If the dislocation is introduced from the side indicated by the arrow, the slipping occurs only on that part of the slip plane on the arrow side of the dislocation. The only component of the slip which has an observable effect on the resolved image of the (*hkl*) planes is that which is perpendicular to the (hkl) planes. This resolved component is readily shown to be equal to $S = (hu + kv + lw)d_{hkl}$ (see reference 9) where d_{hkl} is the spacing of the (hkl) planes; this holds for all kinds of lattices. Therefore, in introducing the dislocation line into the specimen, the lines of the projected lattice image are shifted by $S = Nd_{hkl}$ on the right of the slip plane, relative to the left. For a perfect (i.e. unsplit) dislocation the value of N will always be an integer, so that the slip leaves perfect matching between the lines on the resolved image, away from $A'B'$; but in the vicinity of $A'B'$ there is a mismatch. The N half-lines terminate on the slip plane in the neighborhood of $A'B'$. An example of this is shown in Fig. 9.

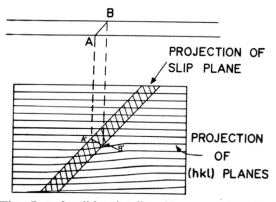

FIG. 23. The effect of a dislocation line AB on a resolved lattice image.

It is worth noting that the condition for a dislocation to be visible on a resolved lattice image is $S \neq 0$, whereas the condition for a dislocation to be visible by diffraction contrast (see Section II, B, 1, b) is $\mathbf{g} \cdot \mathbf{b} \neq 0$. But $\mathbf{g} \cdot \mathbf{b} = N = S/d_{hkl}$, so that these two conditions are identical, and a dislocation which is visible by diffraction contrast in the (hkl) extinction contour will give rise to extra half-lines on the resolved image of the (hkl) planes. The reason for this similarity is that in both cases the contrast effectively depends upon local distortion of the (hkl) planes, which only occurs when the Burgers vector has a nonzero component normal to those planes.

An important consequence of the previously discussed analysis is that the extra terminating half-lines on the image do not necessarily correspond with real extra half-planes in the crystal. This follows from the fact that the image is a two-dimensional lattice projection. Since the only condition for the visibility of a dislocation line which passes from one side of the film to the other is that $S \neq 0$, it follows that screw

dislocations are made visible in exactly the same way as edge dislocations. Thus the main information given by the image is the number
of extra half-lines, which represents the component of Burgers vector
normal to the resolved lattice planes. If other lattice planes can also be
oriented so as to produce resolved images, by suitable tilting of the specimen, the total Burgers vector of the dislocation may be determined.

The analysis has so far concerned only directly resolved lattice
images. It may readily be extended to indirectly resolved lattice images
(i.e., moiré patterns). Optical analogs have been used by Hashimoto and
Uyeda (45) for the case of "rotation" moiré patterns and Pashley et al.

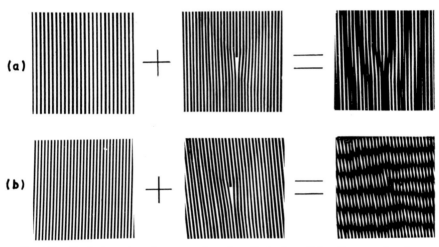

FIG. 24. Optical analog demonstrating the effect of a dislocation on the formation of (a) parallel moiré patterns; (b) rotation moiré patterns.

(85) for "parallel" moiré patterns to show that a dislocation in one
crystal will give rise to extra half-lines in the moiré pattern. This is illustrated in Fig. 24. A geometrical analysis of these situations shows (9) that
if N terminating half-lines are put into the dislocated grating, N terminating half-lines appear in the moiré pattern. For a "parallel" moiré
pattern the dislocation in the moiré pattern has the same sign as that of
the dislocated grating if this is the smaller grating, but the opposite sign
of the dislocation is in the larger grating. An analogous rule was deduced
for "rotation" patterns. As a corollary to these rules it follows that if a
dislocation in one grating is opposite a dislocation of similar sign in the
other crystal no dislocation is observed in the moiré pattern.

This optical analog, and all the rules obtained from it, may be
applied directly to considering the effect of dislocations on moiré patterns. The moiré pattern, for this purpose, may be regarded as the

superposition of the two projected lattices of the overlapping crystals, with diffraction conditions such that the individual periodicities are not resolved (see Section II, A, 2, b). Then if one crystal contains a dislocation, we first consider the effect this has on the projected image of that crystal, and then superpose this projection on that of the perfect crystal.

Many examples of dislocations in moiré patterns have been obtained and analyzed for overlapping (111) films of fcc. metals (9). The planes which formed the projected images were {220} and {422}. The values of N which occur with these planes and a Burgers vector of $[\frac{1}{2}\frac{1}{2}0]$ are given in Table I. The result is well illustrated by the example of Fig. 14.

TABLE I

The Number of Extra Half-Lines (N) Observed in the Periodic Image of the (hkl) Planes for a Dislocation of Burgers Vector $[\frac{1}{2}\frac{1}{2}0]$

(hkl):	(220)	(202)	(022)	($2\bar{2}0$)	($20\bar{2}$)	($02\bar{2}$)
N :	2	1	1	0	1	1
(hkl):	(422)	(242)	(224)	($42\bar{2}$)	($4\bar{2}2$)	($\bar{4}22$)
N :	3	3	2	3	1	1
(hkl):	($24\bar{2}$)	($2\bar{4}2$)	($\bar{2}42$)	($22\bar{4}$)	($2\bar{2}4$)	($\bar{2}24$)
N :	3	1	1	2	0	0

No satisfactory treatment of the effect on a resolved lattice image of dislocations lying parallel to the film plane has so far been given, although observations show that a discontinuity in the moiré pattern occurs as it crosses the image of the dislocation [see, for example, Kamiya et al. (62)].

b. *Partial Dislocations and Stacking Faults.* A dislocation in the fcc system may split into two partial dislocations, according to a dissociation of the type

$$[\tfrac{1}{2}\tfrac{1}{2}0] \to \tfrac{1}{6}[12\bar{1}] + \tfrac{1}{6}[211]$$

When the dislocation is in equilibrium, the separation of the partials can vary between a few angstrom units and several hundred angstrom units, depending upon the stacking fault energy of the metal. The effect of the partials on resolved lattice images may be deduced from the relation $N = hu + kv + lw$. A set of typical values for N is given in Table II.

The nonintegral values correspond to the occurrence of a stacking fault between the two partials. This stacking fault gives rise to a mismatch in the image, provided the displacement vector of the fault is not parallel to the set of planes giving rise to the image. Figure 25 illustrates the four distinguishable cases for the appearance of partials in the projected image of the (220) planes, P_1 and P_2 being the positions of the two partials. When moiré patterns are used, the appearance is similar except that the number of fringes between P_1 and P_2 will be reduced, the amount depending upon the moiré magnification. When the spacing of

TABLE II

THE NUMBER OF EXTRA HALF-LINES (N) OBSERVED IN THE PERIODIC IMAGE OF THE (hkl) PLANES FOR PARTIAL DISLOCATIONS OF BURGERS VECTOR $\frac{1}{6}$ [12$\bar{1}$] AND $\frac{1}{6}$ [211]

(hkl)	[$\frac{1}{2}\frac{1}{2}$0]	$\frac{1}{6}$ [12$\bar{1}$]	$\frac{1}{6}$ [211]
(220)	2	1	1
(202)	1	0	1
(022)	1	1/3	2/3
(2$\bar{2}$0)	0	−1/3	1/3
(20$\bar{2}$)	1	2/3	1/3
(02$\bar{2}$)	1	1	0

the moiré pattern exceeds P_1P_2, the dislocation will appear as though it is unsplit.

c. *Point Imperfections.* The application of periodic images to the study of point defects, or defects which extend over a volume of no more than about one hundred atomic volumes (e.g. vacancy clusters) is not likely to be very rewarding. At best, there will be only a local

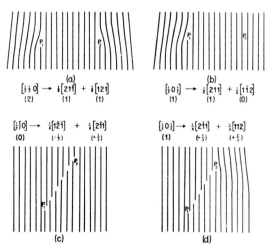

FIG. 25. The appearance of partials and their associated stacking faults in the projected image of the (220) planes. P_1 and P_2 are the two partials. The numbers in brackets indicate the number of extra half-lines associated with each dislocation.

disturbance in the perfection of the periodic image, and it will un-doubtedly be very difficult to recognize these, and to distinguish them from disturbances due to other causes. Likewise, very small dislocation loops will be difficult to detect and characterize.

d. Ghost Imperfections. Although lattice imperfections undoubtedly give rise to recognizable imperfections in a periodic image, care is needed to distinguish these from imperfections which can occur in periodic images due to other causes, associated with the electron optics of the image formation. For example, Hashimoto and Naiki (46) have shown with an optical analog that a wrinkled sheet of transparent paper placed over a perfect grating causes imperfections to occur in the image of the grating unless it is exactly in focus. It is argued that similar effects could occur with electron microscope images when an uneven surface con-taminating film is formed on the specimen. By a careful study of an imperfection observed on a periodic image, involving examination of the effect of both focus change and specimen tilting, it should be possible to decide whether it is a "ghost" imperfection. In particular, any "ghost dislocations" must be produced in pairs of opposite sign, so that a single set of extra half-lines of the same sign, surrounded by perfect periodic structure must be due to a real lattice dislocation.

III. The Observation of Imperfections in Bulk Materials

By means of the techniques described in Chapter 2, it is possible to prepare suitably thin specimens of a large number of metals and alloys. The imperfection structure of a material depends considerably upon the way it is grown, and upon subsequent treatment, and one of the power-ful applications of the electron microscope transmission technique is that it allows a detailed study to be made of the effect of any treatment on the imperfection structure. Further, it allows the properties of mate-rials to be related to their imperfection structure, so that the role of imperfections in determining various properties can be investigated.

Since the imperfection structure of a material depends so much on its previous history, the various types of imperfections which have been observed will be described, without any detailed consideration of the mechanism of formation of the imperfections necessarily being given. Emphasis will be given to the conditions for observing the imperfections, and to the information which can be deduced from the micrographs. In particular, no general consideration is given to the use of electron micros-copy in studying the mode of deformation of bulk materials, because this largely involves the observation of how imperfection structures become changed, rather than observing new kinds of imperfections.

A. General Dislocation Arrangements

A metal may contain dislocation arrangements of three general types, namely single isolated dislocations, irregular tangled arrangements of dislocations, and regular networks or arrays of dislocations. The latter define low-angle subgrain boundaries. All these arrangements are essentially three dimensional, and the thin-film specimens which have to be used represent a randomly selected thin slice taken from this three-dimensional array. In addition, the micrographs effectively give the projected image of the dislocation array onto the lower face of the thin film, so that it is not always easy to deduce from the micrograph the form of the three-dimensional array. This applies especially to the observation of irregular arrangements.

The obvious solution to the difficulty is to attempt to form stereoscopic images by exposing two micrographs from the same area of the specimen, which is tilted between the two exposures. The technique is made difficult and tedious because the contrast of the dislocations is so sensitive to the orientation of the specimen (see Section II, B, 1, b), that the same dislocations are not necessarily in good contrast in both images. The most satisfactory way of ensuring the same contrast conditions is to take one micrograph with the (hkl) reflection operating in the area of interest, and a second micrograph with the $(\bar{h}\bar{k}\bar{l})$ reflection operating. This determines the specimen tilt between the two orientations as twice the Bragg angle for the (hkl) reflection. The tilt is then quite small (one or two degrees) for a low-order reflection, so that if a strong stereoscopic effect is required a fairly high-order reflection should be used. A further source of difficulty is that the dislocation image is displaced from the true position of the dislocation, and this displacement is in opposite senses for orientation on either side of the Bragg setting. If the two images used for a stereoscopic pair are not displaced in the same sense, they will not fuse together perfectly to give a sharp stereoscopic image. It can be deduced that the two images will be displaced in the same sense if the reflecting planes are set at an angle just less than the Bragg angle for one micrograph, and just above the appropriate Bragg angle for the other micrograph. This is equivalent to having the image point of interest displaced in the same direction in each case from the center of the (hkl) and $(\bar{h}\bar{k}\bar{l})$ extinction contours. A further possible technique for ensuring that the contrast conditions are the same for the two stereomicrographs is to rotate the crystal about the normal to the reflecting plane, so that reflection from that plane remains unchanged. This method allows control of the angle of rotation, but is very difficult to carry out in practice. Because of these various difficulties and limitations, very little stereomicroscopy has been carried out with crystalline specimens, and all of what is described later refers to single micrographs on which the three-dimensional dislocation arrangements appear in projection.

1. BURGERS VECTOR DETERMINATION

The basic result which is used for the determination of the Burgers vector of a dislocation is that if $\mathbf{g} \cdot \mathbf{b} = 0$, where $\mathbf{g}$ is the reciprocal lattice reflection vector and $\mathbf{b}$ is the Burgers vector, no contrast arises from the dislocation (see Section II, B, 1, b). This rule applies in most circumstances, but exceptions can occur for edge dislocations (see Section III, B, 1). When $\mathbf{g} \cdot \mathbf{b} = 0$, $\mathbf{b}$ is parallel to the reflecting plane, so that if two nonparallel reflecting planes for which $\mathbf{g} \cdot \mathbf{b} = 0$ can be found, the direction of the Burgers vector is given by the line of intersection of these two planes. The technique requires the use of a tilting stage, preferably with facility for tilting about any axis in the plane of the specimen. Also, it might in some cases be necessary to tilt through angles of 30° and more to obtain two suitable reflections. It still remains to determine the magnitude of the Burgers vector, and also to distinguish between Burgers vectors which are opposite in direction. Although the magnitude of the Burgers vector affects the degree of contrast caused by a dislocation line, the quantitative aspects of the contrast are not sufficiently well established to allow the magnitude to be determined. It is normally asumed that the direction of the Burgers vector effectively gives its magnitude as being the unit lattice displacement in that direction. Since the elastic energy of a dislocation line is approximately proportional to b^2, any dislocation with a Burgers vector which is a multiple n of this unit vector should dissociate into dislocations with the unit Burgers vectors, since $nb^2 < (nb)^2$. Such a dissociation would be observable on an electron micrograph. Thus for a face-centered cubic metal, if the Burgers vector is found to lie parallel to [110], its magnitude would be taken as [$\frac{1}{2}\frac{1}{2}$0] or [$\overline{\frac{1}{2}\frac{1}{2}}$0]. The only method of distinguishing between these two possibilities on grounds of contrast is to make use of the fact that the dislocation image is slightly displaced from the position of the dislocation (see Section II, B, 1, b), and that this displacement reverses sign across an extinction contour. This allows the direction of the displacement on each side of the contour to be deduced. The signs of the image displacement on the two sides of the (hkl) extinction contour determine the sign of the dislocation, provided the directions of the local bending of the film are known. This can be deduced if the relative positions of the (hkl) and $(\overline{hkl})$ extinction contours are observed. Groves and Kelly (44) have described a method involving the use of Kikuchi lines. Clearly, the techniques of analysis just described require repeated correlation between the image and the diffraction pattern as the specimen is tilted. Careful observations of this kind must form a prominent feature of future work in the field.

In many systems, the types of Burgers vectors which are liable to occur are well known, and the determination of the direction of a particular Burgers vector then becomes simpler. If a reflecting plane which contains only one of the possible Burgers vectors is made to operate, the Burgers vector directions for the dislocations which go out of contrast are uniquely determined. Thus for face-centered cubic metals any reflection of the type ($h\bar{h}l$) will uniquely distinguish the dislocations of Burgers vector [$\frac{1}{2}\frac{1}{2}0$] from other $<\frac{1}{2}\frac{1}{2}0>$ values, provided $h \neq 0$ and $h \neq l$.

2. STACKING FAULTS

One of the common types of crystal imperfection is that which involves errors in the way in which successive layers of atoms are stacked

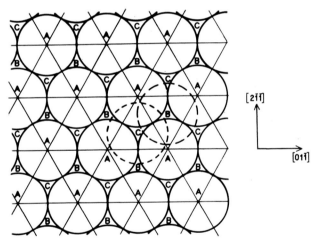

FIG. 26. The stacking sequence of the (111) planes of atoms in a face-centered cubic crystal.

on each other. Such errors sometimes consist of small relative rotations between neighboring crystal planes, and these are commonly found with layer structures. With metals, however, the most common kind of error of this kind is the stacking fault, which is most simply illustrated by reference to the face-centered cubic system. Figure 26 shows how the fcc. structure is built up by stacking close-packed planar hexagonal arrays of atoms upon each other [i.e., by stacking layers parallel to (111)]. The atoms in the second layer are sited above the centroids (B) of alternate unit triangles of the first layer network, while the atoms in the third layer are sited above the remaining centroids (C). The atoms in the fourth layer are above those of the first layer (A), so that the stacking sequence repeats every three layers, and is normally denoted as . . . ABCABC . . . . Any violation of this sequence such as

$$\overset{\downarrow}{\ldots \text{ABCACABC} \ldots}$$

gives rise to a stacking fault (see arrow). Stacking faults can occur during the growth of a crystal, or they can result from deformation, since they can be associated with dislocations. A dislocation in the fcc. system has a Burgers vector $[\frac{1}{2}\frac{1}{2}0]$, and this can dissociate into two partial dislocations according to the equation

$$[\tfrac{1}{2}\tfrac{1}{2}0] \rightarrow \tfrac{1}{6}[211] + \tfrac{1}{6}[12\bar{1}]$$

These partial dislocations have Burgers vectors which cause the crystal planes to be shifted, for example, from a B position to a C position (see Fig. 26) as they glide across the slip plane. Thus they give rise to stacking faults, and when a perfect dislocation (Burgers vector $<\frac{1}{2}\frac{1}{2}0>$) dissociates into two partials, the area between the two partials contains a stacking fault. The dissociation of the perfect dislocation is favored because the elastic energy of the two partials is lower than that of the perfect dislocation, but since there is an energy term associated with the stacking fault the extent of the dissociation is limited. The separation is determined by balancing the total energy of the fault against the gain in elastic energy. The lower the stacking fault energy (per unit area), the wider is the stacking fault.

Observation of stacking faults in thin films allows the width of the faults to be measured in any particular case, and the stacking fault energy can then be estimated. Stacking faults were first observed by Whelan et al. (119) in foils of stainless steel, which has a relatively low stacking fault energy. The nature of the contrast is discussed in Section II, B, 1, a, and examples of the contrast are shown in Fig. 41. For metals of high stacking fault energy (e.g., aluminum) the separation of the partial dislocations is very slight (< 10 A), and this is consistent with the fact that no splitting is observed on the micrographs in such cases. For metals of lower stacking fault energy the expected splitting can be as high as several hundred angstroms, but the micrographs commonly indicate much greater separations. This is explained in terms of stresses present in the foils, probably associated with the formation of a contamination film (see Section V, A). The equilibrium separation for stainless steel is less than 100 A, which gives a lower limit for the stacking fault energy of 14 ergs/cm². If the local stress in a film is deduced from the curvature of one of the partial dislocations bounding a wide ribbon of fault, the stacking fault energy can be estimated from the magnitude of the separation of the partials. For stainless steel a value of less than 19 ergs/cm² was obtained; the stacking fault energy was therefore estimated as approximately 15–20 ergs/cm², which is a typical value for a metal of low stacking fault energy (119). Values determined in this way cannot be regarded as too accurate. More recently stacking fault energies have been determined by measurements on open nodes in hexagonal networks (see Section III, A, 3).

3. DISLOCATION NETWORKS

The most spectacular micrographs of dislocation networks have been obtained with layer structures (discussed later), and some of the earliest examples were photographed by Geach and Phillips (41), with specimens of bismuth telluride. With metals, networks are usually formed in annealed specimens, or more particularly, after deformation followed by annealing, when well-defined subgrain structures are formed. The two basic kinds of networks are the parallel arrays of edge dislocations, representing tilt boundaries, and the hexagonal or similar networks of screw dislocations representing twist boundaries. It has been possible to correlate the spacing between the edge dislocations in a tilt boundary with the misorientation across the boundary as measured by electron diffraction (54). Good order-of-magnitude agreement was obtained. With hexagonal and similar networks it is possible to carry out a detailed analysis of the network structure. The Burgers vectors of the various components of the network can be determined as described previously (see Section III, A, 1). For various orientations of the specimen, one component of the network will be put out of contrast, so that an incomplete image of the network is visible on the micrograph (Fig. 29b). It is therefore essential to examine structures in various orientations, not only as a means of determining Burgers vectors, but also to ensure that the true network formation is revealed. A further complication (discussed later) is that double images, due to the simultaneous occurrence of two strong reflections, can give rise to misleading detailed on the micrographs.

Not all networks are simple and perfect, and one of the advantages of the thin-film technique is that it allows network structures to be analyzed in considerable detail so that any irregularities can be studied. Some examples of this type of observation and analysis are given by Carrington et al. (26) who have studied the arrangement of dislocations in iron. The irregularities arise from the inclusion of stranger dislocations into a network. These stranger dislocations either have a different Burgers vector from those forming the bulk of the net, or they are not parallel to those of the same Burgers vector in the net. Other irregularities can occur when isolated dislocations intersect a network.

The structure of the nodes of a dislocation network is of considerable interest, particularly for metals with low stacking fault energy. Thompson

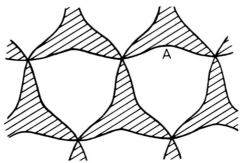

FIG. 27. The open and closed nodes which occur with a hexagonal network in a material of fairly low stacking fault energy. The shaded areas are the stacking faults.

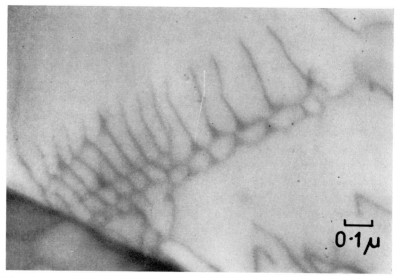

FIG. 28. A hexagonal network in stainless steel showing open and closed nodes. Magnification × 67,000. Micrograph from reference (*120*).

(*113*) was the first to discuss the structure of dislocation nodes of this type. For a hexagonal network the threefold nodes are of two kinds, namely extended and contracted (see Fig. 27). These were first observed by Whelan (*120*) with specimens of stainless steel, as shown in Fig. 28. The dark triangular shaped areas are the regions of stacking fault at the extended nodes. The presence of these triangles of stacking fault provides a means of measurement of stacking fault energy, as discussed by Whelan (120) and others. The stacking fault energy is obtained by equating the surface tension due to the fault and the force due to the line energy and curvature of the partial. If R is the radius of curvature of the partial at A (Fig. 27), and if G is the shear modulus, then the stacking fault energy is given approximately by $Gb^2/2R$, where b is the Burgers vector of the partial. This method of measuring stacking fault energies is useful for materials with low stacking fault energy (say less than 10 ergs cm^{-2}), which exhibit well-defined extended nodes. Among the errors associated with the method is that which arises from neglecting the mutual repulsion between the three partials forming the node. Further, it is assumed that the specimen is stress free, but since stresses are automatically induced during the examination of a specimen (see Section V, A), this assumption is not always necessarily valid. However, because a stress sufficient to move any of the partials belonging to a node would in general affect the various partials differently, the usual criterion is to use a relatively symmetrical looking node. The technique has been used for a variety of materials, including graphite (3, 122), stainless steel (120), and copper-aluminum (58).

Many observations have been made on networks in layer structures. The transmission technique is particularly well suited to the examination of such structures, especially those which can be prepared in the form of adequately thin flakes by simple cleavage procedures. Examples of convenient layer structures are mica, graphite, molybdenite (MoS$_2$), talc, and bismuth telluride. The slip planes of these materials coincide with the cleavage plane, so that the vast majority of the dislocations normally lie parallel to the plane of the cleavage flakes, and are in the most favorable position for observation. Further, the Burgers vectors of the dislocations normally lie in the cleavage plane, so that it is relatively easy to determine the Burgers vectors of the individual dislocations. All that is required is to determine which strong reflection, of those which occur with the electron beam approximately normal to the flake, gives rise to no contrast for the dislocation. The Burgers vector direction is then given by the intersection between the plane of the flake and the crystal plane giving the reflection, since this satisfies the condition $\mathbf{g} \cdot \mathbf{b} = 0$.

Observation on the layer structures usually reveals many dislocations, often lying on overlapping slip planes. Although many of the dislocations occur in very irregular arrays, much more regular arrangements are observed, and most attention has so far been focused on these networks, and the properties of various dislocation intersections. Hexagonal networks of screw dislocations are commonly observed; because the layer

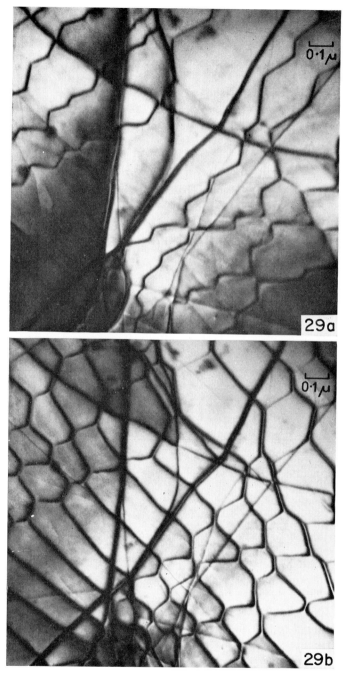

Fig. 29. The image of a hexagonal network in molybdenite for two different diffracting conditions: (a) ($10\bar{1}0$) reflection predominant; (b) two strong reflections operating simultaneously. Magnification $\times$ 60,000. Micrographs from reference (88).

structures commonly give two or more strong Bragg reflections simultaneously, multiple images are often observed. The apparent doubling shown in Fig. 29b is due to this effect, rather than to any real splitting of the dislocations. This is shown by Fig. 29a which is from the same area, after tilting of the specimen. With materials of low stacking fault energy, the characteristic extended and contracted nodes are formed. For extremely low stacking fault energy the hexagonal network degenerates into a triangular network of partial dislocations, which have been found in both graphite (3, 22, 122) and molybdenite (22, 88). With suitable reflections operating, the alternate triangles of stacking fault are in contrast; by tilting the specimen to allow other reflections to operate, the partial dislocations can be put into contrast, and the stacking fault contrast then disappears.

Amelinckx and Delavignette (3) have made a detailed study of graphite, involving a careful study of the structure of the nodes in the dislocation networks, and the way in which they are affected by the stacking fault energy. The results of all their analysis can be explained in terms of the existence of two kinds of stacking fault, both of low energy, which represent two different ways of faulting the stacking sequence of the planes of atoms parallel to the plane of the flake. They determine the stacking fault energy as $3-5 \times 10^{-2}$ ergs cm^{-2}. Williamson (122) has independently determined the stacking fault energy as 10^{-1} ergs cm^{-2}. Whereas all dislocations in graphite appear to split into two partials, in molybdenite two classes of dislocation are observed. The dislocations of one class are not visibly split, and are therefore associated with a high stacking fault energy; the others are always split, and appear to be associated with a stacking fault energy of less than 0.1 ergs cm^{-2} (88). It is suggested that this is evidence that dislocations occur not only between adjacent layers of sulfur atoms, but also between a layer of sulfur atoms and its adjacent layer of molybdenum atoms.

Many interesting dislocation network structures, involving complex arrangements of partial dislocations and stacking faults have been observed in talc (4, 5). One of the most striking observations is that of quarter-dislocations, i.e., the result of dislocations splitting into four partial dislocations all of different Burgers vectors. This phenomenon can easily be interpreted in terms of the known structure of talc.

Due to the presence of packing faults, consisting of occasional small rotations of the crystal on the cleavage or slip planes, moiré patterns are commonly observed with thin flakes of the layer structures. The moiré patterns formed are geometrically equivalent to the dislocation network which accommodates the rotation, and it is not always certain whether the micrographs reveal the dislocation network or the moiré pattern.

Kamiya *et al.* (*62*) have obtained micrographs which show obvious
dislocation networks joining onto obvious moiré patterns, with a region
of continuity in between which exhibits a gradual transition from the
one to the other. It is not clear to what extent this behavior is controlled
by varying diffracting conditions, but it is generally observed that small
rotations give an apparent dislocation network while larger rotations
lead to moiré patterns.

B. Point Defect Aggregates

1. Defects Produced by Quenching

There is no evidence to suggest that individual point defects (i.e.,
vacancies or interstitials) can be observed by transmission electron
microscopy on thin crystalline films. Not only is the resolution thought
to be inadequate but also the contrast is probably insufficient to lead to
an observable effect. However, aggregates of point defects, or features
resulting from the aggregation, have been observed.

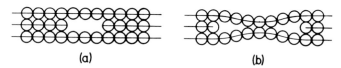

(a)   (b)

Fig. 30. The formation of planar aggregates of vacancies which give rise to dislocation loops.

All crystals in equilibrium contain a concentration of vacancies C
which depends upon temperature according to the relation $C = C_o e^{-U/kT}$
where C_0 is a constant, U is the energy of formation of a vacancy, and
kT has its usual meaning. If the temperature of the specimen is lowered
slowly, the resulting decrease in concentration of the vacancies occurs by
the gradual migration of vacancies to various sinks in the material. The
specimen surface, grain boundaries, and dislocations are all possible
sinks. If the temperature of a specimen is lowered rapidly, to a value at
which no appreciable vacancy migration can occur, a high supersaturation
of vacancies is produced. Comparatively low-temperature annealing can
then cause a condensation of these vacancies, with the formation of
vacancy aggregates. Various authors have discussed the mode of aggregation of such vacancies (e.g., Seitz, *105*, and Read, *101*), and it was
generally supposed that planar aggregates are formed (Fig. 30a). It was
thought that the aggregates occur on (111) planes in fcc metals, and that
above a certain critical size the aggregation causes a collapse of the
lattice in its immediate vicinity, with the formation of a loop of dislocation (Fig. 30b). For a metal of high stacking fault energy, the collapse

must occur in such a way as to produce no stacking fault where the two (111) planes meet (66). This means that the collapse process involves not only a moving together of the two planes along [111] but also a relative shear parallel to (111). It can readily be shown that this causes the dislocation loop to have a Burgers vector of $[\frac{1}{2}\frac{1}{2}0]$, $[\frac{1}{2}0\frac{1}{2}]$, or $[0\frac{1}{2}\frac{1}{2}]$. Further condensation of vacancies can take place at the periphery of the loop to cause it to grow in diameter up to any size.

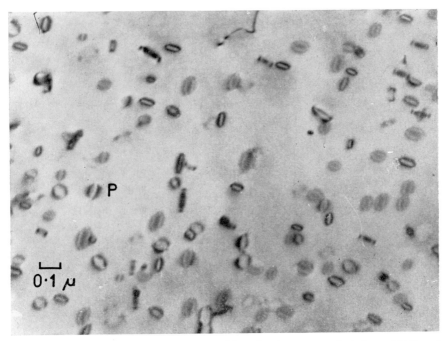

FIG. 31. Dislocation loops in polycrystalline aluminum quenched from 560°C and aged at room temperature. Magnification × 55,000. Micrograph from reference (55).

The first direct evidence for dislocation loops formed in this way in metals was obtained by Hirsch et al. (55) who studied foils of aluminum which had been quenched from a temperature of 600°C. The mobility of the vacancies in aluminum at room temperature is sufficient for aggregation to occur, so that electron microscope examination of the foils after electrothinning revealed numerous loop features, as shown in Fig. 31. The loop diameters vary from about 100 to 1000 A, and so represent aggregates of up to 10^5 vacancies. The shapes of the loops range from perfect circles to well-defined hexagons. Hirsch et al. deduced that the loops were all produced by vacancy aggregation on {111} planes, as described previously, but Kuhlmann-Wilsdorf and Wilsdorf (67) showed that loops on other planes also occur with pure aluminum. In part, this can be explained in terms of a rotation of the loop after formation on a {111} plane. The loop is free to glide on a glide cylinder, whose axis is parallel to the Burgers vector [$\frac{1}{2}\frac{1}{2}$0] of the dislocation loop. Effectively, the plane of the loop can be any plane not parallel to the axis of the glide cylinder, but its lowest energy configuration will be determined by consideration of the circumference of the loop and the elastic energy of the dislocation. The plane of lowest energy is approximately, but not exactly, perpendicular to the cylinder axis, and is not parallel to (111). Rotation of this kind was observed directly on specimens being examined in the electron microscope. However, other mechanisms of loop formation were considered in detail by Kuhlmann-Wilsdorf and Wilsdorf (67). It was found that pairs of loops, separated by distances of 0.1 μ and more, are sometimes formed. These were explained by the collapse of vacancy aggregates on two adjoining planes of types other than {111} (e.g. {100} planes), to produce a metastable dislocation loop which dissociates into two loops that mutually repel each other. Mechanisms such as this were shown to be energetically possible. The formation of near spherical voids due to vacancy aggregation was also considered. The mode of collapse of these spherical voids is thought to lead to the formation of clusters of loops, and a strong tendency to form clusters was noted on the micrographs.

When the temperature of a specimen is raised so that vacancies have to be created to restore the equilibrium concentration, any dislocation loops present in the metal act as readily available sources of vacancies. The loops can give off vacancies and shrink in diameter, provided the vacancy mobility is adequate. This mechanism was very convincingly demonstrated by Silcox and Whelan (111), who annealed previously quenched aluminum foils on a heating stage inside the electron microscope. From the micrographs they measured the rate of decrease in diameter of the loops, as a function of temperature, and they were then able to determine the activation energy for diffusion of vacancies in aluminum.

The contrast effects which are present on micrographs showing the dislocation loops need special consideration. It is commonly found that the contrast of the loops varies around their circumference, being very low or even zero at opposite ends of one diameter (see P on Fig. 31), to give the appearance of two arcs. This arises when the loop lies on a plane steeply inclined to the specimen plane; the two arcs correspond to the parts of the loop approximately parallel to the surface, while the invisible parts of the loop are those which are steeply inclined to the film plane. The kinematical dislocation contrast mechanism developed by Hirsch *et al.* (*56*) predicts low contrast for steeply inclined dislocations. Because, as this latter theory also predicts, a dislocation image is usually displaced to one side of the actual position of the dislocation (see Section II, B, 1, b), the apparent size of a loop is misleading, and can be either smaller or greater than the real value. This applies especially for loops smaller than a few hundred angstroms in diameter. The effect can be well illustrated if two strong reflections are operating in the vicinity of the loop. These can give rise to two concentric images which are quite different in diameter (see reference *56*). Detailed examination of the contrast changes which occur as the specimen is tilted can allow the diameter to be estimated more conclusively; it also allows the Burgers vector of the loop to be determined as described in Section III, A, 1.

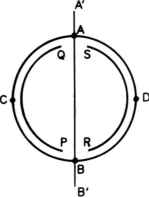

Fig. 32. The image *PQ* and *RS* of a dislocation loop normal to the electron beam, when *A'B'* is the operating reflecting plane.

Even when a dislocation loop is parallel to the plane of the specimen it is possible for a contrast asymmetry to occur for the case of an edge dislocation loop, as discussed by Howie and Whelan (*57*). Consider a dislocation loop parallel to the plane of the specimen, and having a Burgers vector normal to its plane. This pure edge dislocation would not normally give rise to any contrast on the image, since $g \cdot b$ is zero for all reflections. However, the strain field of the dislocation involves some displacement of the lattice sites normal to the slip plane (i.e., the glide cylinder in this case) and normal to the Burgers vector. This strain component was assumed to be unimportant in the original treatment of dislocation contrast (*56*), but in the example being considered is the only one which can be effective, and is therefore of importance. Since the strain component involves radial displacements in the plane of the loop, a contrast asymmetry results. If *A'B'* represents the operating reflecting plane (Fig. 32), no contrast arises at *A* or *B*, since the displacements are parallel to the reflecting plane. At C and D, where the displacements are normal to the reflecting plane, maximum contrast occurs. This effect has been confirmed by observations on large dislocation loops in zinc (57).

Since the earlier observations on aluminum, dislocation loops have been seen in various other quenched metals and alloys by various workers. With metals of low stacking fault energy, one would anticipate that the collapse (see Fig. 30b) which occurs as the aggregate grows above a critical size is such as to leave a stacking fault across the area of the

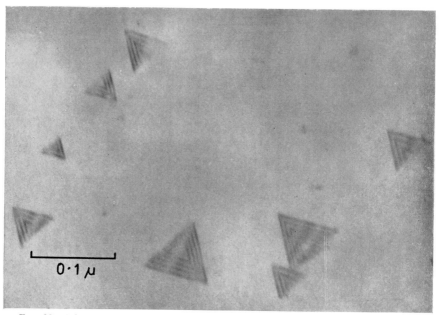

Fig. 33. The appearance of tetrahedra of stacking fault obtained by quenching and aging of gold; (112) orientation. Magnification $\times$ 230,000. Micrograph by R. M. J. Cotterill.

dislocation loop. However, when Silcox and Hirsch (109) examined gold specimens prepared after the metal had been quenched from about 930°C and aged at temperatures between 100° and 250°C, they found the features shown in Fig. 33. These consist of tetrahedra of stacking fault bounded by four triangular stacking faults on the four {111} planes, the six edges of the tetrahedron consisting of low-energy stair-rod dislocations. Although Silcox and Hirsch determine that the tetrahedron of stacking fault has a lower energy than that of the single triangular stacking fault from which it could form (discussed later), so that in this sense the tetrahedron could have been predicted as a stable low-energy defect, such defects had not been postulated previously. This is therefore a clear case where transmission electron microscopy has revealed a hitherto unknown lattice defect. The energy of the fault is determined by adding the energy of the four stacking faults to that for the six stair-rod dislocations, which have Burgers vectors of $\frac{1}{6}<101>$. It is estimated (*109*) that for gold this energy is lower than that of a single triangular stacking fault bounded by Frank sessile dislocations of Burgers vector $\frac{1}{3}<111>$, provided the side of the tetrahedron is less than about 430 A. This agrees well with the observed largest size of tetrahedron of about 500 A along an edge.

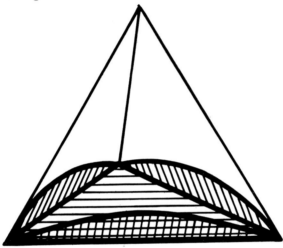

Fig. 34. A possible mechanism for the formation of a stacking fault tetrahedron, by the movement of partial dislocations across the three inclined {111} faces.

A possible mechanism of formation of the tetrahedron has been proposed by Silcox and Hirsch. The collapse of a vacancy aggregate produces a triangular shaped stacking fault bounded by a Frank sessile dislocation which can dissociate on one of the sides of the triangle according to the reaction

$$\tfrac{1}{3}[111] \rightarrow \tfrac{1}{6}[101] + \tfrac{1}{6}[121]$$

This gives rise to the stair-rod dislocation which remains stationary and the partial dislocation of Burgers vector $\frac{1}{6}[121]$ which can glide across the $(1\bar{1}1)$ slip plane and thus extend the stacking fault onto this plane. Similar reactions on the other two sides of the triangle extend the fault onto the $(\bar{1}11)$ and $(11\bar{1})$ planes, as indicated in Fig. 34. These join up to form the low-energy configuration of the tetrahedron. Although no evidence was obtained that this mode of growth actually occurs, the collapse of a tetrahedron by the reverse procedure was observed in some cases.

Silcox and Hirsch point out that the tetrahedron is essentially symmetrical, and that exactly the same configuration would be obtained if the original vacancy aggregate collapse had occurred on another (111) plane. In fact the defect may be regarded as due to a collapse of a spherical shell of vacancies.

No detailed treatment of the contrast due to a tetrahedron of stacking fault has been published. To a first approximation, one can consider the stair-rod dislocations and the stacking faults separately, the latter giving the normal fringe contrast due to an oblique stacking fault, provided it extends in depth in the specimen a distance of significantly more than one extinction distance. Complications arise due to the fact that a fault on one of the faces of the tetrahedron is above part of the fault on another of the faces. The effect of this could be investigated by a direct application of the kinematical column technique (56). Since the defect is bounded by four triangular faces, the shape of its projection varies considerably according to the orientation of the specimen. For example, with a (100) oriented film the shape of the projection is a square.

As stated previously, vacancies readily condense on dislocation lines causing them to climb, and Hirsch *et al.* (55) obtained evidence that dislocation climb had occurred in their quenched aluminum specimens. The climb of edge dislocations occurs by removal of the extra terminating plane or planes of atoms involved by condensation of the vacancies on the edge of the extra planes. A screw dislocation cannot climb in this way, and Weertman (116) has shown that a sufficient supersaturation of vacancies will cause it to climb into a helix with its axis parallel to the Burgers vector. The turns of the helix are then almost pure edge dislocations, and can climb further as normal edge dislocations to increase their diameter. Helices of this kind have been observed (Fig. 35) in quenched aluminum—4% copper alloy by Thomas and Whelan (112), who confirmed that they have the expected Burgers vectors.

2. Defects Produced by Radiation Damage

Various kinds of lattice defects are produced in metals when they are bombarded by sufficiently energetic atomic particles. In some cases the most important damage is produced, not directly by the incident particle, but indirectly by energetic secondary particles (the primary knock-ons) ejected from their normal position in the crystal. For example, most of the damage produced in metals placed in an atomic pile in a position remote from fissile material results from the bombardment by fast neutrons. These neutrons collide with the nuclei of the atoms in the metal once every few centimeters, and transfer ample energy to the impacted atom to eject it. Such ejected atoms interact strongly with the metal crystal, losing energy both by excitation of electrons in their immediate vicinity, and by ejecting other atoms by direct collision. This results in a cascade process giving rise to many vacancy-interstitial pairs in a pear-shaped volume of about 100 A across, and perhaps twice as long. These are the so-called displacement spikes discussed by Brinkman (25). The precise nature of the lattice damage produced by a spike has

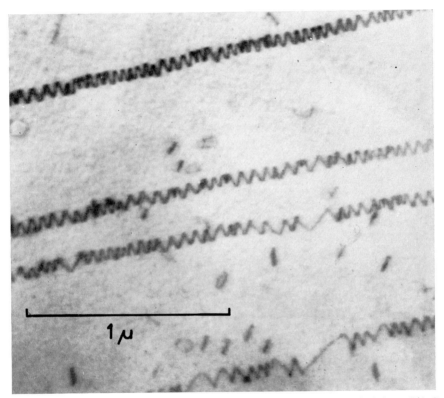

FIG. 35. Helical dislocations viewed side on in Al—4% Cu quenched from 540°C. Magnification × 53,000. Micrograph from reference (112).

been the subject of much speculation. Many of the vacancy-interstitial pairs will rapidly annihilate each other, thus partially restoring the original lattice configuration, but some of those remaining are expected to aggregate to form dislocation loops, regions of local strain, etc.

By means of transmission electron microscopy it is possible to make a direct study of the defects produced during radiation damage, and Silcox and Hirsch (110) have used the technique to investigate the defects produced in copper by fast-neutron irradiation. Figure 36 shows a typical micrograph for a relatively low neutron dose. Although this contains a number of clear dislocation loops (e.g., at L), many features appear as small spots with a diameter of 100 A or less. Some of these might be very small dislocation loops which are not clearly resolved, or else small regions of lattice strain which are either nuclei of loops or loops at various stages of growth. As irradiation proceeds, the average size of

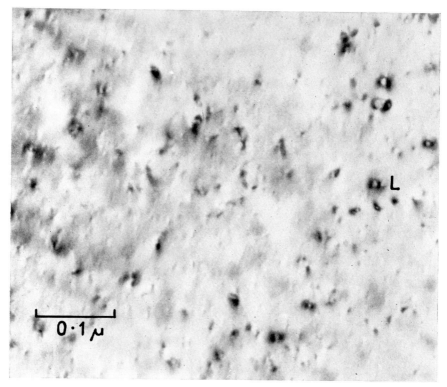

Fɪɢ. 36. Dislocation loops (L) and small regions of strain (black dots) in neutron irradiated copper (low dose). Magnification × 220,000. Micrograph from reference (*110*).

the loops increases, and more of the features become resolvable as loops, which fits with this interpretation. Detailed interpretation, however, is restricted by a lack of understanding of the contrast effects associated with the small features such as shown in Fig. 36. In addition to vacancy clusters, interstitial clusters may be produced, and these can also form prismatic dislocation loops (*110*). The contrast due to an interstitial loop will be very similar to that for a vacancy loop, and careful observations on the change in contrast as the specimen is tilted, together with correlation with the diffraction pattern, would be necessary to distinguish the two on grounds of contrast, see reference (44). There is the further possibility of distinguishing the two by examining their annealing behavior inside the electron microscope. Silcox and Hirsch (110) consider that the annealing of the neutron damage produced in copper is consistent with the defects being due to vacancy clustering.

Observations on copper and aluminum bombarded with 38 Mev α-particles have been carried out by Barnes and Mazey (7), who deduce that interstitial loops are also formed. Due to the heavy interaction between α-particles and a solid, a track of heavy damage about 0.22 mm in length is produced. A high concentration of point defects is produced along the track, and a helium atom is introduced into the metal lattice at the end of the track. In order to distinguish the nature of the damage along the length of the track, Barnes and Mazey used a stack of thin sheets of metal so that the α-particle tracks extended through several of the sheets, which were subsequently thinned and examined separately. The appearance of the electron micrographs obtained from various points along the tracks where no helium was present showed little variation. A number of relatively large dislocation loops ($\sim$200 A in radius) on a background of much smaller dots ($\sim$20 A in radius) was observed. At the ends of the tracks, where helium is certainly present, the general features were very similar, but the dots appeared to be localized around the loops.

A much greater distinction could be made between the middles and ends of the tracks as a result of annealing experiments. In the former case, the loops were annealed out completely after 4 hours at 350°C. In the latter case, the loops enlarged on annealing, and after 2 hours at 450°C they grew so large that they became a tangle of dislocations. This was accompanied by the appearance of small bubbles of helium near the grain boundaries, which took on the appearance shown in Fig. 37 after 2 hours at 750°C. The bubbles form preferentially on dislocation lines. From these results Barnes and Mazey deduced that the dots represent vacancy aggregates, while the loops are the result of the aggregation of interstitials. The helium affects the annealing behavior by providing efficient traps for the vacancies.

Because of its importance as a nuclear reactor material, the damage produced in graphite by fast neutrons has been studied by several workers. Bollmann (20, 21) has obtained particularly clear images by using the dark-field technique. Due to packing faults in the graphite layer lattice, well-defined moiré patterns were present on some of the micrographs. These were useful in that they provided additional evidence on the interpretation of the spot structure produced in the graphite. Bollmann concludes that under some conditions the majority of the defects consist of dislocation dipoles, or clusters of dislocation dipoles. The dipoles are defined by the ends of extra rows of atoms, or missing rows of atoms in single graphite layers.

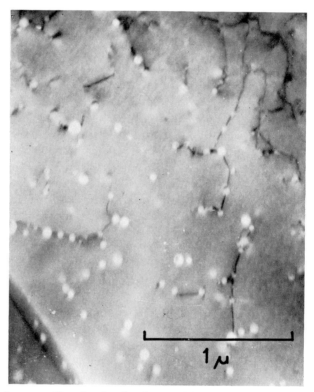

Fig. 37. A copper film after bombardment with α-particles, followed by annealing for 2 hours at 750°C, showing formation of helium bubbles. Magnification × 40,000. Micrograph from reference (7).

3. DEFECTS PRODUCED BY ION BOMBARDMENT

Damage produced in metals during bombardment by relatively low energy particles has also been studied. Since ions of energy less than 100 kev have path lengths in metals which are 1000 A or less, it is possible to produce heavy damage in a specimen which is sufficiently thin to be examined directly by transmission. Extremely low energy (75 ev) argon ion bombardment of gold has been studied by Brandon and Bowden (24). The specimens were prepared by normal electropolishing techniques and bombarded in a specially designed ion gun. The appearance of the damage evident on the electron micrographs closely resembles that produced by fast-neutron or α-particle bombardment, and consists of small spots and small loops. In addition, there is evidence that dislocations become heavily jogged. One interesting observation is the tendency for dislocation loops to line up along <111> directions.

Although very little study has been made of the deliberate ion bombardment of metal films, it has been shown (91) that fortuitous

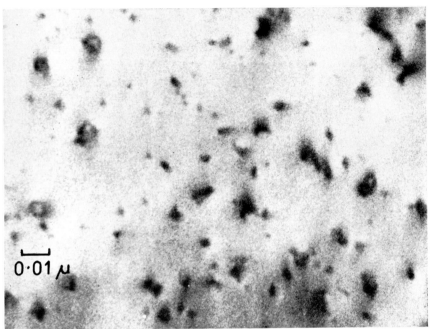

0·01 μ

FIG. 38. Characteristic appearance of the ion damage which occurs in a (100) gold film during observation in the electron microscope. Magnification × 720,000. Micrograph from reference (91).

negative ion bombardment can occur during the observation of a specimen inside the electron microscope. It is thought that the ions originate at or near the tip of the tungsten filament in the electron gun, so that they become accelerated by the full gun voltage. Because the magnetic fields associated with the condenser lenses have only a small influence on the paths of ions of energy 50–100 kev, the ions travel in approximately straight lines, and reach the specimen provided there is a clear path. This will obviously depend upon the alignment of the illuminating system. The proof that fortuitous ion bombardment of the specimen can occur with a Siemens Elmiskop I is based upon the following four observations: (1) Damage in the form of dots or loops (see Fig. 38) occurs in thin gold films while they are under observation. (2) The damage continues to occur if the electron beam is deflected off the specimen by means of a magnetic field just above the specimen. (3) If two gold films are mounted one above the other, the damage occurs in the upper film but not in the lower film. (4) If the filament of the electron gun is coated with a standard oxide electron emitter, which is known to give off large numbers of negative ions, the damage is similar but occurs at a much enhanced rate. The damage produced in single-crystal films prepared by evaporation (Fig. 38) consists of small dots and loops. On the assumption that a single dot or loop feature results from the impact of each ion, the normal rate of ion bombardment at the specimen level is found to vary in the range 10^7–10^9 cm^{-2} sec^{-1}; with the coated filaments, rates as high as 10^{11} cm^{-2} sec^{-1} were observed. The basis of the assumption is that the ions have energies similar to that of the primary knock-ons produced by fast-neutron irradiation. Displacement spikes should therefore be produced, and each spot or loop feature would then result from one spike as discussed, for example, by Silcox and Hirsch (110). However, the close similarity between the micrographs obtained from gold bombarded by 75 ev argon ions, and micrographs such as that of Fig. 38 suggest that another explanation might be possible. Argon ions of energy 75 ev cannot produce displacement spikes, and the aggregates in this case must involve point defects produced by many ion impacts. If the same applies with the 50–100 kev ions, then the previous estimates of the ion flux are not valid.

IV. Growth and Microstructure of Deposited Films

A. Introduction

As already explained in Chapter 2, deposition techniques such as vapor condensation and electrodeposition onto suitable substrates provide a very convenient means of preparing metal films for transmission electron microscopy. Likewise, transmission electron microscopy provides a very powerful tool for studying the microstructure of deposited films at various stages of their growth, so that their mode of growth can be examined in some detail.

In the past, information about the structure of surface films of thickness 1000 A and less has largely been obtained by means of electron diffraction, particularly reflection electron diffraction. Although x-ray techniques have been used, they are far less useful in general, particularly for the thinner layers (say less than 200 A). The diffraction studies have given valuable and precise information on the crystalline structure and orientation of the deposits, as well as giving useful but less precise information on the geometrical form of the deposits at various stages of growth. The presence of lattice imperfections of various kinds has also been indicated in a very qualitative manner. Because electron microscopy allows a detailed point by point examination of a specimen, it is capable of providing much more infromation on the geometrical and imperfection aspects, with the result that in recent years the transmission technique has led to a big increase in knowledge about deposited films. These advances are described in this section. The account is largely confined to studies on evaporated metal films, although some reference is made to studies on electrodeposited metals.

One of the most important results of diffraction studies is that the orientation of the deposit is often influenced by that of the substrate. If a single-crystal substrate is used, the deposit film can often be caused to grow as a single crystal in a particular orientation relative to that of the substrate. This is the phenomenon known as epitaxy (84). Because of these effects it seems desirable to use single-crystal substrates when searching for important fundamental knowledge about the growth of thin surface films. Most of the work to be described will fall into this class.

Good orientation of a deposited film is frequently obtained only at elevated substrate temperatures. For this reason, very little work has been carried out on transmission electron microscopy of films deposited on substrates cooled below room temperature. Such observations might be of limited value anyway, because of the likely possibility of considerable microstructural changes occurring as the deposit is warmed to room temperature for observation. The account given here therefore refers only to films prepared on substrates maintained at room temperature and above. Since any reduction in substrate temperature leads to a lowering of surface mobility, the growth and microstructure of films prepared on cooled substrates is liable to be very different from that described later, particularly with respect to continuity.

B. Experimental Technique

The use of the transmission technique demands that either the deposit film be detached from its substrate for examination, or that the substrate itself be sufficiently thin to allow the composite specimen to be examined by transmission. Most experiments have made use of the former technique, although it is becoming increasingly clear that the latter technique has considerable advantages, particularly for very thin (< 100 A) deposit films. The initial stages of growth of most films consist of the formation of a discontinuous film containing numerous separated crystallites, which would not be self-supporting when detached from their substrate. It is necessary to provide a supporting film for these deposits. This can be achieved very conveniently by evaporating a thin carbon layer onto the specimen surface before the deposit film is detached. The stripping technique is clearly limited to cases where there is a suitable solvent, which dissolves the substrate material without dissolving the very thin deposit. For this reason rock salt, which is water soluble, is a commonly used substrate.

C. The Nucleation and Growth of an Evaporated Film

When a surface film is grown by the evaporation method, the molecules arriving at the substrate surface have a high thermal energy, and a high surface mobility. This causes the molecules to migrate over the surface and to aggregate into small stable groups of nuclei, as discussed by Frenkel (39). The initial nuclei are frequently observed to be three dimensional, so that growth does not proceed atomic layer by atomic layer. This is shown in Fig. 39 for the growth of gold on rock salt, the average thickness of the layer being about 10 A. The individual nuclei are approximately equi-axed, and have diameters of 10–50 A.

Because the supersaturation of the vapor in the vicinity of the substrate is very high, there is no necessity for the substrate surface to have imperfections in order for condensation and growth to occur. Homogeneous nucleation will occur readily on an ideal, atomically smooth substrate. However, when surface imperfections exist on the substrate surface, they are sometimes found to act as sites for preferential nucleation of the deposit. It was found by Bassett (8) and subsequently confirmed by Sella and Conjeaud (108) and others that gold nuclei form preferentially at steps on a rock salt cleavage surface. It can be shown (8) that in many cases these steps are monomolecular in height. In Fig. 39, substrate surface steps are clearly revealed by the lines of gold particles; the band of closely spaced lines of particles is due to a terrace of monomolecular steps. In between the steps and terraces the particle distribution is random, and it is assumed that no preferential sites are normally involved.

These experiments provide a valuable technique for revealing the detailed step structure on a surface, and the technique has been used, for example, in a study of the formation of slip steps on potassium bromide (11); it was found that many monomolecular slip steps, corresponding to unit slip, could be formed in bending.

Although it is clear that in the majority of cases isolated nuclei are formed during the initial stages of growth of an evaporated film, no systematic evidence has been obtained to show how the size, shape, and distribution of the nuclei varies according to the substrates and deposits used. The shapes of the nuclei range from the near equi-axed nuclei shown in Fig. 39 to very platelike nuclei found in other systems. Detailed examination of the shapes is limited not only by the normal difficulties associated with the examination of very small particles, but also by doubts about the validity of studying the deposit after it has been removed from its substrate. There is evidence that the nuclei can, under

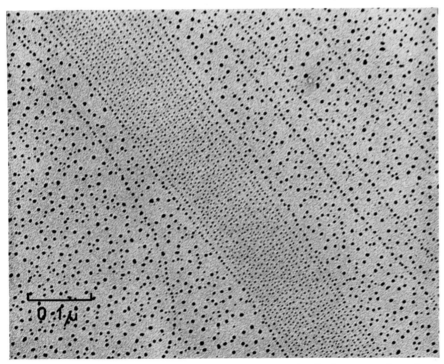

FIG. 39.   The early stage of deposition of gold on a rock salt cleavage surface, showing the decoration of surface steps. Magnification $\times$ 170,000. Micrograph from reference (8).

certain circumstances, change their form during the stripping (discussed later).

After the initial formation of discrete crystallites on a substrate surface, subsequent deposition leads to an increase in size and growing together of these crystallites, until a continuous film is eventually formed. The detailed manner in which this occurs has been studied in only a few cases; the growth of gold on rock salt, at 300°C, is illustrated in Fig. 40. In all cases, the thicknesses quoted refer to average thicknesses, i.e., the thickness the deposit would have if spread uniformly over the substrate. Initially (about 5 A thickness), the density of nuclei is about $10^{11}/cm^2$, and as the thickness is increased this number decreases considerably. Considerable surface migration must be involved. This trend continues until at an average thickness of about 500 A a con-

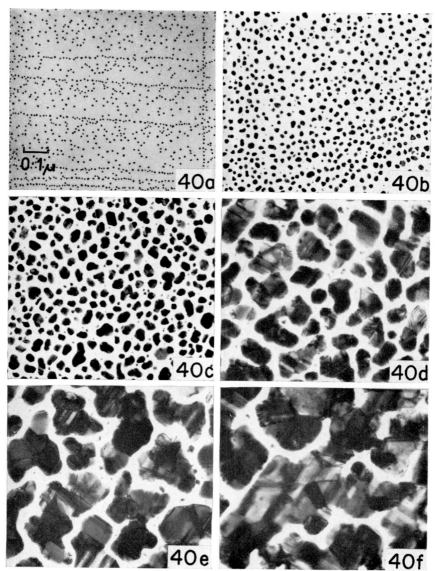

FIG. 40. Sequence illustrating the effect of increasing deposit thickness of gold on rock salt. Approximate deposit thicknesses: (a) 10 A; (b) 30 A; (c) 100 A; (d) 200 A; (e) 350 A; and (f) 500 A. Magnification × 64,000. Micrographs from reference (10).

tinuous film with pronounced channels of 200 A or less in width is formed (Fig. 40f). These channels eventually fill in, and at a thickness of 700–800 A the film is continuous, free of holes, and nearly uniform in thickness (Fig. 41). The local thickness variations are estimated to be at worst no more than 20% from the average thickness.

The thickness at which a near-uniform film is formed is related to the shape of the growing crystallites in the earlier stages of deposition.

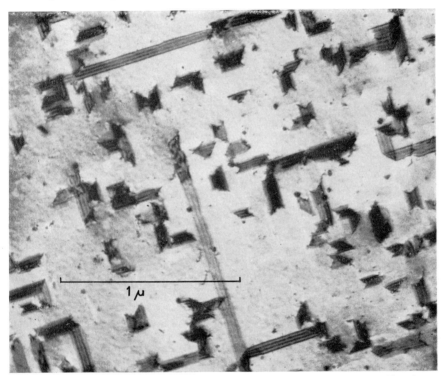

FIG. 41. A (100) gold film of thickness approximately 800 A grown directly on rock salt. Magnification × 48,000. Micrograph from reference (10).

The more platelike are these growing crystallites, the more readily the deposit spreads over the substrate surface, and the sooner a continuous film is formed. The equilibrium shape of the crystallites will be controlled largely by the relative values of the surface energies of the substrate and deposit, and the interfacial energy at their common plane of contact. A pronounced platelike crystallite, which involves a relatively large area of contact, clearly requires a low interfacial energy. Although there is little quantitative data on the required interfacial energies, one would expect low values to occur when: (a) the nature of the bonding in the two substances in contact is very similar; (b) the two crystal structures are similar; and (c) there is only a small misfit between the two lattices at the interface. This seems to be consistent with observations on face-centered cubic metals, since gold layers grown on silver (87) and nickel layers grown on copper (50) become continuous at average thicknesses of less than 100 A. The misfits are 0.2 and 2.5%, respectively. When copper is deposited on silver, with a misfit of 11.5%, platelike crystallites are not formed (65). Other less obvious cases are known; for example, gold spreads very well on sputtered or evaporated layers of

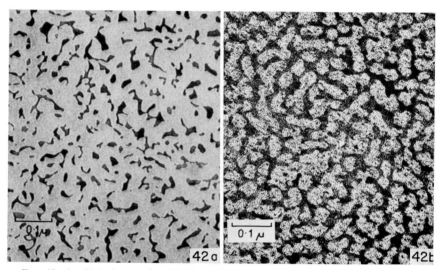

Fig. 42. A 30 A layer of gold electrodeposited onto a (111) silver surface after stripping (a) with a carbon supporting film; (b) with a platinum supporting film. Magnification × 100,000. Micrographs from reference (60).

bismuth oxide (42), and uniform surface films of 50 A and less can be produced in this way.

Studies have been made of the growth mechanism occurring with systems in which uniform films are produced at relatively small film thickness (10, 13), but more recent evidence indicates that the results can be seriously influenced by changes occurring during the stripping of the deposit (60). When a 30 A deposit of gold on a (111) silver surface is detached on a carbon supporting film as described in Section V, B, it appears as shown in Fig. 42a. Attempts to measure the height of the individual crystallites by shadowing the upper side of the carbon film result in complete absence of any shadows, even when a shadowing angle of 10 to 1 is used. However, if the lower side of the carbon film, on which the gold particles are attached, is shadowed the gold crystallites cast well-defined shadows. This is clearly inconsistent with the expected form of the composite carbon-gold film shown in Fig. 43a. This apparent anomaly is readily explained by assuming that the gold particles recrystallize as they become detached from the substrate, to form approximately equi-axed crystallites (Fig. 43b). Although the height of the initial crystallites might be inadequate to cause observable shadows to be cast (this difficulty would be enhanced if the edges of the crystallites are rounded), the near equi-axed crystallites suspended from the lower side of the carbon can be adequately thick to cast easily observable shadows. In the example quoted a crystallite height of 70 A was deduced.

The shape of a very platelike crystallite on its substrate must be

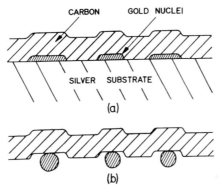

FIG. 43. The recrystallization which occurs when a thin gold deposit is detached from its silver substrate: (a) before stripping; (b) after stripping with a carbon support.

largely controlled by the existence of a very low interfacial energy. It is therefore not surprising that a shape change, or recrystallization, occurs when the crystallite is detached from its substrate. In order to retain closely the crystallite shape which exists on the substrate surface it is necessary to use as a supporting film, in place of the carbon, a layer which will have a low interfacial energy with the deposit (i.e., gold). For this reason a layer of evaporated platinum has been tried, since the occurrence of some alloying at the gold-platinum interface should lower the interfacial energy. The result of using this method for stripping a layer of gold identical to that of Fig. 42a is shown in Fig. 42b. More extensive gold crystallites are observed, confirming that recrystallization occurs when carbon supporting films are used. In addition, the transmission diffraction patterns indicate well-oriented gold layers at all stages of growth when the platinum technique is used, but pronounced arcing of the spots occurs in the early stages when a carbon-supporting film is used. This arcing, which arises from misorientation of the gold crystallites by rotations of up to a few degrees about the [111] axis normal to the film plane, must therefore be due to the changes occurring during the stripping of the deposit, and not, as was originally supposed (13), to an effect associated with the growth of the gold.

Although Fig. 42 refers to electrodeposited gold layers, the same effect occurs with evaporated layers. In view of these results one cannot rely in detail on results obtained by stripping nonuniform and very thin deposits. For the case quoted, one can at least conclude that the initial nuclei are very platelike, and that they grow laterally much faster than they do in thickness.

When silver is used as a substrate, good uniform and continuous single-crystal films of gold can be formed by the evaporation technique, for all thicknesses of about 100 A and above. The silver substrate can itself be prepared by evaporation, for example, on substrates of cleaved mica or rock salt (87), when gold films in (111) or (100) orientation are formed. Alternatively, polished rock salt surfaces cut to any orientation can be used, as described in reference (50), when any desired orientation of gold can be produced, since the orientation of the gold is always the same as that of the rock salt. Another simple technique for preparing any desired orientation of gold is to use electropolished single-crystal surfaces of silver as substrates (23). In all cases, the detached gold film is obtained by dissolving the silver in nitric acid.

D. Lattice Imperfections

Single-crystal films prepared by evaporation are found to contain a high density of lattice imperfections, in the form of dislocations, stacking faults, or microtwins. These faults can usually be observed directly by means of diffraction contrast (see Section II, B, 1), provided the appropriate diffracting conditions are satisfied. For very thin films, dislocation lines nearly normal to the plane of the film give very poor contrast, and much better results can be obtained by using the moiré pattern technique (see Section II, B, 2, a).

Most of the imperfections observed in the face-centered cubic metals (of low stacking fault energy) deposited directly onto rock salt consist of stacking faults on the {111} planes, as shown by the characteristic fringe contrast (Fig. 41). Although many are single faults, some undoubtedly consist of more complex arrangements of overlapping stacking faults, and also of very narrow bands of twins. Clearly, particular sequences of stacking faults are equivalent to narrow twins, but it is very difficult to distinguish experimentally between twins and all the

various possibilities for overlapping stacking faults. Matthews (72) and
Phillips (93), on the one hand, implicitly consider that with silver on
rock salt all faults are single stacking faults on {111} planes, whereas
Nagasawa and Ogawa (76) argue that most features are narrow twins.
In both cases the observed contrast consists, under appropriate conditions, of a set of parallel fringes. These are basically wedge fringes, and
their detailed mode of formation has been considered by Whelan and
Hirsch (117, 118), as discussed in Section II, B, 1, a. The different cases
which can arise are illustrated in Fig. 44. A twin which is sufficiently
wide so that the projections of the two {111} twin boundary planes do
not overlap exhibits fringes at the boundaries, i.e., at AB and CD,
provided the diffraction conditions are appropriate. The fringes will be
identical with wedge fringes if either the matrix or the twin alone is

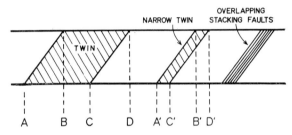

FIG. 44. The contrast due to microtwins in metal films.

diffracting strongly. If both are diffracting strongly, the fringe system
can be either more complex, or nonexistent. For a very narrow twin
(see Fig. 44), which can be regarded as a set of overlapping stacking
faults, the contrast depends upon the twin thickness. If this is such that
the number of overlapping faults is not equal to $3n$, where n is an
integer, then there is effectively a resultant stacking fault or displacement between the matrix above and below the twin. The contrast is
then dominated by this factor, and is largely the same as that of a
single stacking fault. If the number of overlapping faults is equal to $3n$,
there is no resultant displacement between the upper and lower parts
of the matrix, so that no stacking fault fringes occur. A lower contrast
fringe system can arise however; this is demonstrated by considering a
column passing through the twin, and the corresponding amplitude-
phase diagram (Fig. 45). The diagram which would apply in the absence
of the twin is first drawn, giving P'P as the final diffraction vector. When
the presence of the twin is taken into consideration, for the case where
the matrix alone is giving a strong reflection, the wavelets corresponding
to the piece of twin contained in the column must be removed from the

diagram. Suppose *RS* represents the sum of these wavelets. We remove them by adding their negative to the vector **P'P**. The resultant is a vector such as **P'Q**. Since Q rotates about P as the column is traversed along the fault, the resultant **P'Q** fluctuates with a periodicity corresponding to the change in depth of the twin by the equivalent extinction distance t'_o (see Section II, A, 1). The fringes produced will therefore have the same spacing as normal wedge fringes, but will have a very low contrast if the thickness of the twin, in the direction normal to the specimen plane, is small compared to t'_o.

The contrast from a set of random overlapping faults will depend largely upon the resultant displacement of the faults. If there is a non-

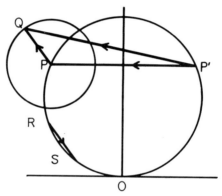

Fig. 45. The amplitude phase diagram for a column passing through a very narrow twin.

zero resultant displacement of the set of faults, then the fringes will be similar to those from the equivalent single fault.

Since there are several situations which lead to almost identical fringe systems, it is difficult to be sure just which type of fault occurs in a particular case. Although many of the faults in specimens such as that of Fig. 41 are probably single stacking faults, there are two pieces of evidence which suggest that both twins and overlapping faults occur. First, the diffraction patterns contain reflections associated with {111} twinning, and these reflections should not occur with single stacking faults. Second, when the specimen is stressed by the formation of contamination during observation (see Section V, A), the movement of the partial dislocations at the ends of the faults sometimes reveals the presence of overlapping faults.

Commonly, the stacking faults on different {111} planes intersect to form various characteristic arrangements with stair-rod dislocations at the lines of intersection. These have been considered in detail by

Matthews (72) and Phillips (93), who analyze all the possible arrangements.

Twins and stacking faults have not been reported for face-centered cubic metals of high stacking fault energy deposited on rock salt. Little work seems to have been done with such systems, but Ogawa et al. (80) report that twins (and implicitly stacking faults) are absent in aluminum films. Presumably the imperfections consist largely of dislocations in this case, although no such evidence was reported by Ogawa et al. at that time.

When gold films are prepared by depositing the gold on silver layers which were themselves formed by deposition onto rock salt (87), the growth faults (Fig. 46) contain many features which are clearly twins. This is revealed by the presence of two sets of fringes to each feature, corresponding to AB and CD on Fig. 44. Also the total width of the images of the faults is variable, due to variations in the widths of the twins themselves. In single-crystal films of uniform thickness, very narrow twins, as with single stacking faults, all give rise to images of the same width, since $A'C'$ and $B'D'$ are very much less than $A'B'$. A conclusive means of detecting narrow twins is to form a dark-field image (Fig. 47) with a diffracted beam resulting from the twinning. The only bright regions of the image occur in one of the four sets of {111} twins. In addition to the twins, these specimens contain dislocation lines which always run across the film, and lie in the {111} slip planes, normally taking the shortest possible path. They appear on the image as very short lines.

The (111) gold films prepared on silver on mica are normally free of twins and stacking faults, but contain many dislocation lines (9, 87). These dislocations have been studied in some detail by means of moiré patterns, and their density has been determined as 10^{10}–10^{11}/cm². The Burgers vectors of the dislocations can be determined by means of the moiré patterns. The six usual $<\frac{1}{2}\frac{1}{2}0>$ Burgers vectors fall into two classes; three lie in the (111) film plane, and three make an angle of 55° with it. The former class give 2, 1, and 1 extra half-lines in the three {2$\bar{2}$0} moiré patterns (see Fig. 14), while the latter class give 1, 1, and 0 half-lines in the {2$\bar{2}$0} moiré patterns, see Table I. Both classes are observed in practice (9).

Occasionally specimens with relatively low imperfection densities are formed. It has been claimed that for nickel deposited on copper on rock salt, the imperfection density is very much reduced if the vacuum is improved beyond 10^{-7} mm Hg (6); most films studied have been prepared in a vacuum of no better than 10^{-5} mm Hg.

There is much interest in understanding how the various lattice imperfections arise in a deposited single-crystal film. A general possibility is that lattice imperfections arise by extending imperfections which exist in the substrate. Clearly this is not the only mechanism, because the dislocation density in the deposited film can be several orders of magnitude higher than that in the substrate. The moiré-pattern technique provides some information on this point. Because a dislocation line which passes through both of two overlapping films gives rise to

Fig. 46. Microtwins in a (100) gold film grown on silver deposited on rock salt. Tilted dark-field on an (002) reflection. Magnification $\times$ 80,000. Micrograph by Pashley and Stowell.

no extra half-lines on any moiré pattern formed (see Section II, B, 2, a) any extra half-lines observed on a moiré pattern must be due to dislocations in one film only. Many such extra half-lines are observed when one metal film is grown epitaxially on another (9), and these must therefore result either from dislocations which are present in the substrate film and are not copied, or from dislocations which grow in the deposit film by some mechanism other than copying. Several investigators (12, 63, 72) have considered the possibility that at least some of the imperfections arise when neighboring growing crystallites on the substrate surface join together.

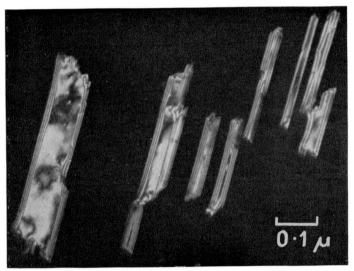

Fig. 47. Specimen as for Fig. 46. Tilted dark-field on a twin reflection. Magnification × 105,000. Micrograph by Pashley and Stowell.

In addition to misorientation between neighboring crystallites being a possible means of introducing imperfections (see Section IV, E) there is the possibility that imperfections arise from displacement misfit between neighboring crystallites. Such misfit is due to the fact that nucleation occurs randomly on a substrate with a different lattice parameter, so that as two crystallites grow together their separation is not equal to an integral number of unit lattice distances along a given lattice direction. The two crystallites will therefore become strained elastically as they join, unless either can become physically displaced with respect to the substrate. This strain can be accommodated by means of a stacking fault. When three crystallites join, elastic strain occurs at all three junctions, and these strains vary in sign and magnitude according to the

FIG. 48. A possible sequence leading to the formation of a dislocation as three nuclei join together. Only displacement misfits exist between the nuclei.

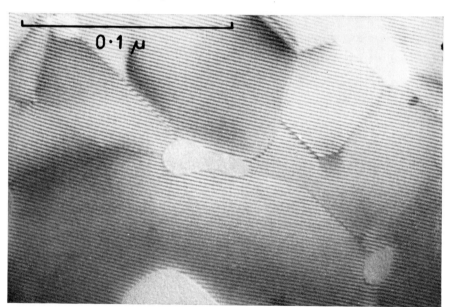

FIG. 49. Moiré patterns revealing the form of growth of silver on molybdenite. The holes contain dislocations in the process of formation. Magnification × 570,000. Micrograph from reference (63).

nature of the displacement misfits involved. Stacking faults can be introduced at any of the three junctions. It is possible for the strains to be such that they can be accommodated to a large extent by a dislocation which is introduced at the line where the three crystallites meet. A possible sequence of events leading to a dislocation being formed in this way is given in Fig. 48. An example of this mechanism has been observed by Kamiya and Uyeda (63), who studied the growth of silver on molybdenite. Moiré patterns are formed because of the 9% misfit between the two lattices, and these occasionally reveal (Fig. 49) an extra half-line when a Burgers circuit is made around a hole in the growing film, the hole occurring where the joining together of three or more crystallites is incomplete. This means that a dislocation must appear when this hole becomes filled.

E. The Growth of Thin Films Inside an Electron Microscope

There are several advantages to be gained by making direct observations on films during their growth by the evaporation technique inside the electron microscope. Changes taking place on one particular area of the specimen can be examined in some detail, so that growth mechanisms can be observed directly rather than being inferred from general changes occurring in sequences of specimens prepared outside the microscope. This means that much more information is obtained in a much shorter time. Since a thin-film substrate must be used, moiré-pattern techniques associated with overlapping crystals can be employed. These give useful information concerning the presence of various lattice defects during growth. Further, no stripping of the deposit from its substrate is involved so that the difficulties of interpretation associated with the possibility of structural changes occurring during stripping are absent. Finally, the direct photography of the fluorescent screen of the electron microscope by means of a cine camera provides a means of making permanent records of the growth mechanism, with the possibility of using frame-by-frame analysis to study any rapid changes at a slower rate than they appear by direct observation.

The difficulties associated with the technique arise from the following: (1) The vacuum system of a normal electron microscope is not very clean, partly because of the presence of many rubber and greased joints; (2) contamination grows on a specimen, due to the effect of the electron beam on adsorbed hydrocarbons; (3) the heating effect of the electron beam leads to uncertainties in the specimen temperature; and (4) because the substrate has a very low thermal capacity, the heat of condensation of the depositing metal and the radiant heat arriving from the vapor source lead to larger temperature rises than they would on more massive substrates. These difficulties have been overcome in part by the technique initially employed by Bassett (*14*), and subsequently used by Pashley and Stowell. Silver has been deposited on several thin-film substrates inside a Siemens Elmiskop I. A liquid air-cooled finger is placed in the specimen chamber of the microscope, so that a dry clean vacuum of about 10^{-5} mm Hg is attained. The specimen is mounted on a heating stage of the type used by Pashley and Presland (*86*), and maintained at 300°C during the deposition so that no con-

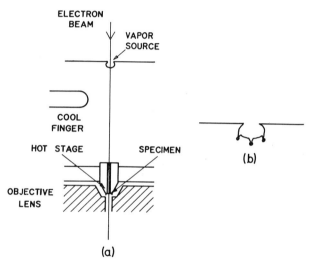

Fig. 50. Arrangement used for growing evaporated metal films inside an electron microscope.

tamination forms. Double-condenser illumination is used to minimize the effect of electron-beam heating. The arrangement is shown in Fig. 50. The normal specimen chamber of the Elmiskop I, with its specimen airlock system, is replaced by a new section which consists of a hollow cylindrical chamber containing several side ports through which any desired device can be inserted. The filament has the form shown in Fig. 50b and effectively provides a ring source of vapor around the incident beam. It is supplied by direct current. Two different rates of evaporation have been used by Bassett (*14*). In order to obtain a series of micrographs on plates showing successive stages in the film growth, rates of growth of about 500 A/hour were used. When cine films were taken, the rates of deposition were increased to 50–500 A/minute. Since the detailed mode of growth is known to depend upon rate of deposition, it does not follow that the growth mechanism was identical in the two different experiments.

Most of the experiments were carried out on molybdenite (MoS_2) as a substrate. It has been shown by Uyeda (114) that well-defined orientation of silver occurs in the temperature range 20–350°C. The silver grows in (111) orientation on the (0001) cleavage face of the molybdenite, with a misfit of 9%, which gives rise to a moiré pattern

FIG. 51. Optical analog demonstrating that parallel moiré patterns are rotated appreciably for a small rotation of one of the component gratings.

of 17 Å between the $\{11\bar{2}0\}$ planes of the molybdenite and $\{2\bar{2}0\}$ planes of the silver. At an early stage of growth there are moiré patterns visible in each silver crystallite. A spread in orientation of the silver of about 3° with respect to rotation about the silver [111] axis, as shown by the transmission electron-diffraction pattern, causes a spread in orientation of these moiré patterns of about 30°. This arises because a rotation of the silver about [111] causes a magnified rotation (the moiré magnification, see Section II, A, 2, b) of the moiré pattern, by a factor of 11 in this case. The optical analog of Fig. 51 illustrates this. Sequences of micrographs taken from the same area of specimen during the growth of the

224   D. W. PASHLEY

silver deposit reveal that the individual crystallites rotate during growth.
This is clearly demonstrated in Fig. 52, which shows three neighboring
silver crystallites before and after they have grown together; thus misorientation between neighboring crystallites can be removed during
intergrowth, so that one of the mechanisms postulated in Section IV, D
for the introduction of lattice imperfections is less prominent than
anticipated. Relative misorientation between neighboring crystallites
does lead to the introduction of dislocations at a later stage of growth,

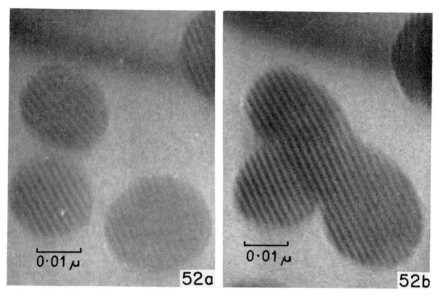

Fig. 52. The coalescence of three nuclei during the growth of silver on molybdenite: (a) before coalescence; (b) after coalescence. Magnification × 1,100,000. Micrographs from reference (14).

and Bassett (14) has published a micrograph of a low-angle boundary
introduced in this way.

Cine films showing the growth of silver on molybdenite at the faster
rates of deposition have been made by Bassett. Although no moiré
patterns appear on these films due to the poorer resolution obtained by
this technique, a considerable amount of detail of the mode of growth
is revealed. The most prominent feature is the extreme liquidlike behavior of the deposit. When two neighboring crystallites touch each
other they tend to coalesce just as two liquid drops on a surface, with
considerable change in shape. Some of the effects are illustrated in Fig.
53, which gives four frames taken from one of the cine films obtained
by Pashley and Stowell, who have used a lower rate of deposition of

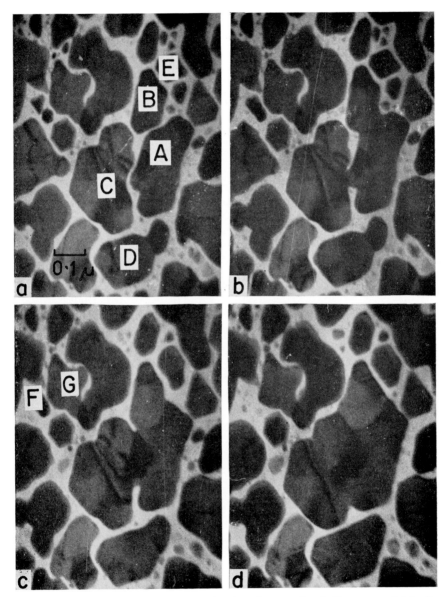

FIG. 53. Extracts from a cine film showing the growth of silver on molybdenite. The photographs were taken after: (*b*) 8 secs; (*c*) 42 secs; (*d*) 102 secs relative to (*a*) as zero. Magnification × 80,000. Micrographs by Pashley and Stowell.

about 20 A/minute. The extreme liquidlike behavior is demonstrated by the island F (Fig. 53c), which coalesces with island G in such a way that most of the substrate surface which it originally occupied becomes bared (Fig. 53d). Less drastic effects occur as the three islands A, B, and C (Fig. 53a) coalesce. A composite island with sharply re-entrant profiles is produced, and these rapidly fill in and become eliminated (Fig. 53c, d). The island E has a very crystallographic form on Fig. 53a, b, but when it coalesces with a neighboring island (Fig. 53c) it becomes very rounded in profile. Subsequently it reassumes a more crystallographic form (Fig. 53d). Similar shape changes occur with the composite island D.

For the reasons given previously, the specimen temperature during the deposition of the silver is uncertain. Although the electron beam does cause some rise in temperature, it is thought that this is not sufficient to have any marked effect on the growth mechanism. The other causes for temperature rise are almost certainly of importance, but there is no doubt that the temperature is well below the bulk melting point of silver. At all stages of growth, the silver deposit gives normal selected area diffraction patterns characteristic of solid crystalline silver. Further, diffraction-contrast features are visible in the islands during coalescence, and these can only arise if the islands are crystalline. It is believed that the observed behavior can be adequately explained in terms of a high surface mobility of the silver, influenced by the surface energy of the silver. The mode of growth revealed by the cine film is thought to be characteristic of the growth of films deposited in a similar manner outside the electron microscope: the one qualification is that the temperature rise is greater, for a given deposition rate, than it would be on a more massive substrate. The mode of growth might therefore be more equivalent to a somewhat higher rate of deposition on a more usual massive substrate.

V. Direct Observation of the Deformation of a Metal

The plastic deformation of a thin metal film can be studied directly in the electron microscope, so that modes of deformation such as slip and twinning can be observed at near atomic level as they occur. Several investigators have constructed devices to allow controlled tensile deformation of a specimen inside the electron microscope, but deformation can also occur fortuitously during the examination of the specimen. Hirsch et al. (54) were the first to observe that dislocations are caused to move as a result of the action of the electron beam, and more recently Fourie et al. (38) found that mechanical twinning was similarly induced in melt-grown tin single crystals.

A. Deformation Induced by the Electron Beam

It was first believed that any fortuitous deformation resulted from thermal stresses arising from electron-beam heating. However, because it is difficult to estimate with any accuracy the temperature rises which are produced by the illuminating electron beam, only approximate estimates of the resulting stresses have been made. Gale and Hale (40) have attempted to measure and calculate the temperature distribution for any given metal under various illuminating conditions. They determine the stress fields produced in the foils by such temperature distributions, and conclude that movement of dislocations should occur in some cases. Other evidence suggested that some other mechanism is operative. It is commonly found (54, 87) that there is a time lag of about 1 minute after a clean area of a metal film is first illuminated with an intense beam, before dislocation motion occurs. This time lag is not caused by a thermal effect, because once an area has been "activated," the electron beam can be cut off for a few minutes, and dislocation motion occurs immediately the intense electron illumination is restored (87). A possible explanation seemed to be that the formation of the so-called carbon contamination film on the specimen is in some way responsible.

This hypothesis has been investigated by Pashley and Presland (91a) who find that the contamination does have a major effect. They constructed a device, such as that first described by Heide (51), which prevents the formation of any contamination, by surrounding the specimen with relatively high pressure oxygen or air. Further, any contamination previously formed can be removed by electron bombardment in this oxidizing atmosphere. The fact that such an electron-beam-induced oxidation reaction does not occur with evaporated carbon films shows that the contamination is not carbon. It is almost certainly a solid polymer film produced by electron-beam-induced cross-linking of hydrocarbon vapor molecules. It is found, when single-crystal gold films prepared by evaporation are used as specimens, that no dislocation motion occurs when contamination is prevented, no matter how prolonged or intense is the electron illumination. As soon as contamination is allowed to form, the specimen begins to buckle, and dislocation motion occurs well within 1 minute. In order to prove that the significant effect of the oxygen is to prevent the formation of contamination, rather than to cool the specimen and lower any thermal stresses, the experiment was repeated with hydrogen in place of oxygen. Although hydrogen is a much more effective cooling agent than the oxygen, pronounced dislocation movement occurred in its presence. Clearly the

hydrogen fails to stop the movement because the formation of contamination is not prevented.

The detailed mechanism by which the contamination stresses the
specimen is not clear. Two general effects are possible. First, the contamination is itself deposited in a state of tensile stress, and this will
lead to a compressive stress in the metal film which will increase as
the contamination-film thickness increases. This could explain well the
observed time lag for dislocation motion to occur. Second, continued
electron irradiation might cause changes in the structure of the already
formed contamination and so lead to increase in the tensile stress in the
contamination.

Although it has been shown that the major cause of dislocation
movement in thin evaporated metal films is the formation of contamination, it is not yet clear whether the same is true for specimens prepared
by thinning bulk material. It is possible that the dislocation movement
is then in part controlled by thermal stresses; however, it seems certain
that the contamination effect is at least a major contributory factor.

Studies of electron-beam-induced dislocation motion are difficult to
interpret in detail, because the stress system is not controllable. However, several fundamental processes of dislocation motion and interaction have been directly observed for the first time by this technique.
The importance of such observations should not be underestimated;
the dislocation theory of crystal plasticity was originally developed
without any direct experimental confirmation of some of its basic concepts. Now that this confirmation is forthcoming, the confidence in
dislocation theory will increase, and further development of the theory
will be very much stimulated.

In face-centered cubic metals, dislocations are seen to move on the
predicted {111} slip planes, and in some metals, e.g., aluminum (54),
pronounced cross-slip takes place from one {111} plane to another.
Cross-slip occurs only with screw dislocations, and provided the stacking
fault energy is not too low. With metals of low stacking fault energy
the dislocations split into two partial dislocations separated by a stacking fault, and these two partials can move to some extent independently
of each other, depending upon the stress field. In some circumstances
the separation of the two partial dislocations can become very large,
and many times greater than that of the equilibrium separation which
applies in bulk metal in the absence of stress. Very extensive stacking
faults of this kind are produced in thin single-crystal gold films (87); they
occur as the two partial dislocations suddenly move apart by long distances. This will arise if the force on one partial dislocation is much dif-

ferent from that on the other, as a result of their different Burgers vectors. The partial dislocations are commonly held apart, so that the wide stacking faults remain; surface pinning of the partial dislocations by contamination is believed to be responsible for this. Many other effects, including dislocation interactions, have been observed. For example, two dislocations of opposite sign are seen to interact and annihilate each other.

Twinning has been induced by the electron beam in tin films grown from the melt (38). The twins tend to be nucleated at the edges of the specimen, or at etch pits and other imperfections in films. No evidence could be found to suggest that nucleation of the twins involved a twinning dislocation mechanism in this case, and it appears that the stress produced during electron irradiation was sufficient to cause homogeneous twin nucleation. Although the authors believe that the propagation of the twins involved the movement of twinning dislocations on the incoherent twin faces, they could not detect any of these dislocations. Two possible reasons for this were advanced. Either the Burgers vectors of the dislocations were too small to lead to adequate contrast, or the spacing between the dislocations, estimated to be only 15 A in some cases, was too small to allow them to be clearly resolved.

B. Thinned Metal on a Straining Device

The deliberate application of controlled tensile stress to a thinned metal film inside the electron microscope presents many difficulties, and the amount of information gained so far by this technique has been much less than was originally hoped by many workers. This is true despite the construction of a number of ingenious devices and the development of several special specimen preparation techniques.

The device constructed by Fisher (34) has been used for studying the deformation of stainless steel (35). Dislocations appear to originate at the edges of holes in the foil, or from grain boundaries; each "source" gives rise to a group of dislocations, 10–400 in number, confined to one slip plane.

Wilsdorf (123, 126) has used a technique which avoids edge effects. The specimen (Fig. 54) is thinned only in the center at A where observations are made, and about 20% of all polished specimens yielded an electron-transparent area without any hole. The tensile specimen is used on the device described in references 123 and 126, so that very slow and controlled rates of deformation can be applied. The system has been used particularly with aluminum and stainless steel. One of the most interesting and important aspects of the work carried out by Wilsdorf has been a study of the nature of dislocation sources in thin films (125). When the grain size of the specimen is small, the majority of the dislocations originate from the grain boundaries, but unfortunately it has not yet been possible to observe the details of the process. Twin boundaries, when present, also provide dislocation sources, and Wilsdorf suggests that such sources probably occur at short sections of noncoherent twin boundary. Polygon walls (low-angle boundaries) emit many dislocations during deformation, and the polygon walls eventually disintegrate. Because the stresses around precipitates can sometimes be very high, the interface between a precipitate and the matrix might be expected to be an ideal location for dislocation sources. In fact, the few precipitates present in the specimens were very often

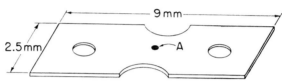

Fig. 54. The microtensile specimen used by Wilsdorf (123, 126) for observing deformation produced inside the electron microscope.

found to be at the origin of dislocation arrays. Again, unfortunately, conditions did not allow any details of the source operation to be observed.

One of the aims of deforming metal films inside the electron microscope has been to observe the operation of multiplication dislocation sources of the Frank-Read type. Because of the severely restricted thickness of the specimen, there have been speculations as to whether such sources are able to operate in thin films. Certainly the geometrical restriction is considerable, but Wilsdorf has succeeded in observing Frank-Read sources operating on slip planes which are obliquely inclined in the plane of the foil, so that the slip planes are sufficiently wide. In addition, he has observed the creation of a dislocation source during glide. A series of micrographs showing the operation of this source has been published (125).

General studies of the motion of dislocations in the thinned regions of the aluminum specimens have been made by Wilsdorf (124), and also by Berghezan and Fourdeux (15, 16), who have used a type of straining device similar to that used by Wilsdorf, but who have prepared their specimens rather differently. They have succeeded, again with aluminum, in thinning similarly shaped tensile specimens to a fairly uniform thickness across the entire width of the specimen. Their results are, in general, similar to those of Wilsdorf. Because their specimens have free edges, Berghezan and Fourdeux (15) were able to observe the formation of slip steps at edges, and correlate the magnitude of the steps with the number of dislocations involved in their production. Two particularly interesting observations (17) were the cooperative movement of dislocations, known as glide polygonization (see Section V, C), and the frequent cross-slip occurring in the vicinity of grain boundaries. This cross-slip is believed to occur to allow adequate distribution of the plastic strain at the grain boundary.

C. Single-Crystal Platelets on a Straining Device

Since one of the major difficulties involved in successfully deforming specimens inside the electron microscope is the preparation of the specimens in a suitable form, any technique which readily provides suitable specimens is certain to lead to interesting results. The use of single-crystal platelets of zinc and cadmium grown from the vapor phase has been exploited with great success by Price (100). The platelets were grown by carefully controlling the atmosphere of the growth vessel, the effective supersaturation of the vapor, the rate of growth of the platelets, and the temperature of the substrate (28). Under certain conditions, large quantities of nearly perfect platelike crystals deposit on the Pyrex substrate, with their large faces parallel to (0001), to (10$\bar{1}$0), or (10$\bar{1}$1) in the case of cadmium (96, 97), and to (0001) only in the case of zinc (94). The platelets were perfect in the sense of containing no dislocations as grown (95, 96) and generally they also had very perfect edges.

All of the platelets examined by Price were transparent to the electrons over their entire area, and many were large enough to be mounted on a straining device with the axis of tension along any desired direction in the platelet plane. Care was necessary to avoid any mishandling which could cause dislocations to be introduced into the platelets. By varying the platelet orientation and the direction of the tensile axis it was possible to examine various modes of deformation, particularly in the case of cadmium.

Dislocation formation during basal glide in (10$\bar{1}$1) cadmium platelets has been investigated (100) with the aid of a low-temperature straining device (99). The initially near perfect crystals contained no internal sources, and dislocations were generated at local stress concentrations along the free edges, as well as at the gripped edges. At large plastic strains, internal sources were initiated at: (1) low-angle boundaries formed as described later; (2) the boundaries and tips of mechanical twins; and (3) the tips of cracks. The dislocations usually moved through the crystals as short lines, and were either in predominantly edge orientation, or of mixed edge and screw character. Both types were normally formed simultaneously. Although the Burgers vectors of the dislocations were not determined by contrast techniques (see Section II, B, 1, b) the two types could be distinguished from the effect of their movement. The dislocations with screw components produced detectable bands of thinning, while the pure edge dislocations produced visible steps at the edges of the crystals in the absence of thinning. Sometimes dislocations were formed at widely separated sources, and they then moved in distinct rows to produce large steps on the edge of the platelets. When many sources on nearby planes were active simultaneously, and when the dislocations were of predominantly edge character, the dislocations were attracted into positions directly above one another. They then moved across the crystal in waves, to produce what is known as glide polygonization. This effect had previously been noted with aluminum by Berhezan and Fourdeux, and sometimes leads to the formation of low-angle boundaries.

It was frequently found that dislocations in adjacent glide bands were of opposite sign, and moved in opposite directions. This leads to the situation whereby a sufficient stress is set up perpendicular to the basal plane to cause a crack to form on the basal plane. Further deformation causes the propagation of the crack, which is accompanied by the nucleation of great quantities of dislocations.

During deformation the dislocations sometimes split into widely separated partial dislocations because in some cases the applied stress was such as to cause the two partials to move in opposite direction (see also Section V, A). In this way, ribbons of stacking fault up to a millimeter in length were produced, sometimes extending right across the crystal.

Nonbasal glide has been studied in (0001) platelets of zinc and cadmium, because the resolved shear stress on the basal plane is zero. It was found that glide occurred on pyramidal planes; the various systems of Burgers vectors were identified, and the glide planes were determined. An interesting observation was the formation of dislocation loops by a dislocation dipole mechanism. The formation of the dislocation dipole could not be followed in any detail at the early stages, but it is considered to occur by a cross-slip mechanism which allows a screw dislocation to bypass an obstacle. The jog produced in the dislocation is not glissile, and the dipole increases in length as the main dislocation continues to glide. Subsequent cross-slip allows the dislocation to return to its original glide plane well beyond the obstacle, leaving an elongated sessile loop on the basal plane. Long loops were able to lower their line energy by splitting up into rows of circular loops. This effect is well illustrated by the sequence of micrographs in Fig. 55, which was taken at 20-second intervals at about —40°C in zinc (99). The total area enclosed by dislocation was found to be conserved during the mechanism illustrated. This was interpreted as due to pipe-diffusion along the periphery of the loops, rather than by volume self-diffusion. Arrays of prismatic loops on the basal planes were frequently observed to occur by the process just outlined.

At high strain rates (0001) zinc and cadmium platelets commonly deformed by a twinning process, and twinning was also observed with $(10\bar{1}0)$ and $(10\bar{1}1)$ cadmium platelets. Detailed studies have been made on (0001) zinc platelets (98). The twins were always nucleated at the edge of the platelet, and they formed preferentially at re-entrant notches in the edges, or at points of localized corrosion. By use of the microtensile machine of Marsh (71), Price was able to measure the stress required to nucleate and propagate the twins, and for very perfect crystals these values agreed well with theoretical predictions. The twins were often nucleated prior to any plastic deformation by glide, from which it is deduced that the twins are formed by homogeneous nucleation, and not by some dislocation mechanism. The twin is always wedge-shaped at its growing tip. The twin plane, which is $(10\bar{1}2)$, makes an angle of 47° with the basal plane, so that a rotation of 180° about the normal to the twin plane causes the c axis of the twin to be very nearly parallel to the plane of the platelet. By very slowly operating the Fisher straining device (36) the wedge-shaped tip of the twin could be advanced at a very slow and uniform rate to the opposite edge of the crystal. The twin could then be widened by a smooth movement of the two bounding twin planes through the matrix. It was even possible in some cases to transform the entire crystal into a twin. An important observation was that there was no evidence for a regenerative dislocation mechanism for the growth of the twin, and Price concludes that the necessary twinning dislocations are nucleated successively at the twin matrix interface, as similarly concluded by Fourie et al. (38) for the formation of deformation twins in tin (see Section V, A). Further observations were made on the dislocation reactions occurring at twin boundaries, and on the subsequent deformation which took place inside the twins.

Although it is clear that the mode of deformation of the zinc and cadmium platelets is influenced by the shape of the specimens, and is therefore not directly relevant to the deformation of bulk crystals, the observations are of considerable interest. The platelets provide a model system for studies on the deformation of nearly perfect crystals, and allow fundamental aspects of the deformation to be investigated. If the effect of the extremely low thickness of the specimens is taken into account adequately, then direct comparison between the observed mode

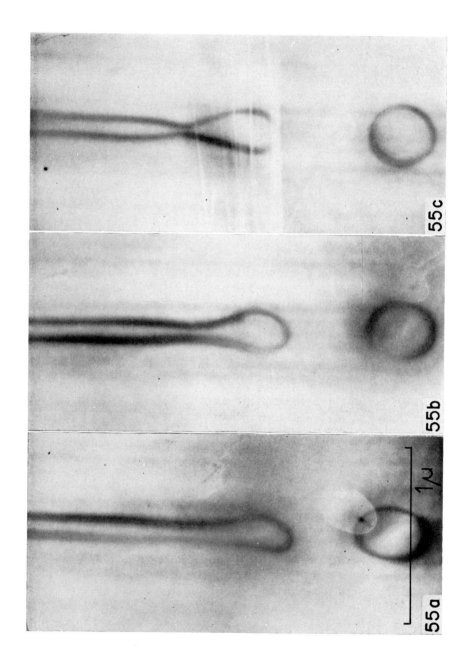

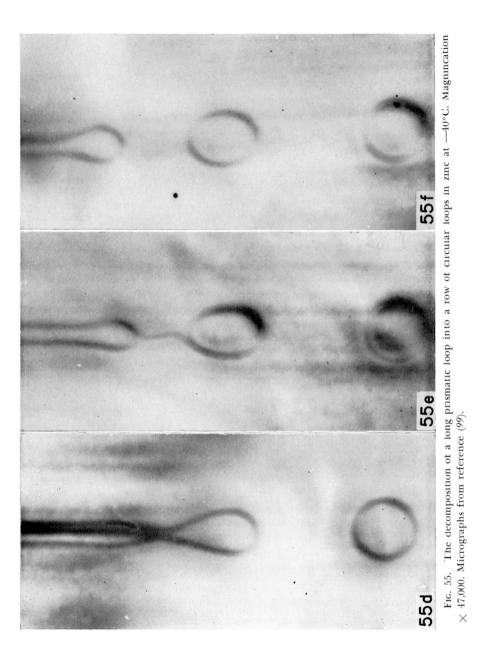

FIG. 55. The decomposition of a long prismatic loop into a row of circular loops in zinc at —40°C. Magnification × 47,000. Micrographs from reference (99).

of deformation and relevant theoretical considerations is of great general value.

D. Evaporated Films on a Straining Device

The thinnest specimens which have been deformed inside an electron microscope are single-crystal films of gold in (111) orientation (*90*). Thicknesses in the range 400–2000 A were investigated. The films were prepared by evaporating silver and gold successively onto heated mica (see Chapter 2), and they were mounted on the specimen support by means of wax before the assembly was immersed in nitric acid. This caused the silver to dissolve, so that the mica could be detached leaving the gold film alone mounted across the slit.

Because the very thin films of gold used for this work have mechanical properties very different from those of bulk material, the mode of deformation is quite different from the modes described in Sections V, B and C. In the first instance no plastic deformation could be observed as the gold film was strained. The high density of grown-in dislocations (10^{10}–10^{11}/cm^2) remained stationary, as far as could be ascertained, and precision electron-diffraction measurements confirmed that considerable elastic strain occurred during the straining of the film. This continued until about 1% elastic strain was produced, when a sudden catastrophic failure occurred. A fracture propagated from the high-strain to the low-strain end of the specimen, and this was found to be a very crystallographic fracture (Fig. 56). The edges of the fracture are parallel to $<1\bar{1}0>$ directions, which are the directions along which the three possible {111} slip planes intersect the film. The micrographs reveal much local plastic deformation in the immediate vicinity of the fracture, but no observable deformation elsewhere. From these observations it was possible to deduce the main features of the fracture mechanism. The grown-in dislocations are presumably locked, partly as a result of the small thickness of the film and partly due to the method of growing the film (i.e., evaporation). A high elastic stress is therefore built up as the specimen is strained, so that when a dislocation source eventually operates it continues to operate because the local thinning produced by the first moving dislocation causes the local stress to increase, thus leading to catastrophic deformation. Dislocations cross-slipping from one (111) plane to another account for the jagged nature of the fracture. It was originally thought that the repeated cross-slipping occurred in order to maintain the general direction of the fracture normal to the tensile axis. Although this is in part true, it has since been determined (*31*) that the specimens used were often appreciably doubly positioned. That is, there were two orientations, both with {111} planes parallel to the film plane, but twin-related so that the plane of the film was effectively the twin plane. The boundaries between the two twin-oriented regions were perpendicular to the film, and parallel to {2$\bar{1}\bar{1}$} planes. The operating slip planes are not continuous across these boundaries, and dislocations moving through a region in one of the orientations will pile up against a double positioning boundary, until sufficient stress is set up to nucleate

Fig. 56. A crystallographic fracture in a (111) gold film deformed inside the electron microscope. Magnification × 40,000. Micrograph from reference (90).

a source on the other side of the boundary. This source could operate on a slip plane at angle which would give the impression that cross-slip had occurred.

Thicker films (> 1000 A) of the same type behaved in a very similar manner, except that examination of the fractures revealed that they were very discontinuous. This confirms that the fracture mechanism involved initial plastic deformation. Where the plastic deformation was highly localized, fracture took place, but where the plastic deformation was more distributed across the film, there was insufficient localized deformation to lead to fracture.

Once a specimen had been fractured, the strain could be increased slowly, and the propagation of the fracture could be examined. However, there were two reasons why this was not very successful. First, during the examination of the specimen a contamination layer formed rapidly at the root of the crack. This seemed to prevent the crack from propagating without a considerable increase in stress. Once the crack started to move, it moved very rapidly over a long distance, so that little or no detail of the mode of propagation was revealed. Second, because of the high magnifications employed with the electron microscope, the speed of any movement is also highly magnified, so that only relatively low actual dislocation velocities can be followed by the eye. It is estimated that at a magnification of $\times$ 40,000 the highest speed of movement which can be followed is about 10^{-2} cm sec^{-1}. This represents a very slow dislocation movement, and a very low strain rate. All electron microscope observations on dislocation motion are, of course, limited by this factor, and in all cases where the motion can be followed the speed of the dislocation is very low compared with that which normally occurs during the plastic deformation of a bulk material.

VI. Ordered Structures in Alloys

The use of the electron microscope to study the phenomenon of ordering in solid-solution alloy systems is included in this chapter because the investigations have developed mainly from the techniques, both of specimen preparation and microscopy, described earlier in the chapter. As with other kinds of study of ordering, the copper-gold system has proved to be the most popular one for investigation, and most of what follows refers to this system.

A. Periodic Antiphase Structures

The first interest concerned periodic structures. There are a number of ordered structures which are characterized by their abnormally long crystallographic unit cells, so that they possess long repeat distances, sometimes well within the resolution limit of the electron microscope.

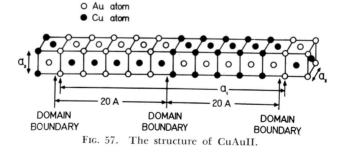

Fig. 57.   The structure of CuAuII.

The unit cell of one of the superlattices of the alloy CuAu is illustrated in Fig. 57. It forms in the temperature range $\sim$380–415°C, and was first studied by Johansson and Linde (61) who used x-ray diffraction powder techniques, and referred to it as CuAuII. The main feature of CuAuII is that the (002) planes contain alternately all gold and all copper atoms, but that these interchange their positions every half-unit

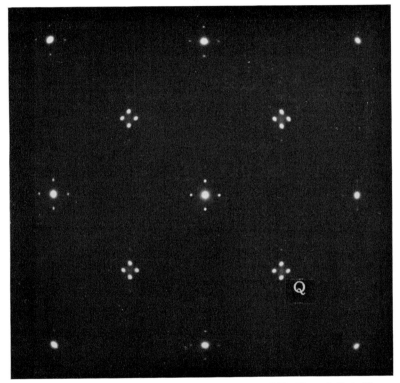

FIG. 58. Electron diffraction pattern from an (001) film of CuAuII.

cell along the a axis, i.e., every five unit cells of the original disordered face-centered cubic structure from which it forms, to give a 20 A periodicity. The interchange is equivalent to a fault plane given by a lattice shift of $\frac{1}{2}(a_2 + a_3)$ on every tenth plane of atoms parallel to (100). Since a second shift of the same amount on the same plane would eliminate the fault, the planes on which such faults occur are known as antiphase boundaries (APB's).

Thin single-crystal films of the alloy, prepared by evaporation, have been studied by electron diffraction (78, 79). A typical pattern is shown in Fig. 58; it is a composite pattern from two different orientations of the CuAuII unit cell. Although the exact origin of the satellite spots immediately surrounding the central spot is not clear (see, for example, references *43* and *81*) they correspond to reflections from the periodic arrangement of *APB*'s, so that (see Section II, A, 2, a) an image formed by allowing all the beams forming a group around the central beam (Fig. 58) to pass through the objective aperture should contain a periodic structure corresponding to the periodic *APB*'s. Such images were first obtained by Ogawa *et al.* (*81*), who made their alloy films by condensing the alloy directly onto rock salt. Similar studies were made by Glossop and Pashley (*43*) who used an improved specimen-preparation technique which gave more uniform and coherent films at lower thicknesses, so that much clearer micrographs were obtained. Gold films in (001) orientation were prepared by evaporation onto a layer of silver on rock salt (see Chapter 2) and the appropriate amount of copper was deposited onto the gold (at 200°C) after it had been detached from its substrate. The alloy was then formed by homogenizing the film at about 300°C *in vacuo*. A micrograph of the CuAuII is shown in Fig. 59. The white lines represent the projection on the image plane of the *APB*'s which are normal to the (001) film plane. There are two directions of the lines, corresponding to the two orientations of the CuAuII referred to previously, and they divide the specimen into areas called "unidirectional zones" by Glossop and Pashley. The *APB*'s are parallel to the two {100} planes normal to the film plane.

A further improvement in image quality is possible if the dark-field technique is used (*43*), and a set of split {110} reflections such as Q (Fig. 58) is selected by means of the objective aperture. Since relatively high resolution is necessary for obtaining these images, the illuminating system must be tilted so that the beams Q pass very close to the objective axis. Under these conditions very good contrast images are produced.

The extreme regularity of the periodic *APB* structure in CuAuII is very remarkable. The long periodicity seems to be controlled by the electronic structure of the alloy, since Schubert *et al.* (*104*) and Wilkens and Schubert (*121*) have shown by means of x-ray diffraction that the addition of elements of a different valency will produce isomorphous antiphase structures, with an *APB* spacing which can be systematically varied by means of composition changes. The effect has been confirmed by Ogawa *et al.* (*82*) who added various proportions of zinc to CuAuII, and obtained micrographs of antiphase structures with spacings down to 8 A. More extensive and systematic observations on the effect of additional elements on the CuAuII periodicity have been made by Sato and Toth (*103*), using electron diffraction on evaporated single-crystal films. A definite relationship between the electron-atom ratio and the periodicity was shown to exist, and on the basis of this result a theoretical model for the periodicity involving the Brillouin zone theory has been formulated. This model fits the experimental observations very well.

Although several periodic antiphase structures are known, the only one which has been resolved by electron microscopy, in addition to CuAuII, is that of Cu_3Pd. This is of special interest, because Cu_3Pd has

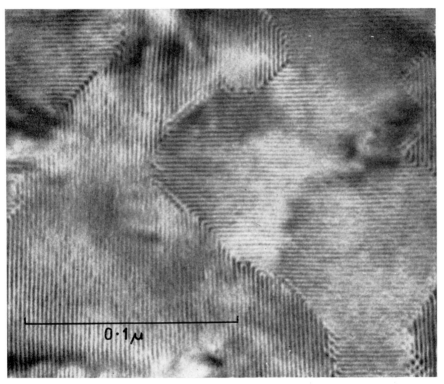

0·1μ

FIG. 59. The image of the periodic *APB* structure in CuAuII. Magnification ╳ 550,000. Micrograph from reference (*86*).

a two-dimensional periodic antiphase structure, as was first deduced from electron-diffraction evidence by Watanabe and Ogawa (*115*), and later confirmed by Ogawa and Watanabe (*83*) who obtained electron micrographs both in bright-field and in dark-field on different groups of satellite reflections.

One reason why such a limited number of systems has been studied is that the conditions of specimen preparation are quite stringent. The film must be thinner than is generally necessary for observations of dislocations, etc., because high resolution is necessary, and the orientation

of the specimen is critical, because the periodic *APB*'s can be observed
only when they are almost exactly parallel to the electron beam. These
requirements are most readily achieved with films grown by evaporation
under epitaxial conditions. All work published so far has been on
evaporated single-crystal films; recently, however, Pashley and Presland
(unpublished) have resolved the CuAuII structure in specimens prepared
by electrothinning of 0.001-inch foils. The unidirectional zone structure
(e.g., Fig. 59) is similar to that found in the evaporated films.

B. General Antiphase Boundaries

Although the number of known periodic antiphase structures is quite
small, less regular arrangements of *APB*'s are present in most ordered

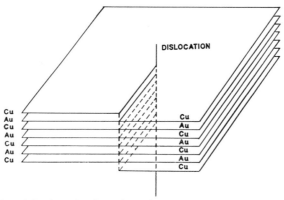

Fig. 60.   The introduction of an *APB* by a dislocation in CuAu.

alloys. These occur for two distinct reasons. First, there are the
boundaries of antiphase domains which normally form as growth faults
during the ordering process, due to the simultaneous nucleation of large
numbers of individual domains. Second, dislocations can introduce
APB's. This is illustrated in Fig. 60, for the particular case of CuAuI,
which is the lower temperature form of CuAu existing below 380°C. It
is a face-centered tetragonal structure ($c/a \sim 0.92$) produced by distorting
the disordered fcc structure, and consists of alternate (002) planes of
copper and gold atoms. A dislocation line intersecting these planes
imparts a helical structure to the (002) planes, whether it be an edge or
a screw dislocation. The pitch of the helix is ($\mathbf{b} \cdot \mathbf{k}$), where $\mathbf{b}$ is the Burgers
vector of the dislocation, and $\mathbf{k}$ is the unit vector along [001]. For the
normal $\langle \tfrac{1}{2}\tfrac{1}{2}0 \rangle$ Burgers vectors this gives a pitch of either zero (i.e., when
$\mathbf{b}$ lies in the (001) plane) or $\tfrac{1}{2}a_3$, the spacing between adjacent (002)
planes. Thus for 2/3 of the dislocations the helical structure must be

accommodated by the existence of a plane across which the gold and copper atoms are interchanged, i.e., an *APB*. This treatment can be readily extended to other superlattices, and with fcc structures (e.g., Cu_3Au) for example, all normal dislocations introduce *APB*'s.

APB's have been observed in CuAuI prepared as single-crystal films as described previously (*86*), and are shown in Fig. 61. The contrast due to an *APB* arises in the same way as that due to a stacking fault (see

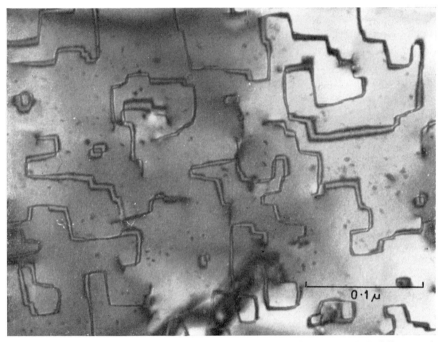

Fig. 61. *APB*'s in an (001) film of CuAuI. Magnification × 310,000. Micrograph from reference (*86*).

Section II, B, 1, a), because the *APB* is a fault across which a phase shift of the lattice occurs. When the *APB* is inclined to the plane of the film, as in Fig. 61, the characteristic fringe contrast (*117, 118*) is obtained provided $\phi = 2\pi \, g \cdot R$ is not an integral multiple of 2π, where **R** is the displacement vector of the fault, and **g** is the reflection vector. Now in CuAuI, **R** is equal to one of $\pm \, (a_1 \pm a_3)$ or $\pm \, (a_2 \pm a_3)$, and the Miller indices for fundamental reflections are either all even or all odd. In all cases ϕ is an integral multiple of 2π. The superlattice reflections have Miller indices of the type (odd odd even) or (even even odd), and this makes ϕ always equal to an odd multiple of π. Thus *APB*'s is this structure are in contrast only where a superlattice reflection is operating, and then all APB's are in contrast together. In the alloy Cu_3Au, however, a similar analysis (37) shows that only 2/3 of the APB's are in contrast where a single superlattice reflection operates. Because the extinction distances for superlattice reflections are long compared with those for fundamental reflections [470 and 520 A for the (001) and (110) super-lattice reflections in CuAu (86), 850 and 1030 A for (100) and (110) superlattice reflections in Cu_3Au (37)], the number of fringes observed in APB images is relatively small, normally two or three. The dynamical theory of stacking fault contrast (117, 118) has been applied by Fisher and Marcinkowski (37) to the determination of detailed intensity profiles of the APB fringes with Cu_3Au, as a function of specimen thickness and the deviation of the illumination direction from the exact Bragg angle. There is good agreement with experimental observations.

Figure 61 shows clearly the two types of APB's, i.e., those which are closed loops and those which terminate on dislocations. For reasons which are not entirely clear, the dislocations are not in good contrast when a {110} superlattice reflection operates, so that the APB's and the dislocations are not easily obtained in good contrast simultaneously. The poor dislocation contrast might arise in part because for all the dis-locations which have associated APB's the value of $\mathbf{g} \cdot \mathbf{b}$ is only 1/2. It is thought that if $\mathbf{g} \cdot \mathbf{b}$ is much less than unity, dislocation contrast is generally poor (see reference 38). A further observation is that the APB's have a strong preference to lie parallel to (100) or (010) planes. This is consistent with the fact that for APB's on these two planes the nearest neighbor relations at the APB are the same as within a domain. The APB energy is thus very low. Nearest neighbor relationships are changed for APB's on any other planes, and so APB's in other orientations will have higher energy.

Individual APB's are much more readily observed in specimens prepared by electrothinning of bulk foils than are the periodic antiphase structures. They have been observed in bulk CuAuI (see reference 89 and Fig. 68) and in bulk Cu_3Au (36) as shown in Fig. 62, which represents the domain structure in the fully ordered alloy. The system is more complex than that of CuAu because the Cu_3Au superlattice can be described as four interpenetrating cubic lattices, one occupied by gold atoms and the other three by copper atoms. Thus there are four distinguishable phases for the domains, since the gold atoms can lie on any one of the four interpenetrating lattices. Two APB's can therefore coalesce without annihilating each other to form an APB corresponding to a different lattice displacement; and three APB's can meet along a common line to form a triple junction. The APB arrangements do not therefore consist of the simple closed loop structures which characterize the *APB* structure of CuAuI in the absence of dislocations. The fact that only 2/3 of the Cu_3Au *APB*'s are in contrast in any one extinction contour is a further complication, and this exaggerates the maze pattern shown in Fig. 62. However, because of this contrast dependence upon the particular superlattice reflection operating, it is possible to distinguish the different types of domains and *APB*'s by examining a particular area

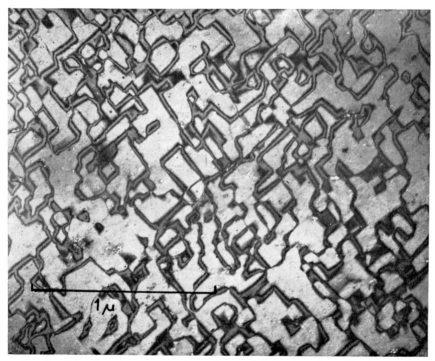

FIG. 62.   The domain structure in well-annealed Cu_3Au. Magnification $\times$ 48,000. Micrograph from reference (*36*).

of the specimen as it is tilted to cause different superlattice reflections to occur.

Extensive observations on ordered alloys other than those of the copper-gold system have been made more recently. Marcinkowski and Brown (*69, 70*) have examined thin foils of Fe_3Al which forms two distinct superlattices, both based upon the body-centered cubic system. The higher temperature modification has only two distinguishable domains, as with CuAuI, and therefore the *APB*'s form closed surfaces. Whereas the *APB*'s in CuAuI are very crystallographic, because the (100) and (010) boundaries are of much lower energy than all others, the *APB*'s in Fe_3Al are not at all crystallographic, due to a much smaller dependence of *APB* energy on orientation. The lower temperature Fe_3Al structure can be described in terms of four interpenetrating face-centered cubic lattices, and thus is similar to Cu_3Au in having domains of four distinguishable phases.

Since both dislocations and *APB*'s in ordered alloys can be observed directly on electron micrographs, it is now possible to examine in detail the interaction between dislocations and *APB*'s in ordered lattices, and so gain information which has an important bearing on the mechanical properties of such alloys. One consequence of the introduction of *APB*'s by dislocations in ordered lattices is that dislocations are easier to move through ordered lattices in pairs (*29*), joined by a narrow ribbon of *APB*, so that no increase occurs in the area of the *APB*. The existence of these closely spaced pairs of dislocations (superdislocations) has been confirmed on electron micrographs of Cu_3Au (*68*), the observed separation of 130 A agreeing well with calculated values.

C. Direct Observations of Transitions in Ordered Structures

The study of ordered structures can be further extended by heat treating thin alloy films inside the electron microscope. In this way, transitions between order and disorder, and from one ordered state to another, can be observed as they take place. As with all experiments carried out inside the electron microscope, considerable caution is necessary in deducing the behavior of bulk material from observations made on thin films. However, since ordering occurs when preferential interchange of atoms takes place as a result of the local migration of point defects (e.g., vacancies), it is reasonable to suppose that the general mechanisms which occur in a thin film give a very good indication of what happens in the bulk.

The most detailed study of this kind so far carried out is the CuAuI to CuAuII transition (*86*), which occurs at $\sim 380°C$. As already described, CuAuI and CuAuII are effectively the same basic crystal structure with different domain structures. In CuAuI the domains vary in size, becoming larger as annealing is continued, and are preferentially bounded by *APB*'s on (100) and (010) planes. In CuAuII the domains are periodic, consisting of an alternating plate structure parallel to (100), each plate being 10 atomic planes (20 A) thick. An evaporated single-crystal film of well-ordered CuAuI, with (001) parallel to the film plane, was heated slowly through the transition temperature, by means of a specially designed heating stage, and the nucleation and growth of the periodic CuAuII was observed. Within a single domain of the CuAuI, especially beside an existing *APB*, groups of antiphase domains are

FIG. 63. A fairly late stage in the CuAuI-CuAuII transition. Magnification ×
650,000. Micrograph from reference (86).

nucleated as indicated at P and Q in Fig. 63 which shows a fairly late stage in the transition. The antiphase domains consist of small discs, already about 20 A across and 20 A apart, right from the earliest observable stages. When the antiphase domains do not extend completely through the thickness of the film (see Fig. 64), the domains themselves appear in contrast against the background. This is readily understood in terms of the column theory (see Section II, A, 1), because diffracted wavelets in antiphase with each other (for a superlattice reflection) arise from a column such as *AB* passing through the antiphase domain. This causes the transmitted intensity through the antiphase domain to be modified compared with that for the surroundings since the diffracted wavelets from a column such as *CD* are all in phase. However, when the antiphase domain extends through the film (Fig. 65), only the *APB*'s give rise to

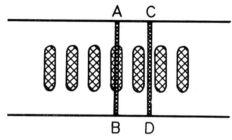

Fig. 64. The contrast from a periodic array of antiphase domains which do not extend through the film thickness.

contrast, since the diffracted wavelets from a column passing through the middle of the domain are all in phase. The nucleated domain discs, which are perpendicular to the film plane, grow by increasing their diameter until they extend through the thickness of the film, and further growth is restricted to directions in the film plane. The antiphase domains are always nucleated on either the (100) or (010) planes, so that two sets of groups are formed. The final CuAuII structure is produced as these sets intergrow with one another. Figures 65 and 66 show how two perpendicular groups of antiphase domains intergrow, to form the boundary between two neighboring unidirectional zones. The structure of a boundary formed in this way is shown in Fig. 67; in general the *APB*'s are continuous from one unidirectional zone to its neighbor, but irregularities occur due to the detailed mode of intergrowth of the perpendicular sets of domains, as illustrated in Fig. 65. Figure 67 also shows an irregularity due to the mode of joining of intergrowing parallel sets of antiphase domains (see reference *86*).

Thus by means of the observations on specimens annealed inside the

electron microscope, it has been possible to study in full detail the way
in which the CuAuI structure shown in Fig. 61 is transformed to the
CuAuII structure revealed in Fig. 59.

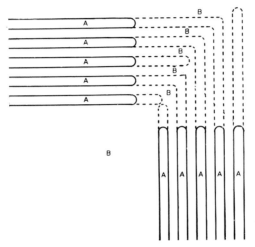

FIG. 65. The intergrowth of two perpendicular sets of antiphase domains A in a
single domain B.

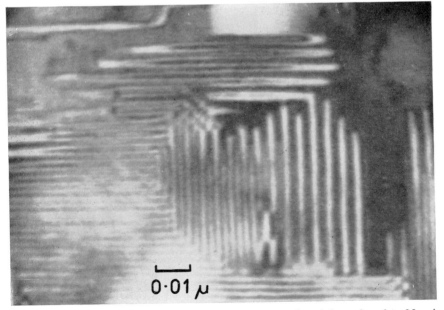

FIG. 66. The intergrowth of two perpendicular sets of antiphase domains. Magnification $\times$ 900,000. Micrograph from reference (86).

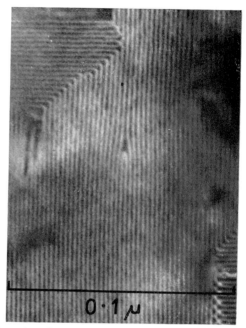

Fig. 67. The boundary between two unidirectional zones in CuAuII. Magnification × 600,000. Micrograph from reference (86).

D. Twinning Produced by Ordering

When the tetragonal CuAuI structure is formed by annealing the cubic disordered alloy, there is no unique single orientation of the CuAuI, but always several equivalent orientations. For example, if the principal axes of the two structures are parallel, there are three equivalent orientations involving the CuAuI c axis being parallel to one of three cube axes of the disordered alloy. Further, when the ordering occurs, the transition from a cubic to a tetragonal structure involves expansions of the lattice in some directions and contraction in others. These would lead to very large long-range lattice strains if only one single orientation of the CuAuI were to form. Such long-range strains are reduced in practice by the occurrence of the equivalent orientations, so that in a particular direction expansion in one region is balanced by contraction in a neighboring region. Transmission electron microscopy offers a powerful means of determining the equivalent orientations which occur, and the manner in which they are distributed. Foils of the alloy, 0.001–0.002 inch in thickness have been heat-treated and then electro-thinned (89). The electron micrographs from the thinned regions reveal a banded structure (Fig. 68) which has been analyzed in detail by means of selected area diffraction. It is shown that the bands represent micro-twinning on the {101} planes, and that within a restricted area such as that of Fig. 68 the alternating twin structure contains only two of the many equivalent orientations of the CuAuI. In neighboring regions of the specimen the twins occur on other {101} twin planes. Thus a complex twinned structure is shown to exist. This type of structure is similar, crystallographically, to that which occurs during martensitic transformations.

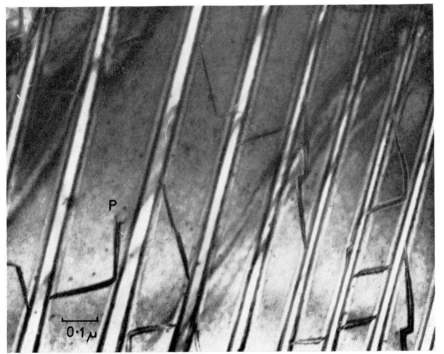

FIG. 68. Twin lamellae and *APB*'s in bulk CuAuI. Magnification × 90,000. Micrograph from reference (*89*).

The contrast of the twins shown in Fig. 68 is as described in Section IV, D, this being a case where no overlap of the twin boundaries occurs. The boundaries therefore give rise to a set of fringes. In addition, *APB*'s are visible in Fig. 68 (e.g., at P). The *APB*'s are visible in only one of the two sets of twins, because in only the one set is there a super-lattice reflection operating.

The {101} twinning just described did not normally occur in the evaporated single-crystal films of CuAu (see Section VI, A). This arises because the evaporated films were so mounted that any contraction in the plane of the film resulting from the cubic to tetragonal transition during ordering would lead to high stresses. Contraction normal to the film leads to no such stresses, and expansion in the plane of the film results in nothing worse than buckling of the film. The orientation with the c axis normal to the film ($c/a = 0.92$) is therefore favored, and this is the one observed. Thus the observations on the CuAuI-CuAuII transition made on the thin evaporated films are equivalent, as regards bulk alloy, to the transition which occurs within one of the twins such as those revealed in Fig. 68.

REFERENCES

1. Abbe, E., *Arch. mikroskop. Anat. u. Entwicklungsmech.* **9**, 413 (1837).
2. Agar, A. W., *Brit. J. Appl. Phys.* **11**, 185 (1960).
3. Amelinckx, S., and Delavignette, P., *J. Appl. Phys.* **31**, 2126 (1960).
4. Amelinckx, S., and Delavignette, P., *Phil. Mag.* [8] **5**, 533 (1960).
5. Amelinckx, S., and Delavignette, P., *J. Appl. Phys.* **32**, 341 (1961).
6. Anderson, J. C., *Proc. Phys. Soc. (London)* **78**, 25 (1961).
7. Barnes, R. S., and Mazey, D. J., *Phil. Mag.* [8] **5**, 1247 (1960).
8. Bassett, G. A., *Phil. Mag.* [8] **3**, 1042 (1958).
9. Bassett, G. A., Menter, J. W., and Pashley, D. W., *Proc. Roy. Soc. (London)* **A246**, 345 (1958).
10. Bassett, G. A., and Pashley, D. W., *J. Inst. Metals* **87**, 449 (1958-1959).
11. Bassett, G. A., *Acta Met.* **7**, 754 (1959).
12. Bassett, G. A., Menter, J. W., and Pashley, D. W., "Structure and Properties of Thin Films," p. 11. Wiley, New York, 1959.
13. Bassett, G. A., *Proc. 4th Intern. Conf. on Electron Microscopy, Berlin, 1958* p. 512 (1960).
14. Bassett, G. A., *Proc. European Reg. Conf. on Electron Microscopy, Delft, 1960* p. 270 (1961).
15. Berghezan, A., and Fourdeux, A., *Compt. rend. acad. sci.* **248**, 133 (1959).
16. Berghezan, A., and Fourdeux, A., *Proc. 4th Intern. Conf. on Electron Microscopy, Berlin, 1958* p. 567 (1960).
17. Berghezan, A., and Fourdeux, A., *J. Appl. Phys.* **30**, 1913 (1959).
18. Bethe, H., *Ann. Physik* [4] **87**, 55 (1928).
19. Bollmann, W., *Phys. Rev.* **103**, 1588 (1956).
20. Bollmann, W., *Proc. European Reg. Conf. on Electron Microscopy, Delft, 1960* p. 330 (1961).
21. Bollmann, W., *J. Appl. Phys.* **32**, 869 (1961).
22. Boswell, F. W. C., *Proc. European Reg. Conf. on Electron Microscopy, Delft, 1960* p. 409 (1961).
23. Brame, D. R., and Evans, T., *Phil. Mag.* [8] **3**, 971 (1958).
24. Brandon, D. G., and Bowden, P., *Phil. Mag.* [8] **6**, 707 (1961).
25. Brinkman, J. A., *J. Appl. Phys.* **25**, 961 (1954).
26. Carrington, W., Hale, K. F., and McLean, D., *Proc. Roy. Soc. (London)* **A259**, 203 (1960).
27. Castaing, R., *Rev. mét.* **52**, 669 (1955).
28. Coleman, R. V., and Sears, G. W., *Acta Met.* **5**, 131 (1957).

29. Cottrell, A. H., "Relation of Properties to Microstructure," p. 131. Am. Soc. Metals, Cleveland, Ohio, 1956.
30. Cowley, J. M., *Acta Cryst.* **12**, 367 (1959).
31. Dickson, E. W., and Pashley, D. W., *Phil. Mag.* [8] **7**, 1315 (1962).
32. Dowell, W. C. T., Farrant, J. L., and Rees, A. L. G., *Proc. 3rd Intern. Conf. on Electron Microscopy, London, 1954* p. 279 (1956).
33. Dowell, W. C. T., Farrant, J. L., and Rees, A. L. G., *Proc. Reg. Conf. on Electron Microscopy, Tokyo, 1956* p. 320 (1957).
34. Fisher, R. M., *Rev. Sci. Instr.* **30**, 925 (1959).
35. Fisher, R. M., and Szirmae, A., *ASTM Spec. Tech. Publ.* **262**, 103 (1960).
36. Fisher, R. M., and Marcinkowski, M. J., *J. Appl. Phys.* **31**, 1687 (1960).
37. Fisher, R. M., and Marcinkowski, M. J., *Phil. Mag.* [8] **6**, 1385 (1961).
38. Fourie, J. T., Weinberg, F., and Boswell, F. W. C., *Acta Met.* **8**, 851 (1960).
39. Frenkel, J., *Z. Physik* **26**, 117 (1923).
40. Gale, B., and Hale, K. F., *Brit. J. Appl. Phys.* **12**, 115 (1961).
41. Geach, G. A., and Phillips, R., *Proc. 4th Intern. Conf. on Electron Microscopy, Berlin, 1958* p. 571 (1960).
42. Gilham, E. J., and Preston, J. S., *Proc. Phys. Soc. (London)* **B65**, 649 (1952).
43. Glossop, A. B., and Pashley, D. W., *Proc. Roy. Soc. (London)* **A250**, 132 (1959).
44. Groves, G. W., and Kelly, A., *Phil. Mag.* [8] **6**, 1527 (1961).
45. Hashimoto, H., and Uyeda, R., *Acta Cryst.* **10**, 143 (1957).
46. Hashimoto, H., and Naiki, T., *J. Phys. Soc. Japan,* **13**, 764 (1958).
47. Hashimoto, H., Howie, A., and Whelan, M. J., *Phil. Mag.* [8] **5**, 967 (1960).
48. Hashimoto, H., Mannami, M., and Naiki, T., *Phil. Trans. Roy. Soc. London* **253**, 459, (1961).
49. Hashimoto, H., Howie, A., and Whelan, M. J., *Proc. Roy. Soc. (London)* **A269**, 80 (1962).
50. Heavens, O. S., Miller, R. F., Moss, G. L., and Anderson, J. C., *Proc. Phys. Soc. (London)* **78**, 33 (1961).
51. Heide, G., *Proc. 4th Intern. Conf. on Electron Microscopy, Berlin, 1958* p. 82 (1960).
52. Heidenreich, R. D., *J. Appl. Phys.* **20**, 993 (1949).
53. Hillier, J., *Natl. Bur. Standards (U.S.) Circ.* **527**, 413 (1954).
54. Hirsch, P. B., Horne, R. W., and Whelan, M. J., *Phil. Mag.* [8] **1**, 677 (1956).
55. Hirsch, P. B., Silcox, J., Smallman, R. E., and Westmacott, K. H., *Phil. Mag.* [8] **3**, 897 (1958).
56. Hirsch, P. B., Howie, A., and Whelan, M. J., *Phil. Trans. Roy. Soc. London* **A252**, 499 (1960).
57. Howie, A., and Whelan, M. J., *Proc. European Reg. Conf. on Electron Microscopy, Delft, 1960* p. 194 (1961).
58. Howie, A., and Swann, P. R., *Phil. Mag.* [8] **6**, 1215 (1961).
59. Howie, A., and Whelan, M. J., *Proc. Roy. Soc. (London)* **A267**, 206 (1962).
60. Jacobs, M. H., and Pashley, D. W., *Proc. 5th Intern. Congr. for Electron Microscopy, Philadelphia, 1962* p. GG1 (1962).
61. Johansson, C. H., and Linde, J. O., *Ann. Physik* [5] **25**, 1 (1936).
62. Kamiya, Y., Ando, K., Nonoyama, M., and Uyeda, R., *J. Phys. Soc. Japan* **15**, 2025 (1960).
63. Kamiya, Y., and Uyeda, R., *Acta Cryst.* **14**, 70 (1961).
64. Kamiya, Y., and Uyeda, R., *Proc. Phys. Soc. Japan* **16**, 1361 (1961).
65. Kehoe, R. B., Newman, R. C., and Pashley, D. W., *Phil. Mag.* [8] **1**, 783 (1956).

66. Kuhlmann-Wilsdorf, D., *Phil. Mag.* [8] **3**, 125 (1958).
67. Kuhlmann-Wilsdorf, D., and Wilsdorf, H. G. F., *J. Appl. Phys.* **31**, 516 (1960).
68. Marcinkowski, M. J., Brown, N., and Fisher, R. M., *Acta Met.* **9**, 129 (1961).
69. Marcinkowski, M. J., and Brown, N., *Acta Met.* **9**, 764 (1961).
70. Marcinkowski, M. J., and Brown, N., *Phil. Mag.* [8] **6**, 811 (1961).
71. Marsh, D. M., *J. Sci. Instr.* **36**, 165 (1959).
72. Matthews, J. W., *Phil. Mag.* [8] **4**, 1017 (1959).
73. Menter, J. W., *Proc. Roy. Soc. (London)* **A236**, 119 (1956).
74. Menter, J. W., *Advances in Phys. (Phil. Mag. Suppl.)* **7**, 299 (1958).
75. Mitsuishi, T., Nagasaki, H., and Uyeda, R., *Proc. Japan Acad.* **27**, 86 (1951).
76. Nagasawa, A., and Ogawa, S., *J. Phys. Soc. Japan* **15**, 1421 (1960).
77. Niehrs, H., *Optik* **13**, 399 (1956).
78. Ogawa, S., and Watanabe, D., *Acta Cryst.* **7**, 377 (1954).
79. Ogawa, S., and Watanabe, D., *J. Phys. Soc. Japan* **9**, 475 (1954).
80. Ogawa, S., Watanabe, D., and Fujita, F. E., *J. Phys. Soc. Japan* **10**, 429 (1955).
81. Ogawa, S., Watanabe, D., Watanabe, H., and Komoda, T., *Acta Cryst.* **11**, 872 (1958).
82. Ogawa, S., Watanabe, D., Watanabe, H., and Komoda, T., *J. Phys. Soc. Japan* **14**, 936 (1959).
83. Ogawa, S., and Watanabe, D., *in* "Direct Observation of Imperfections in Crystals" (J. B. Newkirk and J. H. Wernick, eds.), p. 523. Wiley (Interscience), New York, 1962.
84. Pashley, D. W., *Advances in Phys. (Phil. Mag. Suppl.)* **5**, 173 (1956).
85. Pashley, D. W., Menter, J. W., and Bassett, G. A., *Nature* **179**, 752 (1957).
86. Pashley, D. W., and Presland, A. E. B., *J. Inst. Metals* **87**, 419 (1958-1959).
87. Pashley, D. W., *Phil. Mag.* [8] **4**, 324 (1959).
88. Pashley, D. W., and Presland, A. E. B., *Proc. European Reg. Conf. on Electron Microscopy, Delft, 1960* p. 417 (1961).
89. Pashley, D. W., and Presland, A. E. B., *Proc. European Reg. Conf. on Electron Microscopy, Delft, 1960* 429 (1961).
90. Pashley, D. W., *Proc. Roy. Soc. (London)* **A255**, 218 (1960).
91. Pashley, D. W., and Presland, A. E. B., *Phil. Mag.* [8] **6**, 1003 (1961).
91a. Pashley, D. W., and Presland, A. E. B., *Phil. Mag.* [8] **7**, 1407 (1962).
92. Phillips, R., *Brit. J. Appl. Phys.* **11**, 504 (1960).
93. Phillips, V. A., *Phil. Mag.* [8] **5**, 571 (1960).
94. Price, P. B., *Phil. Mag.* [8] **5**, 417 (1960).
95. Price, P. B., *Phil. Mag.* [8] **5**, 873 (1960).
96. Price, P. B., *J. Appl. Phys.* **32**, 1746 (1961).
97. Price, P. B., *J. Appl. Phys.* **32**, 1750 (1961).
98. Price, P. B., *Proc. Roy. Soc. (London)* **A260**, 251 (1961).
99. Price, P. B., *Phil. Mag.* [8] **6**, 449 (1961).
100. Price, P. B., "Electron Microscopy and Strength of Crystals," p. 41. Wiley (Interscience), New York, 1963.
101. Read, W. T., "Dislocations in Crystals," p. 105. McGraw-Hill, New York, 1953.
102. Riecke, W. D., *Optik* **18**, 278 (1961).
103. Sato, H., and Toth, R. S., *Phys. Rev.* **124**, 1833 (1961).
104. Schubert, K., Kiefer, B., Wilkens, M., and Haufler, R., *Z. Metallk.* **46**, 692 (1955).
105. Seitz, F., *Advances in Phys. (Phil. Mag. Suppl.)* **1**, 43 (1952).
106. Seki, Y., *J. Phys. Soc. Japan* **6**, 534 (1951).

107. Seki, Y., *J. Phys. Soc. Japan* **8**, 149 (1953).
108. Sella, C., Conjeaud, P., and Trillat, J. J., *Compt. rend. acad. sci.* **249**, 1987 (1959).
109. Silcox, J., and Hirsch, P. B., *Phil. Mag.* [8] **4**, 72 (1959).
110. Silcox, J., and Hirsch, P. B., *Phil. Mag.* [8] **4**, 1356 (1959).
111. Silcox, J., and Whelan, M. J., *Phil. Mag.* [8] **5**, 1 (1960).
112. Thomas, G., and Whelan, M. J., *Phil. Mag.* [8] **4**, 511 (1959).
113. Thompson, N., *Proc. Phys. Soc. (London)* **B66**, 481 (1953).
114. Uyeda, R., *Proc. Phys.-Math. Soc. Japan* **24**, 809 (1942).
115. Watanabe, D., and Ogawa, S., *J. Phys. Soc. Japan* **11**, 226 (1956).
116. Weertman, W., *Phys. Rev.* **107**, 1259 (1957).
117. Whelan, M. J., and Hirsch, P. B., *Phil. Mag.* [8] **2**, 1121 (1957).
118. Whelan, M. J., and Hirsch, P. B., *Phil. Mag.* [8] **2**, 1303 (1957).
119. Whelan, M. J., Hirsch, P. B., Horne, R. W., and Bollmann, W., *Proc. Roy. Soc. (London)* **A240**, 524 (1957).
120. Whelan, M. J., *Proc. Roy. Soc. (London)* **A249**, 114 (1958).
121. Wilkens, M., and Schubert, K., *Z. Metallk.* **48**, 550 (1957).
122. Williamson, G. K., *Proc. Roy. Soc. (London)* **A257**, 457 (1960).
123. Wilsdorf, H. G. F., *Rev. Sci. Instr.* **29**, 323 (1958).
124. Wilsdorf, H. G. F., *ASTM Spec. Tech. Publ.* **245**, 43 (1958).
125. Wilsdorf, H. G. F., "Structure and Properties of Thin Films," p. 151. Wiley, New York, 1959.
126. Wilsdorf, H. G. F., Cinquina, L., and Varker, C. J., *Proc. 4th Intern. Conf. on Electron Microscopy, Berlin, 1958* p. 559 (1960).

CHAPTER 6

In Histology and Cytology

DON W. FAWCETT

I. Introduction

As long as the morphologist, seeking to investigate smaller and smaller components of tissue structure with the compound microscope, was limited by the wavelength of light; and as long as the chemist, seeking to determine the structure of larger and larger protein molecules, was limited by the complexity of his methods of stereochemical analysis, there remained a serious gap in the continuity of our information about the structural organization of protoplasm. The histologist was usually describing the appearance and behavior of units several orders of magnitude larger than those involved in the reactions studied by the biochemist, and the discoveries of the one field were therefore of very limited value for interpretations in the other. The boundary between the disciplines was clearly defined by a *terra incognita* extending from the limits of resolution of the compound microscope downward in size to structures of macromolecular dimensions. The electron microscope has now opened up this large and important frontier for visual exploration, and in so doing, has completely revitalized the fields of histology and cytology. Never before has the microscopist been able to provide information so directly pertinent to the problems of the biochemist and cell physiologist. It is evident that the new discoveries in the area of cell fine structure are rapidly effacing the traditional boundaries between the structurally and functionally oriented disciplines and are achieving an integration of the sciences basic to biology and medicine such as could not have been imagined a generation ago.

Some 20 years have now passed since the commercial development of the electron microscope and about a decade since the development of the methods for embedding and thin sectioning which made possible the application of this instrument to the analysis of cell and tissue ultrastructure. The extraordinary rate at which significant technical advances have followed one another in this period and the large volume of work accomplished make it quite impossible to assess, in this chapter, all of the important contributions of electron microscopy to histology and cytology. Therefore we shall only undertake in the first section of this chapter to describe a few of the more significant changes that it has wrought in our understanding of the organization of the cell and the structure of its organelles. The routine methods of specimen preparation currently in general use will be discussed in a second section, together with some of the newer techniques whose application to the study of cells and tissues appears to hold unusual promise for the future.

II. The Fine Structure of the Cell and Its Organelles

Few contributions of biological electron microscopy have had as far reaching an effect upon our concept of the cell as the discovery of the key role played by lipoprotein membranes in the structural organization of protoplasm. Not only do such membranes form the surface of the cell but they bound most of the classic organelles and several new ones that escaped detection with the light microscope. An account of the submicroscopic architecture of the cell is now, in large part, a description of the disposition of the membrane that encloses it and those that delimit the several functionally interrelated systems of compartments within its cytoplasm. It is appropriate, therefore, to begin this section with a review of the development of our present understanding of the cell surface membrane, and to proceed from there to a description of the membrane-bounded cell organelles, presenting, at the same time, the current interpretations of their respective functions in cell metabolism.

A. The Cell Surface

1. THE STRUCTURE OF THE MEMBRANE

The boundary between a cell and its environment has long been at the focus of investigative interest, for in the structural and chemical organization of the plasmalemma lies the key to its selective permeability, its specific enzyme activities, its capacity to conduct an impulse, and many of its other vital properties. The cell membrane was too thin to be studied with much profit with the light microscope but the application of ingenious indirect methods for analysis of its physical properties and dimensions led to the conclusion that it probably consisted of a bimolecular leaflet of mixed lipid between two layers of protein (31). This hypothetical model for the molecular organization of the cell membrane was accorded widespread acceptance and for the past two decades has been the basis for much of the speculation about transport of substances into and out of cells.

The increased resolution afforded by the electron microscope and the development of methods for cutting and staining thin sections of cells made possible, for the first time, a direct visual approach to the investigation of the plasmalemma. In thin sections of osmium-fixed cells examined at relatively low powers of the electron microscope, the surface membrane was visualized as a dense line about 80 A thick. At higher magnification (Fig. 1) the membrane was found to have a substructure consisting of three layers that were resolved in sections as two parallel dense lines ($\sim$25 A) separated by a less dense intermediate line ($\sim$30 A). This complex, about 80 A in thickness, was designated the *unit membrane (146, 147)*. Its trilaminar appearance was interpreted as visual confirmation of the general features of the Danielli model for the molecular organization of the cell membrane. It was quickly assumed by some workers that the parallel dense lines seen after osmium fixation represented the protein layers of the membrane, and that the less dense intermediate line either represented saturated hydrocarbon chains of the lipid or the site of a lipid component that had been extracted during specimen preparation. Owing to inadequate understanding of the chemical mechanism of fixation and staining by osmium and permanganate, it was not possible to arrive at once, at general agreement among investigators as to the correspondence between the distribution of densities in the electron microscopic image and the distribution of the various molecular species comprising the membrane.

Valuable information bearing upon the troublesome problem of interpretation of the dense lines representing membranes in electron micrographs came from studies of the myelin sheath of nerves. As early as

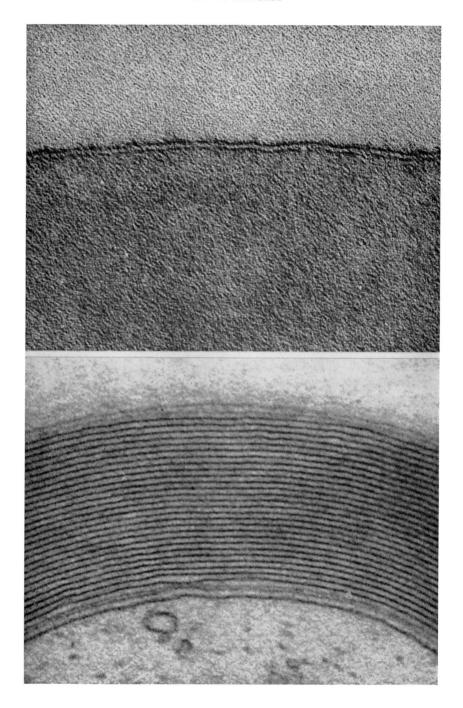

1950, Fernández-Morán (47) succeeded in cutting frozen sections of nerves thin enough to demonstrate a layered structure in the sheath. As improved methods of embedding and sectioning evolved, micrographs regularly revealed a repeating pattern of major dense lines 120 A apart, with thinner intraperiod lines midway between them (Fig. 2). The direct pertinence of the study of the myelin sheath to the general problem of the molecular organization of the cell membrane was not immediately apparent, but examination of unmyelinated peripheral nerves (53) disclosed that the axons occupy deep recesses in the surface of the accompanying Schwann cells and are closely invested by the plasma membrane of these cells. Subsequent studies of the embryonic development of peripheral nerves (54) led to the important discovery that the sheath of myelinated axons arises as a spiral prolongation of the *mesaxon,* the name given to the double-layered structure formed by the apposition of the plasma membrane of the enveloping Schwann cell where its margins close around the enclosed axon. The myelin sheath was thus demonstrated to be a local specialization of the plasmalemma of the sheath cell which remains continuous with the rest of the surface membrane of the Schwann cell throughout development. The *major dense lines* in the electron micrographs of myelin sheaths were later shown to originate by apposition of the cytoplasmic surfaces of the Schwann cell membranes and the thinner *intraperiod* line, to arise from the coaptation of the outside surfaces of the Schwann cell membranes (*144, 145*). With these discoveries it became evident that the origin of the myelin sheath from the Schwann cell surface and its regular laminated structure made it ideal material for detailed analysis of the cell membrane by physical and chemical means.

Studies combining x-ray diffraction and electron microscopy (*50*) established a close correspondence between the radial repeating unit in the low-angle x-ray diffraction pattern of the myelin sheath and the layer spacings observed in electron micrographs of the same material. Observations by both of these complementary methods after controlled

FIG. 1. High-magnification electron micrograph of the plasma membrane of an erythrocyte in thin section illustrating the trilaminar structure of the so-called unit membrane—two dense lines about 25 A thick separated by a less dense layer of similar thickness. Potassium permanganate fixation. (Courtesy of Dr. J. D. Robertson, McLean Hospital, Harvard Medical School.)

FIG. 2. Electron micrograph of a sector of the myelin sheath of an axon in the sciatic nerve. Only the major dense lines of the sheath are shown here. At higher magnification they can be shown to be formed by the apposition of the cytoplasmic surfaces of two Schwann cell membranes. (Courtesy of Dr. H. DeF. Webster, Massachusetts General Hospital, Harvard Medical School.)

extraction procedures, revealed that the dense osmiophilic lines had a considerable resistance to lipid solvents. Although this evidence was not considered conclusive, it strongly suggested that the densely stained lines in electron micrographs were due to concentration of osmium either in the protein layers or at the lipid-protein interfaces rather than among the hydrocarbon chains of the lipid. The findings were therefore considered to be consistent with the prevailing concept of the cell membrane as a bimolecular leaflet of lipid flanked by layers of protein.

The value of these combined electron microscopic and x-ray diffraction studies was not limited to the light they shed upon the nature of the cell membrane, or to the clues they offered for interpretation of the light and dark components of membranes in electron micrographs. They also provided a means of quantitating the dimensional changes introduced by osmium and permanganate fixation and by the subsequent steps in specimen preparation. When the diffraction patterns of fresh nerve were compared with those after fixation, it was shown that osmium treatment resulted in a shrinkage of the layer spacings by about 20 A. The change produced by permanganate was even less. The distortions introduced by dehydration and methacrylate embedding were appreciable, but on the whole, the alterations in dimensions attributable to the various steps in the preparative procedures for electron microscopy were less than had been feared. These results justified increased confidence in the faithfulness of preservation achieved by the methods of specimen preparation then in general use.

Another fruitful approach to the interpretation of cell membranes in electron micrographs has been the study of model systems consisting of phospholipid and phospholipid-protein complexes that form laminar structures upon hydration *in vitro*. These myelin forms of lipid can be fixed and sectioned in the same way as tissue and their electron microscopic images compared with those of cell membranes. Thin sections of such myelin figures containing no protein gave electron microscopic images showing alternating dense and less dense layers that bear a striking resemblance to those in sections of the membranes of cells (*137, 161*). The facile interpretation of the dark lines in micrographs of cell membranes as protein, and the light lines as lipid, thus appeared to be an oversimplification. Further studies bringing both electron microscopy and x-ray diffraction methods to bear upon the study of myelin figures enabled Stoeckenius and his co-workers to establish 40 A as the thickness of a bimolecular leaflet of phospholipid, and to present evidence that the dense lines of the unit membrane in electron micrographs could either represent the reaction product of osmium with double bonds of unsaturated fatty acid chains or its binding at the hydrophilic surfaces of the bimolecular layers. In the former case, the dark lines would mark the center of a bimolecular leaflet, in the latter, it would mark the two hydrophilic surfaces. In the multilayered myelin figures which were being studied, a clear choice between these alternatives could not be made for the reason that the measurements would be the same whether a bimolecular leaflet corresponded to one dense line and halves of the two adjacent light lines, or to one light line and halves of the neighboring dense lines (164). Myelin figures, believed to consist of one bimolecular leaflet of lipid with a layer of globin on either side, yielded images that corresponded closely in dimensions with those of cell membranes. Although these investigations of model systems have not brought a definitive interpretation of the molecular organization of the cell membrane, they have clarified the problem of interpretation of osmium fixation and staining and have provided additional morphological evidence compatible with the Danielli and Davson theory of membrane structure.

Electron microscopy of thin sections of cell membranes has brought forth no evidence of structural heterogeneity within the plane of the membrane and hence, has provided no support for other models which have invoked the presence of polar pores or a mosaic of lipid and non-lipid areas to account for the observed permeability properties of cell membranes (30, 119). The new technique of negative staining for electron microscopy reopened the subject of membrane structure with some surprising new findings. A centrifugal fraction of a tissue homogenate, believed to consist of fragments of cell membranes, was treated with saponin, then negatively stained with phosphotungstic acid and examined in surface view with the electron microscope (33). Such preparations revealed pits or pores 80 A in diameter arranged hexagonally with a center-to-center spacing of about 150 A. Each was surrounded by a ring about 30 A thick, hexagonal in outline, and separated from the next adjacent ring by a minimum distance of 10 A. No such appearance could be detected in surface views of cell membranes without preliminary treatment with saponin. The impressive regularity and reproducibility of the pattern led these authors to conclude that this pretreatment achieved a controlled degradation or chemical dissection of the membrane that disclosed a real heterogeneity in its structure that otherwise escapes detection. The further interesting finding that digitonin blocks the action of saponin invited the speculation that the latter extracts a specific component of the membrane such as cholesterol. These observations seemed to raise anew the possibility of a mosaic structure of cell membranes, but the excitement they engendered was short-lived.

The conclusion that saponin treatment disclosed a true heterogeneity of membrane structure present in the living cell was soon challenged by Bangham and Horne (3) who demonstrated that dried-down solutions of lecithin, lecithin and cholesterol, or cholesterol alone, when negatively stained and examined with the electron microscope show an hexagonal lattice with 80 A holes and a center-to-center spacing of 140 A—a pattern essentially identical to that observed in saponin-treated natural membranes. Thus, instead of being a result of selective extraction of certain components from the membrane as suggested by Dourmashkin et al. (33), this pattern appears to represent a transitional phase of a mixture of saponin, water, and membrane lipid resulting from the incorporation of saponin into the membrane. Similar experiments carried out independently by Glauert et al. (56) led to the same conclusion, namely, that the hexagonal pattern produced in membranes by saponin represents a molecular organization that is assumed by a complex of saponin with cholesterol and does not reflect a pre-existing arrangement of lipid and protein in the cell membrane. The studies of Bangham and Horne (3) and of Glauert and co-workers (56) are further examples of the insight into the nature and behavior of cell membranes that can be gained by the use of model systems of phospholipids in vitro to simulate the patterns encountered in cells. Although the observations of Dourmashkin et al. (33) no longer can be interpreted as offering support for a mosaic theory of membrane structure, they nevertheless continue to be of great interest. They suggest that the hemolytic mechanism of saponin may depend upon the production of pores in the membrane by complexing with it and causing a rearrangement of its lipid components. A further intriguing possibility raised by these studies is that vitamin A and other biologically active compounds causing hemolysis may also act by bringing about reversible alterations of the lipid structure of the membrane. Similar molecular rearrangements may be involved in the changes in permeability of cells that take place under normal physiological conditions (56).

The description of the general occurrence of the so-called unit membrane and the documentation of examples of continuity between the plasmalemma and the endoplasmic reticulum and between the latter and the Golgi complex led some investigators to regard all cell membranes as more or less interchangeable and similar in function as well as in structure. This emphasis upon the uniformity in organization of cellular membranes has now given way to a quest for visual evidence of those regional differences in specific biochemical mechanisms which must exist, and which are unquestionably more important from a functional viewpoint than the generalized trilaminar lipoprotein framework. Several authors have recently reported dimensional variations in the unit membrane from one cell type to another, and indeed, on different surfaces of the same cell (*181, 38*). Differences in the dimensions of various types of cellular membranes make it possible to differentiate between mitochondrial membrane elements (50–60 A thick), Golgi membranes (60–70 A thick), other cytoplasmic membranes, and the plasma membrane (80–95 A thick) (*158a*). Corresponding variations in thickness of the layers can be obtained in model systems *in vitro* (*162*), and study of these synthetic membranes again promises to cast further light upon the meaning of the dimensional differences in naturally occurring membranes in terms of their molecular organization.

2. ACTIVITIES OF THE FREE SURFACE

The dynamic concept of the cell surface that developed from cinematographic observations on living cells has been extended by electron microscopic studies that reveal more clearly than before, the behavior of the membrane in phagocytosis and pinocytosis. *Phagocytosis,* as it is seen in living cells with the light microscope, begins with the adherence of a foreign particle to the cell surface. Pseudopodia rapidly form on either side and these extend and ultimately fuse on the other side of the particle. The cytoplasm thus appears to flow around the object incorporating it in a clear vacuole. The sharpness of its outline suggests that the vacuole is probably limited by a membrane but this cannot be established with the light microscope. Electron micrographs have now verified the fact that the newly formed vacuoles are bounded by a membrane derived from the plasmalemma of the engulfing pseudopodia.

The mechanism of *pinocytosis* appears to be quite different. It can be observed best with the optical microscope at the thin margins of living cells flattened against the solid substrate of a tissue culture vessel. In one or more peripheral regions, the cell can be seen to extend an extremely thin, transparent *undulating membrane* that is constantly in motion. Thin folds projecting upward from its surface give it a ruffled appearance. These ruffles in their elaborate sinuous movements somehow trap droplets of the fluid medium which then suddenly appear in the undulating membrane as clear spherical vacuoles among the serpentine contours of its surface folds. From there they move slowly inward and accumulate in great numbers in the vicinity of the cell center. In their centripetal migration, the vacuoles become progressively smaller as though their contents are being concentrated by withdrawal of water into the cytoplasmic matrix. A variety of cell types exhibit pinocytosis *in vitro*, but while we were limited to the light microscope it could not be determined whether it also occurred *in vivo* or whether it was a cellular response peculiar to the abnormal environment of tissue culture. Electron micrographs of tissue sections have now established that this kind of surface activity does occur *in vivo* but it is apparently not so widespread as observations on tissue cultures might lead one to expect. It has been found in the peripheral parts of endothelial cells and in leucocytes, macrophages, ascites tumor cells, and other free cells. The morphological details of the process are different from those of phagocytosis. The struc-

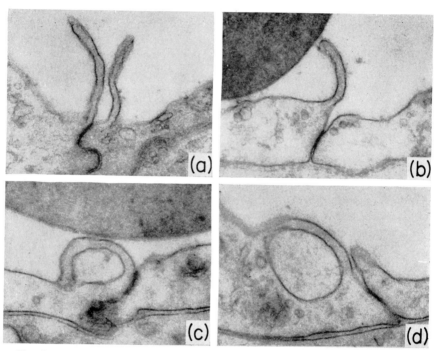

FIG. 3. (a) and (b) At the junction of endothelial cells one or both cells have thin folds that overlap the junction or project upward into the vessel lumen. In section, these have the appearance of microvilli but instead are probably thin ruffles or folds. The marginal folds are believed to be motile like the undulating membranes of cells engaged in pinocytosis in tissue culture. (c) and (d) The fold may recurve and its free edge contact and coalesce with the plasma membrane in such a way as to impound a sizeable drop of fluid in a vacuole. The vacuole then moves toward the cell center and a new fold forms at the cell margin. This behavior is believed to be the *in vivo* counterpart of *pinocytosis* observed *in vitro* with the light microscope. [From Fawcett (45).]

tures involved are not broad, amoeboid pseudopodia but instead are thin folds extending upward from the cell surface (Fig. 3). These contain a layer of cytoplasm only 80–100 mµ in thickness and are devoid of organelles and inclusions. In endothelium, they usually project into the vascular lumen at the cell margins where the attenuated edges of adjacent cells overlap or interdigitate. In the case of free cells, the folds may occur anywhere on the surface. Study of fixed images in electron micrographs suggests that two of these cytoplasmic folds or ruffles meet and fuse at their margins to impound a droplet of fluid. Or, in other instances, a single fold of this type may curve over so that its free edge falls back onto the cell surface and coalesces with the plasmalemma to enclose a droplet of fluid in a vacuole (*45, 46, 125*).

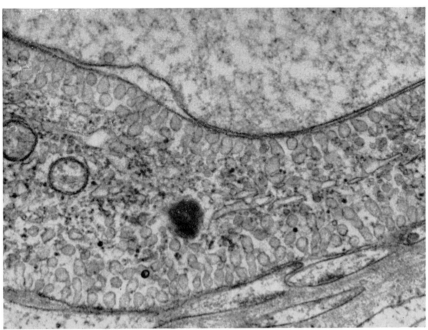

Fig. 4. Electron micrograph of a portion of a capillary wall showing numerous small pinocytosis vesicles associated with both the luminal and basal surfaces of the endothelial cell.

In addition to these microscopically visible manifestations of surface activity that have long been familiar to cytologists, the electron microscope has revealed a hitherto unknown mode of incorporation of fluid and macromolecules into cells. By formation of large numbers of submicroscopic invaginations of the plasma membrane small quanta of fluid are enclosed in pockets 80–100 mμ in diameter (Fig. 4). Constriction of the mouths of these minute invaginations severs their connection with the surface membrane and permits them to move into the cytoplasm as small spherical vesicles. Palade (*104*) who first described this kind of surface activity in capillary endothelium, interpreted it as a submicroscopic form of pinocytosis. The terms *pinocytosis* or *micropinocytosis* are appropriate here only to the extent that this process, like that originally described by Lewis (*79a*), involves incorporation of fluid in bulk or "drinking" by cells. The mechanism of fluid uptake is, however, very different—simple invagination of submicroscopic vesicles in the one case, and infolding of large droplets by folds or evaginations of the surface in the other case. In recognition of this fundamental difference Policard and Bessis (*125*), retain *pinocytosis* for the uptake of microscopically visible droplets and propose *rhopheocytosis* (from rhopheo: I aspirate) for the submicroscopic vesiculation of the cell surface.

The observation that submicroscopic inpocketings were present in great numbers at both the luminal and basal surfaces of endothelium led to the suggestion that they might participate in transport across the capillary wall by taking up fluid from the lumen, moving across the cell as closed vesicles, and discharging their contents into the perivascular space (*104, 108*). Subsequent experiments using electron-dense particulate markers have, thus far, failed to produce compelling evidence that these vesicles are vehicles of transport in a preferred direction across endothelial cells. They have, however, provoked renewed interest in the mechanism of transcapillary exchange and have directed attention again to the possibility that endothelial cells may participate more actively in capillary physiology than is generally supposed. Regardless of whether such vesicles prove to be vehicles of transport across cells, their abundant occurrence on smooth muscle cells, fibroblasts, and numerous other cell types, suggests that they may well constitute an important mechanism for uptake of material by cells for their own use.

Phagocytosis, pinocytosis, and rhopheocytosis all involve the movement of large areas of membrane from the cell surface into the cytoplasm. A circulation or cycling of membrane substance between the surface and the interior of the cell is postulated but morphological studies to date have failed to demonstrate the site or mechanism of replacement of the considerable areas of the plasmalemma that presumably are lost in these activities. Intriguing ultrastructural and biochemical problems related to the turnover of cell membranes still await solution.

3. EXTRANEOUS COATINGS OF THE CELL SURFACE

With more successful preservation of extracellular components, there is increasing interest in the extraneous coats of cells which may play a supportive or protective role or may influence the permeability of the cell surface. Nearly all cells of mesenchymal origin, except actively motile elements of the blood and connective tissues, are coated by a thin layer (50–70 mμ) of material of appreciable density which appears amorphous at low magnification. When examined at higher power it can be resolved into a feltwork of exceedingly fine filaments dispersed in an amorphous matrix. A mantle of this kind is regularly observed on the sarcolemma of skeletal and cardiac muscle, smooth muscle, Schwann cells of nerves, fibroblasts, and adventitial cells of blood vessels. It appears to be a glycoprotein, and is probably a product of the cell itself and not simply a condensation of the ground substance of the surrounding connective tissue.

Epithelial cells rest upon a continuous layer of similar material with variable amounts of collagen associated with its outer surface. These components together evidently correspond to the "basement membrane" of light microscopy. Although this term is now often applied to the amorphous or finely fibrillar layer seen in electron micrographs immediately adjacent to the cell base, it is probably preferable to call this the "basement lamina" or "basal lamina," reserving "membrane" specifically for the linear densities that represent lipoprotein components of cells. The basement lamina of epithelia appears to be a specialization of the extraneous coat that is of general occurrence on cells of many kinds. Its permeability properties and its effect upon transport and exchange of metabolites between the epithelium and the blood stream are yet to be elucidated.

The membrane bounding the microvilli on the free surface of many epithelia possess a pile or nap of fine filaments 20–30 A in diameter and up to 0.5 μ in length (Fig. 5). These project perpendicularly from the outer layer of the unit membrane as though one end were firmly anchored in its surface. Such filamentous excrescences appear to correspond to the thin layer of periodic acid Schiff (PAS) positive material observed on epithelial cell surfaces with the light microscope. Among the epithelia possessing them are those of the gall bladder (*182*), the intestine, the stomach (*67*), the toad bladder (*21, 120*), and the pancreatic acini. The origin of these filaments is still in doubt. Some regard them as an adherent secretory product arising from granules that are often found in the apical cytoplasm of the same cells. In the intestine, however, where the cells involved lack visible secretory granules the PAS-positive material would presumably arise from the associated goblet cells. The presence of a similar coating on the pancreatic acinar cells which have no associated mucous cells is more difficult to explain. Reasons have been presented elsewhere for believing that these filaments are, in all instances, a product of the cell that they coat (*44*). Their uniform distribution and precise orientation strongly suggest that their relation to the underlying membrane is more intimate than would be expected if they simply represented an adherent layer of extraneous mucus. A corresponding filamentous coating on amoebae has been found to bind particles of thorotrast or ferritin which are subsequently taken into the cell by pinocytosis (*14*).

Transport of substances by vesiculation or membrane flow as proposed by Bennett (8) must involve selective binding in or near the cell surface, and it has been proposed that the PAS-positive filamentous layer on vertebrate epithelial cells might act as a cationic ion exchanger binding ions that are then taken into the cell by pinocytosis as the first step in vesicular transport (14, 21). Interesting as this suggestions is, this type of

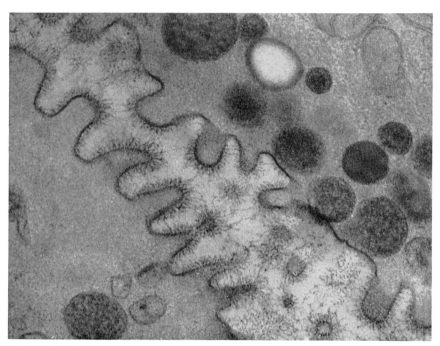

Fig. 5. Micrograph of the free surfaces of two neighboring epithelial cells in the gastric mucosa. The plasmalemma covering the short microvilli is covered by a dense nap of fine filaments oriented perpendicular to the membrane surface. (Courtesy of Dr. S. Ito, Harvard Medical School.)

coating is present on a number of cell types not notably involved in transport and it seems unlikely that this is its only or indeed its principal role. There are other ways in which it could affect the permeability properties of the cell surface and its origin and function will no doubt continue to be a subject of intensive investigation.

4. SURFACE CONTACTS AND CELL COHESION

According to the traditional interpretation, cells were held together by an adhesive intercellular cement, or by a specific attraction like that of antibody for antigen, or by the formation of chemical bonds between the membranes. Electron microscopic observations have forced us to alter our views concerning the nature of the contact between cells and the mechanism of their cohesion. The unit membranes of adjoining cells are usually separated by a distance of 150–200 A, and the dimensions of this intercellular space remain extremely constant whether the cell boundaries are relatively straight or elaborately convoluted (Fig.

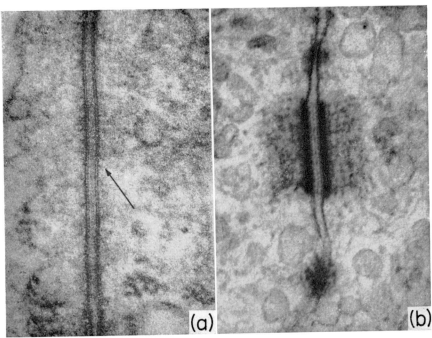

Fig. 6. (a) Electron micrograph of the junction of two cells showing the trilaminar structure of the apposing membranes and the very uniform width of the intercellular cleft. (Courtesy of Dr. Jane Overton, Whitman Laboratories, University of Chicago.)

(b) A typical desmosome or macula adherens on the boundary between two endothelial cells in a fish capillary. Above and below are two smaller attachment devices wherein the membranes lack the dense layer that is characteristic of typical desmosomes, and the intercellular gap is narrower.

6a). The space appears to have a content which is probably a thin layer of mucopolysaccharide. Although no filamentous substructure has been resolved, it is reasonable to believe that this intercellular substance is akin to the filamentous coating of the free surface and to the layer of fine fibrillar material that constitutes the extracellular basement lamina (basement membrane). The reality of this intercellular gap seems to be established beyond question, and its considerable width would seem to

eliminate the possibility that cell cohesion is maintained either by formation of chemical bonds between the lipoprotein membranes themselves
or by the intervention of small ions such as calcium. The same considerations make it equally unlikely that the mechanism of cohesion involves
the coaptation of specific complementary groups on the opposing protein
surfaces. It is clear nevertheless that some cohesive force acts over the
entire surface to maintain the constancy of the 150–200 A intercellular
gap. In addition to the general attraction of the surfaces for each other,
there are local differentiations of the opposing membranes called *desmosomes* where the cells are attached more tenaciously (Fig. 6b). At these
sites the membranes on either side of the intercellular cleft are thickened
and the subjacent cytoplasm is condensed and reinforced by a feltwork
of interwoven fine filaments (*42, 60, 101*). Tonofilaments in the cytoplasm
often converge upon the desmosomes and terminate in the dense fibrous
plaques on their cytoplasmic surfaces. Desmosomes are distributed at
irregular intervals over the contact surfaces of most epithelial cells.

A similar differentiation called a *terminal bar* is found on the
boundary between epithelial cells near the apical surface. These attachment devices differ from desmosomes mainly in their shape, being long
bands that extend around the perimeter of each polygonal cell in a plane
parallel to the free surface of the epithelium. The thickening of the opposing cell membranes is less apparent than in desmosomes and the limits
of the associated condensation of cytoplasm are less clearly defined. In
epithelial cells having a terminal web its filaments end in the terminal
bar. The distance between cells at these specializations is about the same
as at desmosomes (150–200 A). Between the terminal bar and the free
surface, the membranes of the two cells converge and come into very
close apposition in a band of variable width that girdles the cell parallel
to the terminal bar. The intercellular gap is narrowed in this region to
20 A or less, and in a considerable number of epithelia it is apparently
completely obliterated by the fusion of the outer leaflets of the opposing
unit membranes (*109*). These close junctions are of particular significance
because they effectively close the intercellular space preventing extracellular passage of materials through the epithelium.

In an effort to develop a consistent terminology for the various junctional complexes, Farquhar and Palade (*38*) propose *zonula occludens* for
the close junctions obliterating the intercellular space; *zonula adherens*
for the bandlike attachments formerly called the terminal bars; and
macula adherens for the disc-shaped sites of adhesion now commonly
called desmosomes. While these new designations have considerable
merit for the description of the junctions of epithelial cells, it is clear
that they will not be applicable to all such specialized relations between

cells. Close adhesions occur in the myelin sheath and the "external compound membrane" of peripheral nerves (147) and in a variety of synaptic complexes in the central nervous system (115, 123). In these, the concept of occlusion or adherence may be less pertinent than the significance of these relations for the electrical events concerned with impulse transmission.

We are left with no satisfactory explanation for the fact that there are, in general, two principal degrees of separation between cell surfaces—a gap of the order of 150–200 A or one less than 20 A. Curtis (26) finds attractive the possibility that cell cohesion at these distances may result from the interaction of electrostatic forces of repulsion between similarly charged cell surfaces, on the one hand, and London-van der Waals' forces of attraction on the other. In support of this theory, he cites work (170) showing that such forces between surfaces tend to balance in two situations, namely, a primary point at 5–20 A separation of the surfaces and a secondary point at about 100–200 A. Although there is no experimental evidence that these London and electrostatic forces operate in living systems, the agreement between the primary and secondary points of balance and the two prevailing distances of separation of cell surfaces, make this a provocative suggestion.

B. Nucleus

The prevailing interpretation of the mechanism of heredity is based upon the idea that the genes are arranged at specific sites in linear sequence along the length of the chromosomes. Although the chromosomes are readily visible in both living and fixed cells during division they are not seen in the nondividing nuclei of somatic cells in vertebrates. It is commonly assumed, however, that they retain their identity through interphase, even though their limits cannot be defined with the light microscope. They are believed to become unevenly dispersed in the karyoplasm in such a way that more hydrated and loosely organized regions (euchromatin) stain faintly or not at all, while other regions (heterochromatin) maintain nearly the same degree of condensation observed in mitotic chromosomes and these regions stain intensely throughout interphase. The irregularly shaped clumps of chromatin, the *karyosomes*, in fixed and stained nuclei are interpreted as incompletely dispersed portions of the interphase chromosomes. Their number and distribution determines the characteristic pattern assumed by the chromatin in each cell type. The expectation that higher resolution would reveal many further details of chromosome structure in mitotic and interphase chromosomes has not been fulfilled despite intensive investigation.

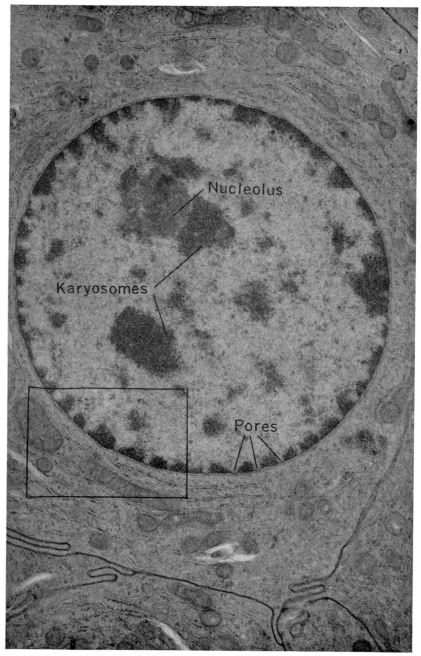

FIG. 7. A typical nucleus in an epithelial cell of the epididymis showing part of
the nucleolus, a number of karyosomes of varying size, and an irregular accumulation

The electron microscope has, in fact, contributed surprisingly little to our understanding of the organization of the nucleus. The reason for this disappointing outcome is still not clear. The coarse patterns which result from traditional fixation and staining for the light microscope may have raised unrealistic expectations. On the other hand, it is quite possible that current methods of specimen preparation for electron microscopy, although very satisfactory for cytoplasmic components, may simply be entirely inadequate for preservation of the nucleoplasm.

1. THE INTERPHASE NUCLEUS AND MITOTIC CHROMOSOMES

After osmium tetroxide fixation the nucleoplasm of resting somatic cells is often rather homogeneous in electron micrographs, as it is indeed, in the living cell (Fig. 18). In some cell types, however, it shows a pattern of density variations that resembles the distribution of chromatin in stained cytological preparations viewed with the light microscope (Fig. 7). This pattern can be brought out in better contrast by staining with uranyl acetate.

At higher magnification, the interphase nucleoplasm is a confusing conglomeration of minute particles of various sizes and densities. Local differences in the concentration and in the relative proportions of the several categories of particles are responsible for the pattern of density variations observed in low-power micrographs. Some of the small granules have the same size and density as the ribonucleoprotein particles in the nucleolus and the ribosomes of the cytoplasm. Others are considerably larger and more irregular in outline. One component of intermediate density tends to be concentrated in fine textured masses from which the coarser and denser particles are largely excluded. The segregation of the various kinds of particles at the periphery of these masses is incomplete, however, and their boundaries are therefore poorly defined. These masses are often closely associated with the nuclear envelope and with the nucleolus but also occur elsewhere in the nucleoplasm. It has been established by optical examination of Feulgen-stained, adjacent, thick sections that these areas, in electron micrographs, correspond to the chromatin in light microscopic images of the same nucleus (62, 93a).

Not all investigators accept this poorly ordered mixture of particles as a valid representation of the organization of nucleoplasm in life. Observations on selected living cells in tissue cultures and on the same cells in electron micrographs after preparation by currently accepted methods,

---

of heterochromatin around the periphery, interrupted at intervals by areas of lower density opposite the nuclear pores. The high contrast of the chromatin in this micrograph is a consequence of staining with uranyl ions. The area enclosed in the rectangle is shown at higher magnification in Fig. 8.

have led Bloom and Leider (11) to mistrust osmium tetroxide as a pre-
servative of nuclear structure. They employ instead, neutral formalin
in Tyrode solution, followed by staining in alcoholic phosphotungstic
acid. Prefixation by ultraviolet irradiation has also been advantageous
for their purposes. Their preference for these methods over those in more
general use is based upon the fact that the chromosomes have more
clearly defined limits and less evidence of extraction. Moreover, after
localized ultraviolet radiation of chromosomes, fine structural alterations
can be detected with these methods that correspond to the paling and
apparent loss of chromosomal substance seen to occur in living cells as
a consequence of the irradiation. Osmium fixation, on the other hand,
fails to retain evidence of this structural alteration. In their preparations,
the chromosomes consist of a homogeneous or finely fibrillar material of
low density filling the meshes of a coarse irregular reticulum of anastomosing strands 40–300 A in diameter. This reticulum not only permeates
the chromosomes but extends into the interchromosomal areas and indeed throughout the nucleoplasm. The homogeneous light component
is interpreted as the deoxyribonucleoprotein of the chromosome. Nuclear
fine structure after these methods of specimen preparation is so different
from that seen after osmium-containing fixatives that the images obtained
with the two procedures cannot be compared with the expectation of
establishing any correspondence between the components revealed. Although Bloom and Leider's interpretation of the structure of chromosomes based on these unorthodox methods has not been accorded general acceptance, it is important to have before us this striking reminder
of the degree to which our interpretations of fine structure have come to
depend upon a single fixative, osmium tetroxide. Orthodoxy in methods
may not prove to be the best approach to truth in this area of science.

A more popular view accepts buffered osmium as faithfully preserving the ultrastructure of the nucleoplasm and attributes the apparent
lack of organized structure in electron micrographs to the difficulties
inherent in interpreting the three-dimensional configuration of minute
structures in ultrathin sections that are essentially two-dimensional (143).
The fine punctate areas that appear to be granules are interpreted instead as transverse or oblique sections of elementary fibrils 100 A thick
and of indefinite length. These are regarded as subunits of the uncoiled
chromonemata of swollen, hydrated, interphase chromosomes. According to this interpretation, the changing appearance of the chromosomes
during condensation before cell division is mainly the result of closer
spacing and a greater degree of coiling of the elementary fibrils comprising the chromonemata. Fibrils 100 A thick have now been described
by many authors and interpreted as the common component of chromo-

somes from protozoa to man (*12a, 71, 95, 143*). A fibrillar organization for the chromosome has considerable appeal because it can most easily be brought into accord with current genetic theory and with the observations of classic cytology. The fact is, however, that many workers remain unconvinced that the appearance of thin sections adequately supports this interpretation. While it is true that the majority of profiles of randomly oriented fibrils in thin sections would be punctate and indistinguishable from granules, one would expect the 100 A fibrils to coincide with the plane of the section with sufficient frequency to leave no doubt as to their presence. Such extended profiles of fibrils of these dimensions are rarely seen.

A novel interpretation of the structure of the deoxyribonucleoprotein component of the nucleus has recently been advanced by Hay and Revel (*62*). In nuclei of salamander cells, regions corresponding to the chromatin in Feulgen-stained preparations were found in high-magnification electron micrographs to consist of an interlacing pattern of filaments 50–75 A in thickness which appeared to branch and anastomose constituting a fine meshwork, or a three-dimensional lattice with interstices less then 200 A wide. This meshwork shows regional variations in the thickness of its filament and the size of its interstices, being more loosely organized and less dense in areas corresponding to the euchromatin, and more closely compacted and dense in areas of heterochromatin. Recognizable chromosomes appear to form in prophase by closer aggregation and condensation of this filamentous meshwork. Except for the difference in their density and degree of dispersion, the chromosomes are believed to have essentially the same reticular organization as the chromatin of the interphase nucleus. Both are visualized as a meshwork of interconnected deoxyribonucleoprotein macromolecules constituting the solid phase of a reticular gel. From observations on the sites of labeling and the relative rates of thymidine uptake, it is speculated that the loosely organized, dispersed chromatin of the interphase nucleus is the form that is most active in synthesis of deoxyribonucleic acid (DNA) and that the condensed chromatin in karyosomes or chromosomes is metabolically inert.

It is clear that much remains to be learned about the organization of the nucleus. Before a great deal more can be accomplished with existing methods there is an imperative need for fundamental investigations that will establish to what extent the fine structural components seen in electron micrographs represent precipitation patterns of protein whose form depends largely upon the nature of the fixative, and to what extent they represent the preservation of pre-existing formed elements present in the living nucleus.

2. THE MEIOTIC CHROMOSOMES

The first and only continuous longitudinal structures observed in electron micrographs of chromosomes were the fibrous cores found in prophase of the first meiotic division of spermatocytes (*40, 93a*). These structures occur in meiotic prophase only at the stage of synapsis and hence have been called *synaptonemal complexes.* They consist of three parallel strands in the axis of the chromosome. The lateral dense strands are about 300 A in diameter and 1000 A apart. The less clearly defined intermediate line is about 170 A wide. The two lateral fibers may have a spiral course along the axis of the chromosome and are often seen terminating on the inner aspect of the nuclear envelope. Arranged around the core complex and making up the bulk of the chromosome are fine granules or radiating fine filaments interpreted by some workers as strands of deoxyribonucleoprotein (*93*). Nothing comparable to the synaptonemal complex has been found in mitotic chromosomes. It is of interest that in *Drosophila,* where crossing over occurs in the female but not in the male, the synaptonemal complex is present in the oocytes but not in the spermatocytes (*88*). It appears that these structures are related in some way to the chromosome pairing and recombination in meiosis but their actual role in this process remains unknown.

3. THE NUCLEOLUS

The nucleolus in different cell types has many different configurations, but its appearance is usually quite characteristic and consistent within a given cell type. A common, but by no means a universal, feature of nucleolar organization is a dense strand of uniform thickness in the form of a tangled skein or a close-meshed plexus. This threadlike component is called the *nucleolonema.* At high magnification it is found to be composed of closely packed 150 A dense particles that greatly resemble the ribosomes of the cytoplasm and are presumed to be ribonucleoprotein. Within the irregular spaces bounded by the meshes of the nucleolonema is a fine textured component that has been identified as deoxyribonucleoprotein by its characteristic fine structure and its labeling with tritiated thymidine (*61*). The nucleolonema is often organized around one or two, more-or-less spherical areas having a lower density and a more finely granular texture than the nucleolonema (Fig. 18). The nucleoli of certain cell types have a third component of intermediate density. This may form a central mass, flanked by two rounded areas of low density and surrounded by the nucleolonema. In others, these fine granular components of varying density may be arranged concentrically. The meaning of the regional differentiations of the nucleolus and its different configurations is obscure, and almost nothing is known of the

chemical nature of its components other than that of the ribonucleoprotein of the nucleolonema and the deoxyribonucleoprotein found in its
interstices and around its periphery. The study of functional changes
in the organization of the nucleolus with the electron microscope is
hampered by the fact that its appearance varies greatly depending
upon the plane of section. The prospect of resorting to serial sections
and reconstruction is too laborious to attract many workers in this period

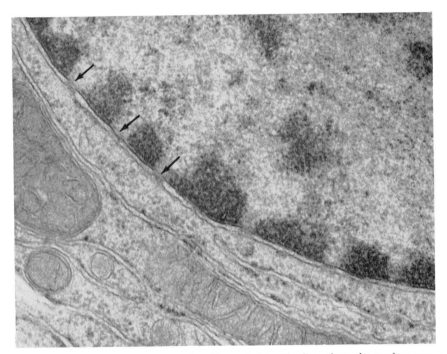

FIG. 8.   A sector of the same nucleus illustrated in Fig. 7 to show the nuclear pores
at higher magnification.

of rapid exploitation of the electron microscope, when other problems
will yield a generous return with a smaller investment of time and effort.

4. THE NUCLEAR ENVELOPE

The nuclear envelope was seen with the light microscope as a thin
dark line at the interface between the deeply stained chromatin of the
nucleus and the paler cytoplasm. It was interpreted as a single membrane with permeability properties not unlike those of the cell-surface
membrane. The first challenge to this traditional interpretation came
in 1950 when Callin and Tomlin (17) devised a simple technique for

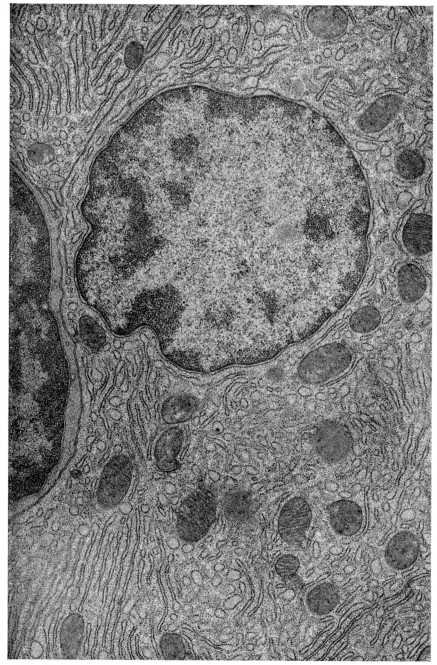

FIG. 9. Electron micrograph of a gastric zymogenic cell showing numerous mitochondria and an elaborate granular endoplasmic reticulum consisting of both

isolating and spreading on Formvar films, nuclear envelopes from amphibian oocytes. In electron micrographs of such preparations, they established the bilaminar nature of the envelope and the presence of a regular pattern of pores. Later work utilizing thin sections confirmed, in all cells examined, the existence of a nuclear envelope consisting of two membranes ∼ 80 A thick separated by a space 200–300 A across and penetrated by pores 400–500 A in diameter (175) (Fig. 7). The inner and outer membranes of the nuclear envelope are continuous with one around the margins of each circular pore (Fig. 8). The apparent patency of these openings and the regular occurrence of areas of rarefaction in the chromatin in the vicinity of the pores, suggests that they may constitute pathways for the interchange of substances between the nucleus and the cytoplasm. Examination of these structures at high magnification often reveals an exceedingly thin membrane or diaphragm across the middle of the pore. The influence of this, if any, upon the passage of materials through the pore is not known. The cytoplasmic surface of the outermost membrane of the nuclear envelope is studded with ribonucleoprotein particles and is often observed to be continuous with tubular and cisternal profiles of the granular endoplasmic reticulum (106, 127). For this reason, the nuclear envelope is considered to be an integral part of the endoplasmic reticulum. In recognition of this relationship the space between the layers of the envelope is sometimes called the *perinuclear cisterna*. In late prophase of meiosis and mitosis, the nuclear envelope breaks up into vesicles and tubules indistinguishable from other profiles of the endoplasmic reticulum and, in late telophase, elements of the reticulum coalesce to reconstitute the nuclear membranes of the daughter cells (4, 131). The nuclear envelope is thus regarded by some as the most constant and fundamental portion of the endoplasmic reticulum (128).

C. Endoplasmic Reticulum

The system of cytoplasmic membranes now known as the endoplasmic reticulum is a new organelle whose discovery had to await the development of the electron microscope. It was first described in electron micrographs of intact tissue culture cells by Porter (125a, b) and later in thin sections of a variety of cell types by Palade and Porter (109a). It became clear in retrospect that certain aggregated forms of this organelle had been seen earlier as coarse basophilic bodies in the cytoplasm of some

tubular and cisternal profiles. In addition to the ribosomes associated with the membranes large numbers are present in the cytoplasmic matrix. The nucleus shows a peripheral disposition of chromatin and several karyosomes of varying size. Collidine-buffered glutaraldehyde fixation, osmium tetroxide postfixation, and uranyl acetate-lead citrate staining. (Courtesy of Dr. S. Ito, Harvard Medical School.)

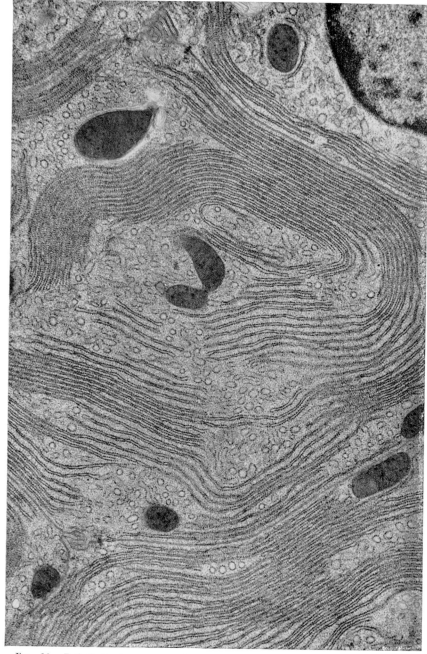

Fig. 10. Relatively low-power electron micrograph of a pancreatic acinar cell including a small portion of the nucleus at the upper right, and a typical area of

cell types and had been called *ergastoplasm* or *chromidial substance*. However, its membranous structure, its canalicular organization, and its almost universal occurrence in cells could not be appreciated with the light microscope. It is basically an intercommunicating system of tubules extending throughout the cytoplasm (Fig. 9). The tubules may be locally expanded into broad flat sinuses called *cisternae* which have a tendency to associate in close parallel array (Fig. 10). It was only such aggregations of cisternae which were visible with the light microscope. The anastomotic character of the profiles included in single sections suggests that the system is continuous throughout the cytoplasm. Further evidence for this has been provided by the study of serial sections covering limited segments of cells. These clearly demonstrate the confluence of profiles that appear to be separate in single sections. The tridimensional configuration of the reticulum and the relative proportions of tubules and cisternae vary with the cell type and in different physiological conditions of the same cell type. Although potentially continuous throughout the cytoplasm, it is not always so, and in some cells it is represented by a population of isolated vesicles.

As indicated earlier, the nuclear envelope or perinuclear cisterna is considered to be an integral part of this system, and through its communications with other elements of the reticulum affords a pathway for dissemination of genetic information or of nuclear metabolites to all regions of the cytoplasm. Continuity of the endoplasmic reticulum with the plasma membrane has also been reported (*35, 105*) and is prominently figured in several widely reproduced diagrammatic representations of the typical cell (*146*). Such depictions create an erroneous impression of the frequency and physiological importance of this relationship. If communication between the lumen of the reticulum and the extracellular space does exist, it is relatively rare and probably quite transient.

Inasmuch as the perinuclear cisterna is the most constantly occurring part of the reticulum it has been suggested that it may be conceptually useful to think of the cytoplasmic part of this system as an "outgrowth of the nuclear envelope" (*128*). The value of this suggestion resides mainly in the emphasis that it places upon the contiguity and functional unity of these two parts of the system and may not go beyond that for, at

---

basal cytoplasm with its graceful parallel aggregations of cisternae of the endoplasmic reticulum interspersed with areas occupied by transverse and oblique sections of tubular elements of the reticulum. A higher magnification of a group of these cisternae showing the relation of the ribosomes to the membranes is shown in Fig. 12. Collidine-buffered glutaraldehyde fixation with postfixation in buffered osmium, Epon embedding, and uranyl acetate-lead citrate stain. (Courtesy of Dr. S. Ito, Harvard Medical School.)

present, there is no good evidence that the cytoplasmic elements of the reticulum do, in fact, develop by growing out from the nuclear envelope. One can as logically support the view that the nuclear envelope is an outgrowth of the general cytoplasmic portion of the reticulum since, at each cell division, it fragments and is later reconstituted in the daughter cells by fusion of tubular and cisternal elements which persist in the cytoplasm (131). In at least one instance it has been possible to assemble a series of micrographs representing intermediate stages in differentiation of a primitive cell lacking cytoplasmic membranes, into a specialized cell type possessing an abundant and highly complex reticulum. In this case the reticulum seemed to arise in the cytoplasm as discontinuous vesicles and tubules which elongated and coalesced into a continuous system of channels that secondarily established continuity with the nuclear envelope (159). Additional studies of differentiating cells are needed to clarify the ontogeny of the endoplasmic reticulum and its relation to the nuclear envelope and to the Golgi complex.

Two principal morphological types of endoplasmic reticulum are distinguished: (1) the *granular* or *rough-surfaced reticulum* which has large numbers of small dense particles of ribonucleoprotein, the *ribosomes,* adhering to the outer surface of its membranes and (2) the *agranular* or *smooth-surfaced reticulum* which lacks these granules. The distinction between the two goes considerably beyond the mere presence or absence of associated ribosomes. There are differences in function, in the configuration of the tubular and cisternal elements, and in the stability of the membranes. Generally, one form of reticulum greatly predominates over the other. Thus, cell types with well-developed agranular reticulum have very little granular reticulum, few ribosomes, and are generally acidophilic in stained histological preparations. Conversely, cell types with abundant granular reticulum usually have little or no agranular reticulum and are basophilic in histological preparations. The liver cell is unusual in having both types of reticulum well represented. Its aggregations of ribosome-studded cisternae correspond in electron micrographs to the basophilic bodies in the light microscopic image. The loose networks of agranular reticulum in the glycogen-rich areas of cytoplasm are not resolved with the light microscope but they no doubt contribute to the acidophilic staining of these regions.

1. THE GRANULAR ENDOPLASMIC RETICULUM

The degree of development of the granular reticulum and its form vary with the biochemical activity of the cell type. In those synthesizing a modest amount of protein, the reticulum is a meandering system of tubules with occasional cisternal expansions. In secretory cells synthesizing large amounts of protein, the reticulum is apt to consist of extensive arrays of parallel cisternae (Figs. 11 and 12). In an admirable series of correlated biochemical and electron microscopic studies, the *microsomes* of the biochemist have been identified as vesicular fragments of the endoplasmic reticulum produced during homogenization. The small 150 A *ribosomes* associated with their surface have been shown to be the sites of protein synthesis (*81, 105, 110, 111*). In the elaboration of the pancreatic secretions, isotopically labeled amino acids are first incorporated into protein on or near the ribosomes. The protein is then transported across the membrane into the lumen of the reticulum where it accumulates in amorphous form or in intracisternal granules depending upon the species (Figs. 13 and 14). From there is is channeled into the supranuclear region of the cell where it is concentrated in membrane-bounded secretion vacuoles or granules and then released into the apical cytoplasm for storage (*112, 155, 156, 156a*). Essentially the same intracellular pathway appears to apply to all cells elaborating a protein secretory product, but in those producing a modest volume of secretion, the granular endoplasmic reticulum is not nearly as extensively developed as in the liver, pancreas, salivary glands, and gastric zymogenic cells.

The mechanism of transport of the product from its site of synthesis on the ribosome across the membrane into the lumen of the reticulum, and the means of its transfer from the reticulum to the Golgi complex remain somewhat obscure. Sites of continuity between the granule-studded membranes of the reticulum and the smooth-surfaced elements of the Golgi complex have been described but are not found with sufficient frequency to support the contention that free communication between the lumens of these two organelles is the normal condition. It seems more likely that they are in transient, intermittent communication, or that agranular vesicles containing quanta of the cell product bud off from the ends of the reticulum and fuse with the thin cisternal vacuoles of the Golgi complex. Our present lack of detailed knowledge of the topographical relations and functional interchanges between these two organelles is the weakest morphological link in our understanding of the intracellular mechanisms involved in secretion.

Great interest is now centered on the possible biochemical differences in the synthetic activity of the ribosomes that are attached to the membranes of the reticulum compared to those that are free in the matrix, and in the relation of the ribosomes to each other, to the membranes, and to the so-called messenger ribonucleic acid (RNA). Although these would seem to be problems well beyond the reach of microscopic analysis, refined methods of cell fractionation and the application of high-resolution electron microscopy with negative staining are yielding exciting

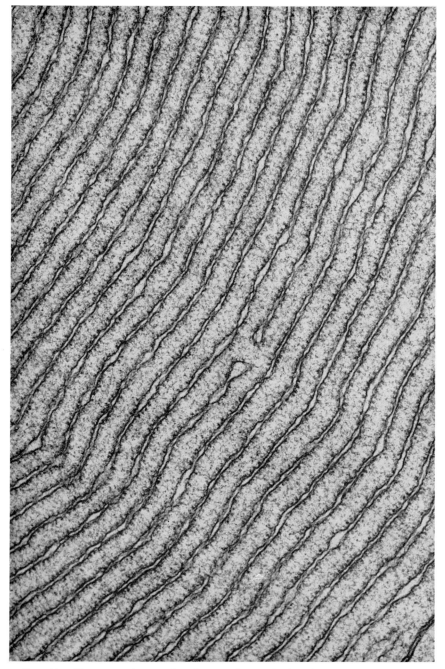

FIG. 11. Electron micrograph of granular endoplasmic reticulum in a cell elaborating a protein-rich secretory product. In such cells the cisternal form of the

results. Warner *et al.* (*173*) have isolated ribosomes from rabbit reticulocytes and have shown that the site of hemoglobin synthesis *in vivo* is
not the single ribosome but clusters of ribosomal particles termed *poly-*
ribosomes. The great majority of the polyribosomes in the active fraction consist of five ribosomal units. High-resolution electron micrographs
often show these associated in a clump, but under favorable conditions
of specimen preparation it can be shown that the ribosomal units are
arranged in linear array about 340 A apart and connected by a slender

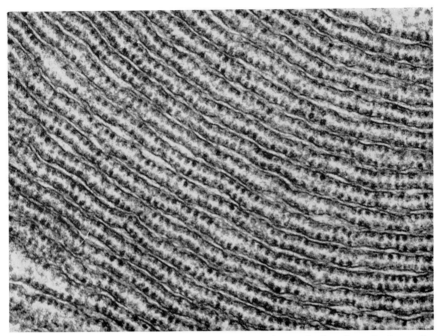

FIG. 12. A parallel array of cisternae of granular endoplasmic reticulum of a
pancreatic acinar cell, showing the ribosomes uniformly distributed along the outer
surfaces of the membranes. There is no evidence of their clustering to form
polyribosomal aggregates. It is instructive to compare the discrete outline and
spherical shape of the ribosomes in this preparation with the smaller size and poorly
defined limits of those in Fig. 11 fixed by another method. This specimen was fixed
in collidine-buffered glutaraldehyde, post-osmicated, and stained with uranyl acetate-
lead citrate. (Courtesy of Dr. S. Ito, Harvard Medical School.)

reticulum usually predominates over the tubular and vesicular elements. The membranes here are well preserved with minimal distortion, the contents of the lumen are
extracted, the ribosomes associated with the outer surface of the membranes are
preserved but are smaller and have less clearly defined limits than those in Fig. 12.
Collidine-buffered osmium tetroxide fixation, Epon embedding, and lead-citrate stain.
(Courtesy of Dr. S. Ito, Harvard Medical School.)

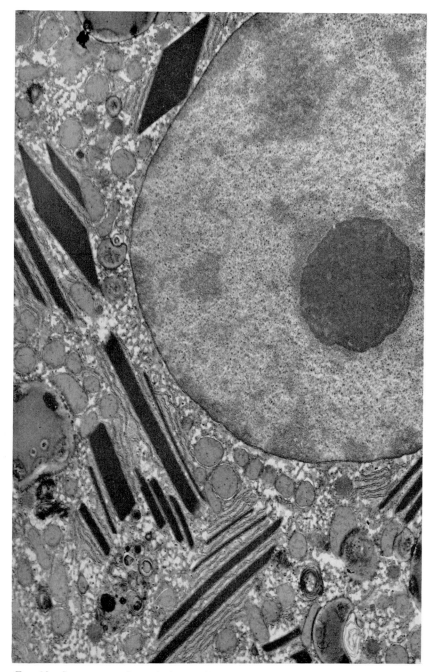

FIG. 13. Low-power view of the nucleus and adjacent cytoplasm of a liver cell
from the salamander *Batrachoseps*. The nucleus shows a compact nucleolus, in which

thread 10 to 15 A units in diameter. These dimensions are consistent with the speculation that the ribosomes in each cluster are held together by a single strand of RNA. It is suggested that this strand may be the messenger RNA carrying the information for assembling the amino acids in hemoglobin (173).

In micrographs of thin tissue sections, the ribosomes associated with the membranes of the reticulum are not always randomly arranged but are often grouped in rosette patterns or short beaded strands. In other

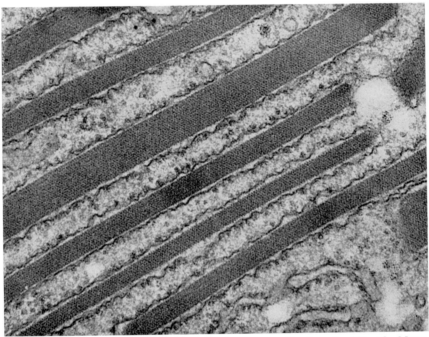

FIG. 14. Crystals of the kind seen at lower magnification in Fig. 13. Macromolecules about 65 A in diameter can be resolved in the crystal lattice. The crystals lie within the lumen of cisternae of the reticulum which have typical ribosomes on the outer surface of their membranes. In this instance a protein product of the cell is sufficiently concentrated by the reticulum to crystallize in its lumen. The nature of the protein has not been determined.

the nucleolonema is scarcely distinguishable. Areas of heterochromatin are represented by irregularly shaped masses of finely granular material associated, for the most part, with the nuclear envelope and nucleolus. The cytoplasm is highly heterogeneous with mitochondria, granular and agranular reticulum, lipid inclusions, and conspicuous protein crystals that develop within the cisternae of the granular endoplasmic reticulum. This specimen was fixed in collidine-buffered glutaraldehyde, postfixed in osmium, embedded in Epon, and stained with uranyl acetate and lead citrate.

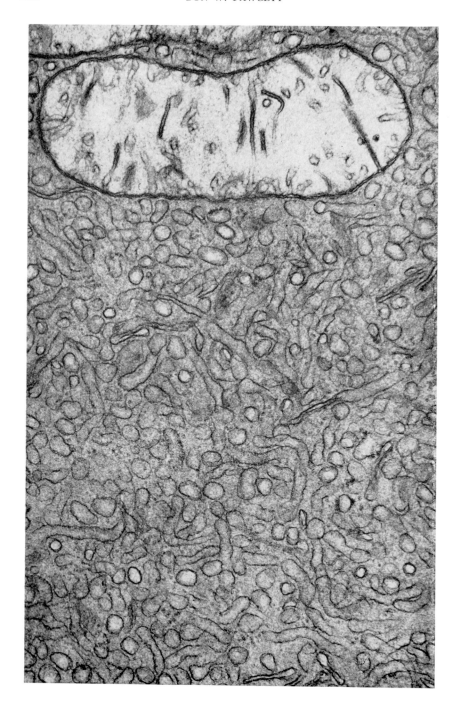

cell types, however, they appear to be distributed individually and uniformly over the membrane surface (Fig. 12). The report that only the pentameric clusters or linear chains of reticulocyte ribosomes are active in hemoglobin synthesis raises the interesting question as to whether, in other cell types, the number of particles involved and the pattern of their association on the membranes is in any way specific for the protein being synthesized. The ribosomes in the acinar cells of the pancreas appear to be individually distributed, yet the reticulum in this organ is very active in synthesis of a variety of digestive enzymes. This suggests that association of ribosomes in clusters of a particular size is not a requirement for synthesis of the pancreatic enzymes as it appears to be for the synthesis of hemoglobin by reticulocytes. One cannot, of course, rule out the possibility that clusters which may have existed in the living pancreas cell are dissociated and redistributed in the course of specimen preparations, but this seems unlikely.

2. AGRANULAR RETICULUM

This term was first applied to aggregations of smooth-surfaced membranes forming the walls of vesicles and flattened saccules in the perikarya of neurons (116). These structures were later identified as the Golgi complex of classic cytology and were thenceforth so designated. The term agranular reticulum was subsequently applied instead, to close-meshed networks of tubules found in the cytoplasm of liver cells in animals refed after a period of fasting (39). The smooth-surfaced tubular elements of these networks were often continuous with typical granular endoplasmic reticulum and at first were considered to be an intermediate stage in the regeneration of granular reticulum which had been depleted during the previous period of fasting. This interpretation had to be abandoned when a well-developed, although somewhat more dispersed, agranular reticulum was found in the livers of normal animals (130). The origin of the agranular reticulum and its relation to the Golgi complex and to the granular reticulum remain to be clarified. For the present it seems reasonable to consider this smooth-surfaced canalicular component of the cytoplasm and the granular reticulum as alternate forms of the same organelle. There are indications, however, that in addition to the presence or absence of associated granules, there

FIG. 15. An area of cytoplasm from an interstitial cell of the mammalian testis, showing a mitochondrion at the top of the figure, and the extensive development of agranular endoplasmic reticulum characteristic of steroid-producing cells. This type of reticulum usually consists of a close-meshed branching and anastomosing system of tubules. Collidine-buffered glutaraldehyde fixation, osmium postfixation, Epon embedding and uranyl acetate-lead citrate stain.

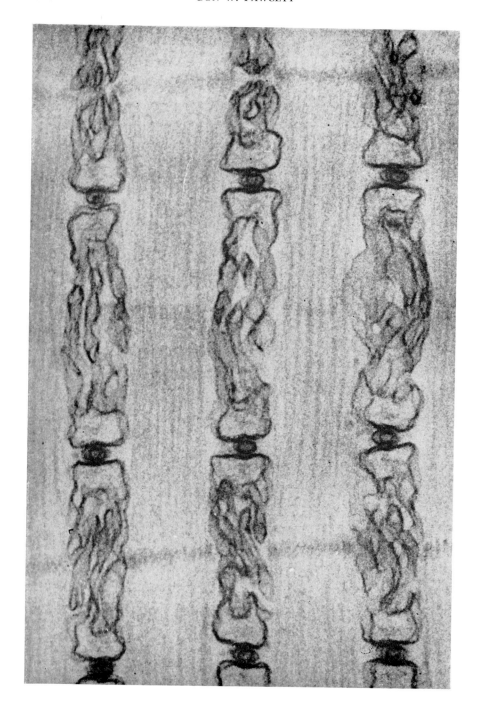

are fundamental differences in the properties of the membranes in the two forms of reticulum. For example, the granular reticulum is easily preserved by routine methods of fixation and dehydration and is extraordinarily resistant to post-mortem autolysis, whereas the agranular reticulum is difficult to preserve in continuity and breaks up rapidly after death of the animal (57).

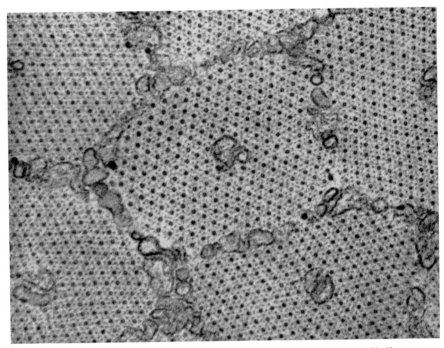

Fig. 17. Cross sections of myofibrils in copepod muscle. The myofibrils are not only surrounded by tubular elements of the sarcoplasmic reticulum but these penetrate into the myofibrils and run longitudinally within their substance. (Courtesy of Dr. W. H. Fahrenbach, Harvard Medical School.)

Fig. 16. High-magnification electron micrograph of the sarcoplasmic reticulum of striated muscle, a specialized form of agranular endoplasmic reticulum. Shown here is the reticulum associated with one sarcomere length of four myofibrils. The smooth-surfaced tubules run longitudinally in the interfibrillar clefts, but terminate in expansions called terminal cisternae that run transversely, or in this case, in the direction perpendicular to the page. Between each pair of terminal cisternae and running parallel to them is a slender intermediate tubule. The two terminal cisternae and the intermediate tubule constitute a "triad" of the reticulum. There are usually two triads to each sarcomere, occurring at the junctions of the A- and I-bands of the myofibrils. Veronal-acetate buffered osmium tetroxide fixation, Epon embedding, and lead hydroxide staining. [From Fawcett and Revel (44a).]

There are several different patterns of organization, different degrees of post-mortem stability and different biochemical functions within the category of agranular reticulum. It is clear, therefore, that the two general classes of reticulum, granular and agranular, will not long suffice for the descriptive purposes of cytologists but there will be need for other more specific designations appropriate to the distinctive patterns of organization and different functional properties of this organelle in various cell types.

The most typical configuration of the agranular reticulum is that found in the liver cell where it forms networks of anastomosing tubules of rather uniform diameter. These occasionally communicate with the Golgi complex and with elements of the granular reticulum, but they only very rarely form smooth-surfaced cisternae and never appear to open onto the cell surface. The function of the agranular reticulum in the liver is not known but it seems likely that it is concerned with the lipid and cholesterol metabolism of the liver cell. Agranular reticulum of similar configuration attains its most spectacular development in cells engaged in the biosynthesis of steroids such as the interstitial cells of the testis (Fig. 15) (22), the cells of the corpus luteum (34, 94, 183), and those of the adrenal cortex. It is also present but less extensively developed in the Meibomian gland (114), the intestinal epithelial cells (165), and the pigment epithelium of the retina (133), cell types not involved in steroid synthesis but nevertheless having an active lipid metabolism.

The sarcoplasmic reticulum of striated muscle (Figs. 16 and 17) must also be regarded as a special form of agranular reticulum (132). It comprises an elaborate system of longitudinal tubules surrounding each myofibril and communicating at regular intervals with transverse elements of larger caliber called *terminal cisternae*. These occur in pairs that run parallel to one another on either side of a third slender tubule to form the so-called *triads* of the sarcoplasmic reticulum (Fig. 16). There is evidence that the membrane of the intermediate element of the triad has properties different from those of the rest of the system (134). The agranular reticulum of muscle consisting of longitudinal sarcotubules and transverse triads comprises an elaborate multicomponent system organized in repeating units that bear a precise topographical relation to the cross-banded pattern of the myofibrils. Its function is clearly unrelated to lipid or steroid metabolism. Instead it is probably concerned with initiation and coordination of contraction. It is thought that some component, possibly the intermediate element of the triads, functions in intracellular impulse conduction, while the other components are involved in distribution of metabolites or in the action of "relaxing factors."

A third kind of agranular reticulum is found in the pseudobranch gland (25), in the chloride cells of fish (124), and in the hydrochloric acid-secreting cells of the amphibian (152) and mammalian (67) stomach. Reticulum of similar appearance is also found in cells of the nephron of euryhaline fish (59). In all of these organs the cells are believed to be engaged in secretion or active transport of ions. In contrast to the forms of agranular reticulum described previously, the tubular elements in these examples communicate freely with the cell surface.

The term granular reticulum is now associated in the minds of most cell biologists with synthesis of protein, but the term agranular reticulum as yet has no such specific functional implications. When its varied morphological patterns and diverse biochemical properties become better known it will probably be found to have a variety of quite different functions.

D. The Golgi Complex

The reticular apparatus discovered in cells in 1898 by Camillo Golgi using silver-impregnation methods, has had a long and controversial history. Its universal occurrence in differentiated cells and the changes observed in its size and position in different phases of cellular activity convinced many that it was an essential cell organelle. A voluminous and contradictory literature accumulated describing its form in virtually all cell types. Because it was difficult to verify its presence in living cells before the development of phase-contrast microscopy, it was regarded by many cytologists as an artifact of the chemical procedures required for its demonstration. This interpretation gained supporters in increasing numbers, and investigative interest in the Golgi complex gradually declined in the 1940's to a very low level.

Phase-contrast and electron microscopic observations have since established the reality of the Golgi complex beyond doubt. At the same time it has been shown that the canalicular form of the organelle revealed in classic Golgi preparations is, in part, artifactitious. The Golgi complex is not a system of anastomosing canals as might have been anticipated from light microscopic images of silver-impregnated specimens but instead, appears to be a heterogeneous assemblage of lamellar systems of membranes and associated minute vesicles and larger vacuoles (Fig. 18). The proportions of these components vary. The most consistent and characteristic is the multilayered array of parallel, smooth-surfaced membranes. These membranes are associated in pairs, and the members of each pair are continuous at the ends of the profile thus delimiting flat cavities. These closed, bilaminar units comprising the

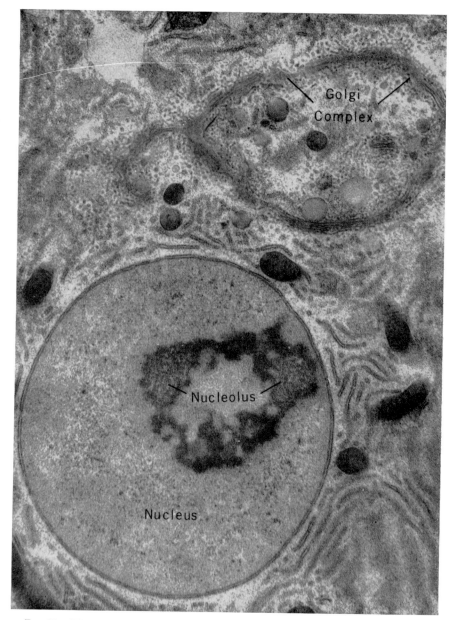

FIG. 18.   Electron micrograph of the nucleus and juxtanuclear Golgi complex of a pancreatic acinar cell. With this method of preparation the nucleoplasm is quite homogeneous, except for the nucleolus which shows a loose-meshed nucleolonema organized around two granular areas of slightly different texture and density (see at ends of lead lines). The Golgi complex appears to be in a relatively inactive phase

lamellar portions of the Golgi complex are similar to the cisternae of
the endoplasmic reticulum in that they are flat, saccular structures piled
one upon the other. They differ, in that they have narrower lumens,
are more closely spaced, and are bounded by smooth-surfaced membranes. It has been established that the parallel membranes at the periphery of the Golgi complex are the site of metal deposition in classic
Golgi preparations. These, therefore, correspond to the *Golgi externum*
while the vesicular and vacuolar components remain essentially unstained and correspond to the *Golgi internum* (28).

Among the many functions that have been attributed to the Golgi
complex, that of segregating and concentrating the product of secretory
cells is the one which has received the most support from electron
microscopic studies. A number of investigations of protein-synthesizing
cells have shown the product accumulating within Golgi vacuoles which,
at first, have a content of low density and later become increasingly
dense and homogeneous as they are transformed into secretion droplets
or granules (*111a, 62a, 43*). Concentration of the products of protein synthesis in the Golgi complex of the pancreatic acinar cell has also been
demonstrated by autoradiographic methods (*18, 174*).

The mechanism by which the protein synthesized in the endoplasmic
reticulum gains access to the Golgi vacuoles is one of the more poorly
understood steps in the intracellular pathway of secretion. It has been
suggested that the small vesicles of the Golgi complex bud off from the
ends of neighboring elements of the endoplasmic reticulum carrying
with them small droplets of fluid containing the cell product in relatively dilute form (*112, 184*). Within the Golgi complex the vesicles are
thought to coalesce into larger vacuoles which concentrate the product
by removing water. Agranular areas of the endoplasmic reticulum in
the vicinity of the Golgi complex have been called "transitional elements" to indicate that they are the source of the small Golgi vesicles and
to suggest the role they may play in transfer of materials between the
ergastoplasmic membranes and the Golgi system (*112, 184*). The view
that there is a flow of smooth-membrane derivatives from the endoplasmic reticulum through transitional elements to the Golgi complex
has recently gained further support from fine structural and cytochemical studies on hepatomas (*36*). It is proposed on the basis of these
observations that the influx of transitional elements not only serves to

with extensive lamellar aggregations of smooth-surfaced membranes around the
periphery and myriad minute vesicles. Vacuoles containing secretory product are few
and small. Veronal-acetate buffered osmium fixation, Epon embedding, and lead-
cacodylate stain.

transfer secretion product from the endoplasmic reticulum to the Golgi complex but maintains the integrity of this organelle in spite of continuous loss of its membrane during intense secretory activity. Such a dynamic state of the cytomembranes is an attractive concept in relation to the activities of secretory cells. However, the implication that the integrity of the Golgi complex depends upon contributions of membrane from the endoplasmic reticulum is not consistent with observations on differentiating cells which suggest that the Golgi complex is present and well developed before the appearance of the endoplasmic reticulum (159), nor does it account for the maintenance of an active Golgi complex in nonsecretory cell types that have little endoplasmic reticulum. An equally strong case could be made for the Golgi complex as a site of membrane synthesis and a reservoir of smooth membrane that might acquire granules and contribute to the enlargement of the endoplasmic reticulum.

The possibility that the Golgi complex may participate in the synthesis as well as the concentration of products rich in carbohydrates has not been ruled out. It plays a prominent part in the formation of the acrosome of spermatozoa. During acrosome formation, the spermatids have a discontinuous and rather poorly developed endoplasmic reticulum, and there is no clear morphological indication of transfer of material from the reticulum to the Golgi complex. Instead, large numbers of small vesicles appear to arise by budding from the ends of the Golgi cisternae. These vesicles acquire a dense content and fuse to form proacrosomal granules which, in turn, coalesce to form the acrosome (16). The development of numerous small vesicles at the expense of the cisternae and their progressive coalescence to form vacuoles that contain the acrosomal substance, represents a rather different process from that proposed for the liver and pancreas. There, the Golgi cisternae are presumed to open up to form large vacuoles and the small vesicles are regarded as a derivative of the endoplasmic reticulum (99).

Much remains to be learned about the role of the Golgi complex in secretory cells, and our ignorance of its function in nonsecretory cells is still more profound. The only successful efforts to isolate and characterize the Golgi complex chemically have been applicable only to the epididymis where the function of the epithelium is in doubt (73). Progress toward an understanding of this important organelle is slow because any organelle which has not yet captured the interest of the biochemist suffers considerable lack of patronage. It is to be hoped that techniques for centrifugal isolation of the intact Golgi complex from liver and pancreas or methods for identification of its contribution to the microsome fraction will soon be found.

E. Mitochondria

From the time of their discovery in 1894 by Altmann until about 1940, mitochondria were mainly of interest to descriptive cytologists. Their function was not known but it was inferred from their universal occurrence that they were of vital importance in cell physiology. Their intimate association with secretion granules and their tendency to be mobilized at sites of intense metabolic activity formed the basis for the speculation that they were probably involved in the secretory and respiratory processes of the cell. There was no indication from light microscopy that they possessed a limiting membrane and the most prevalent conjecture as to their physicochemical nature was in terms of tactoids or coacervates. The actual composition and function of mitochondria could not be ascertained until methods were developed for their centrifugal isolation from cell homogenates (10, 23a). In the decade that followed, a flood of significant biochemical investigations determined their composition (151) and defined the series of cyclic chemical reactions by which they trap, store, and transfer energy (58, 76). The highly ordered, sequential nature of the reactions involved could best be explained by assuming that the participating enzymes were arranged in particular patterns on a structural framework within the mitochondrion. One of the signal achievements of biological electron microscopy was the demonstration in 1952 that the mitochondrion does, in fact, have a highly differentiated internal structure (103, 158). It is now common knowledge that it possesses a continuous outer limiting membrane and an inner membrane which is plicated at intervals to form thin folds or *cristae* that project into the amorphous matrix occupying the interior of the organelle (Fig. 19). Conspicuous granules are irregularly distributed in the matrix between cristae. The mitochondrion is thus composed of two concentric compartments of unequal size; the larger being the cavity occupied by the matrix and limited by the irregular contour of the inner membrane; the smaller, being the narrow space between the inner and outer membranes and its extensions between the leaves of the cristae. Although this basic organizational pattern holds for mitochondria of nearly all cells of vertebrate species there are wide variations in shape, length, number, and orientation of the cristae. In general, the complexity of the internal structure of mitochondria is related to the metabolism of the particular cell type, the cristae being longer and more numerous in those cells with high energy requirements.

Since the discovery of the internal organization of the mitochondrion, investigative effort has been focused upon localization of specific biochemical functions to its several structural components. The soluble

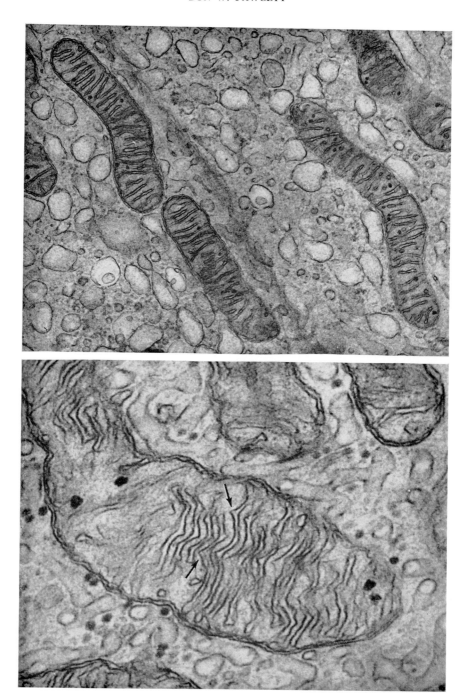

enzymes catalyzing the citric acid cycle are found to be associated with the matrix while the enzymes involved in the highly ordered energy-transport mechanism appear to be associated with the membranous framework of the organelle. The electron microscope has played an indispensable role in the attempts to break up this framework into smaller and smaller morphologically identifiable fragments for the purpose of discovering its ultimate functional unit. It is now believed that the smallest unit of function is an assembly of enzymes and structural protein molecules arranged in a particular pattern on or within the membranes of the cristae. These assemblies are believed to repeat at regular intervals along the membrane. Although this concept is still highly speculative, it has stimulated further examination of mitochondria for possible differences between its membranes and others in the cell, and particularly for visual evidence of periodic substructure within the cristae.

The membranes of the cristae have a tendency to form angles at intervals along their length (138). The angulation often occurs alternately, first on one membrane of a crista and then on the other giving it a zigzag profile (Fig. 20). Other expressions of this tendency may lead to coalescence of neighboring cristae at the sites of their angulation, resulting in a honeycomb pattern of membranes in the mitochondrion. In rare instances, prismatic cristae are formed which are triangular or quadrangular in section. The significance of these angulations is not clear but they would seem to bespeak an underlying structural discontinuity in the molecular organization of the membranes of the mitochondrial cristae that is not present in the outer membrane or in other membranes of the cell.

Not all of the structural components of mitochondria are preserved by the preparative procedures ordinarily used for electron microscopy of thin sections. When negatively stained fragments of isolated mitochondria are examined at high magnification the membranes of the cristae are found to be covered by a profusion of minute particles, roughly spherical in shape and about 85 A in diameter (Fig. 28) (49, 163). These were originally considered to be an integral part of the membranes comprising the leaflets of the cristae, but according to a more recent

FIG. 19. Mitochondria from mouse epididymis showing their characteristic elongated form with cristae oriented perpendicular to the limiting membrane and dense granules in the intercristal matrix.

FIG. 20. Mitochondrion showing periodic angulations of the membranes of the cristae (see at arrows) giving them a zigzag course. The significance of this common tendency for angulation of the membranes of the cristae is not known. It is not seen in other membranes of the cell. (Courtesy of Dr. C. W. Philpott, Harvard College.)

interpretation the particles are outside of the membrane and are attached to it by slender stalks 40–50 A long (*163*). They appear to be
completely destroyed by all of the conventional fixatives employed for
electron microscopy, including osmium tetroxide. Thus no trace of them
is seen in micrographs of thin sections even though the membranes of
the cristae are well preserved. The particles are present on the inner
limiting membrane of the mitochondrion as well as on the cristae, but
they are absent from the outer membrane and have not been found on
other biological membranes examined to date. It has been suggested
that these particles are fixed enzyme complexes and as such may be the
morphological units whose arrangement establishes the appropriate
spatial relationships for the enzymes of oxidative phosphorylation.

   There has been a tendency to attribute to all mitochondria the same
enzymic activities that are so well established for those of the liver.
There is accumulating a considerable body of morphological and histochemical evidence for biochemical heterogeneity among mitochondria
from different sources. This comes as no great surprise to cytologists who
have long been more aware of the organ-specific differences in the structure of mitochondria than have biochemists who are obliged to work
with a more limited variety of organs which have relatively homogeneous
cell populations. The mitochondria of the proximal and distal convolu-
tions of the amphibian nephron have recently been found to differ in
their fine structure and histochemical staining reactions (*70*). They also
vary according to the environmental conditions. In freshly collected
summer frogs, cytochrome oxidase can be demonstrated in mitochondria
of both the proximal and the distal convolution. However, in winter
frogs or in summer frogs fasted 10 days or longer, the enzyme is no longer
demonstrable histochemically in the proximal tubule whereas it remains
unchanged in the distal convolution. Associated with the loss of enzymic
activity in the proximal tubule there are striking changes in form of the
mitochondria, particularly in the orientation of their cristae (*69*).

   Equally gratifying to morphologists has been the impressive array of
evidence for the dependence of optimal biochemical function on the
structural integrity of the mitochondrion. Numerous biochemical investigations carried out with fine structural correlation have shown
that mitochondrial swelling *in vitro* is associated with uncoupling of
oxidation from phosphorylation (*77*). An intriguing clinical example of
the unity of structure and function in mitochondria has recently been
reported (*85*). A woman of 35 with severe hypermetabolism of many
years duration, unrelieved by subtotal thyroidectomy and antithyroid
drugs, was found upon biochemical study of her isolated mitochondria,
to have a loosely coupled state of oxidative phosphorylation. Electron

microscopic studies revealed increased numbers of mitochondria, with many exhibiting bizarre and abnormal internal structure. It was concluded that the hypermetabolic state of this patient was caused by a defect in mitochondrial enzyme organization. This first clinical instance of a disease apparently resulting from structural and functional disorder of a cell organelle may be a harbinger of a new era in pathology when many metabolic disturbances will be interpretable in terms of specific structural defects at the subcellular level of organization.

III. Modern Methods for Analysis of Cell Structure

It has been our objective in the first section of this chapter to present the structure of the major cell organelles in sufficient detail to provide a preliminary orientation for the novice in the field of biological ultrastructure. It is hoped that such a reader will also have gained an appreciation of the extraordinary progress which the electron microscope has made possible in our understanding of the cell. The initial phases of exploitation of this instrument for descriptive histology and cytology appear to be drawing to a close. Its great potentialities for the future lie in its application to experimental cell research; in further correlation of ultrastructural and chemical analysis; in the development of methods for microscopic identification of specific substances, and for the localization of metabolic events within cells and tissues. In the following section we consider some current problems of specimen preparation and a few of the modern methods that are rapidly extending the usefulness of electron microscopy in promising new directions.

A. Specimen Preparation for Routine Descriptive Histology and Cytology

The primary objective of the biological electron microscopist, and one most difficult to attain, is the preservation of near normal structure during specimen preparation. Although this is an old and familiar problem for the histologist, its difficulties have been compounded by the forward leap in resolution achieved with the change from the light to the electron microscope. Since living cells cannot be examined in high vacuum, it is necessary to kill, dehydrate, embed, and section in order to obtain a preparation suitable for examination. It is a cruel paradox that in seeking to satisfy our curiosity about the structural organization of living matter we must destroy, at the outset, those vital properties of protoplasm which we desire most to understand. At best we deal with the lifeless remnants of cells and we have an imperative need to know to what extent the residual structure we observe resembles that which prevailed in life. At the level of the light microscope, comparing the image of the fixed cell with the appearance of the living cell examined under phase contrast was a possibility. If the components visible in the living cell were retained after fixation without appreciable distortion of size or shape, the preservation was considered to be good. No corresponding criterion is available for judging the adequacy of fixation for the electron microscope. Furthermore, experience has shown that the great majority of the time-honored fixatives which meet this challenge, actually produce a precipitation of proteins which is intolerably coarse when viewed under the electron microscope. The increased resolution of this instrument has set such exacting requirements for chemical fixation that very few of the scores of empirical mixtures in the armamentarium of the classic cytologist continue to be useful.

1. Procedures for Fixation and Dehydration

Of all the traditional fixing agents, only osmium tetroxide (*102*) and osmium-dichromate mixtures (*53*) have been successfully adapted to meet the new standards imposed by the great resolving power of the electron microscope. Both consistently permit highly magnified images sufficiently free of distortions and coagulation artifacts to be accepted as reasonably faithful representations of the structure of the living cell. The buffered 1 or 2% osmium is more widely used, possibly because it yields images of better contrast than the osmium-dichromate mixture. To these standard fixatives have been added three others that were not used for light microscopy: potassium permanganate (*82*), acrolein (*83*), and glutaraldehyde (*150*). Permangate has been extensively used for the study of membranous components of cells but it destroys, or fails to preserve, many other constituents and is therefore of limited use as a general fixative. Acrolein and glutaraldehyde have the advantage of rapid penetration of relatively large pieces of tissue. They have no staining action and are usually followed by a period of postfixation in buffered osmium tetroxide. Treatment with either of these agents gives the tissue a firm consistency which makes it possible to cut the specimen into small blocks prior to osmium postfixation with minimal mechanical damage. Many of the distortions introduced by mincing fresh tissue are thus avoided and normal tissue interrelations are preserved to a degree rarely seen in tissues fixed directly in osmium. The quality of cytological preservation after glutaraldehyde is superior to that obtained with acrolein. With it, there appears to be a retention of components of the cytoplasmic matrix that are ordinarily extracted by the usual buffered osmium. Glutaraldehyde has not been applied long enough or to a wide enough variety of biological materials to permit a full appraisal of its usefulness, but when employed in combination with osmium it appears to have some real advantages over other fixatives now in general use.

The importance of the control of pH during fixation to the range 7.2–7.6 has been thoroughly established (*102*). The veronal-acetate buffering system formerly in routine use for this purpose has gradually been supplanted by others which are reputed to improve, in minor respects, the quality of preservation. Among these, chromate-dichromate (*29*), S-collidine (*9*), and phosphate (*88a*) buffers are the ones most commonly used. Earlier concern over the tonicity of the fixative appears to have been exaggerated. While it is reasonable to use balanced salt solution as the vehicle for the fixative or to add polyvinylpyrilodone (*32*) or sucrose (*20*), others omit these osmotically active ingredients with apparent impunity. The need for such precautions evidently varies with the material being studied.

Considerable importance is attributed to measures for minimizing the effects of anoxia and for preventing post-mortem alterations in fine structure by rapid fixation. It is common practice simply to excise the tissue immediately after death or take it from a living anaesthetized animal and cut it into small blocks while immersed in a few drops of cold fixative. Some, however, prefer to initiate fixation *in situ* by injecting the solution of osmium tetroxide into a hollow viscus, or by flooding the exposed organ in the anaesthetized living animal (*116, 122, 179*). Others recommend topical application of hyaluronidase before exposure to the fixative in order to facilitate its penetration (*118*). In all of these procedures the tissue is excised after a suitable interval of prefixation *in situ,* and is immersed in fresh cold fixative for an additional period of up to 2 hours. These measures unquestionably result in improved preservation of some tissues. For example, the retention of the patency of the lumen of the renal proximal convoluted tubule seems to depend upon preliminary *in situ* fixation of the kidney exposed in a living animal (*121, 140*). The gains from such precautions are especially obvious in the nervous system which is exceptionally sensitive to oxygen deprivation and unusually susceptible to mechanical damage in handling. In small laboratory animals, a still greater degree of success with this difficult material can be assured by vascular perfusion with the osmium tetroxide fixative (*117*). This procedure requires specialized equipment and considerable operative skill to carry out the dissection and cannulation with dispatch. The chest is opened while the anaesthetized animal is maintained on artificial respiration. After slow intracardiac injection of sodium nitrite as a vasodilator, the aorta is cannulated through the left ventricle. Perfusion of a small volume of warm balanced salt solu-

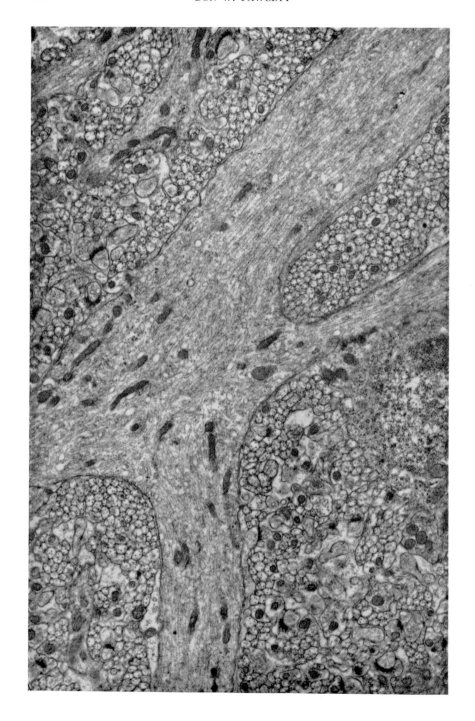

tion is followed by a large volume (100–150 ml) of chilled osmium tetroxide fixative containing added calcium. The perfusion extends over a period of 20–40 minutes. The brain is then excised, sliced, and small blocks are cut from the desired areas which can easily be identified under a dissecting microscope. These blocks are further hardened by immersion in fresh fixative. Under optimal conditions uniform fixation of nearly the entire central nervous system is achieved (Fig. 21). This permits accurate selection of specific areas and analysis of undisturbed relations between cells with a degree of validity not possible with other methods of fixation. The tissue is free of distortions, open spaces, swollen myelin sheaths, dark and light cells, and other common artifacts that have long frustrated efforts to apply the electron microscope to the nervous system.

The excellent preservation achieved by perfusion is not limited to the central nervous system but there is evidently less to be gained by applying this elaborate and rather costly procedure to organs more tolerant of anoxia and less subject to mechanical damage in preparation. Recent systematic studies of the fine structural alterations in cells after death have revealed that the membranous organelles possess a surprising degree of stability (66). The results of these studies suggest that for many tissues there may be less urgency for immediate fixation than is commonly assumed (Fig. 22 and 23). Excised liver and kidney, after 3 hours at room temperature, showed cytological structure scarcely distinguishable from that of blocks fixed immediately. At later time intervals, 4 to 6 hours, the plasmalemma and agranular reticulum exhibited early regressive changes and the mitochondria were rounded up. After 10 hours the mitochondria were swollen and distinctly altered in their internal structure but nevertheless retained 50% of their original succinoxidase activity. The granular endoplasmic reticulum was found to be particularly stable, remaining largely intact after 48 hours when the deterioration of mitochondria and other membranous structures was far advanced.

It is evident that many of the distortions earlier attributed to delayed fixation were not an accurate reflection of the condition of the tissue at the time of fixation but were the results of a post-mortem increase in

---

FIG. 21. A low-magnification electron micrograph of an area of the molecular layer of the cerebellum. A primary dendrite of a Purkinje cell extends diagonally across the figure. Around it are a multitude of cross sections of small axons of granule cells. This figure exemplifies the uniform good preservation, absence of free space, and freedom from distortion which can be achieved by fixation of the nervous system by perfusion of buffered osmium followed by Epon embedding. [Courtesy of Dr. Sanford Palay, Harvard Medical School, from Palay et al. (117).]

their susceptibility to the polymerization damage associated with methacrylate embedding. When these artifacts are eliminated by Epon embedding the tissue is found to retain a near normal appearance for some time after death. These observations should not constitute an excuse for delay where prompt fixation is possible. They do, however, remove some of the sense of urgency that may lead the inexperienced to inflict more damage out of haste than would occur from autolytic changes in

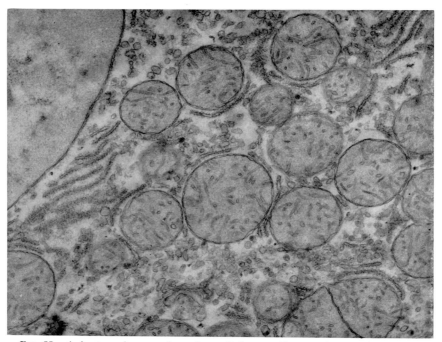

Fig. 22. A juxtanuclear portion of a cell from a liver excised from the animal and left for 10 hours at room temperature. The mitochondria are rounded up but have essentially normal internal structure. The granular and agranular reticulum are largely intact. The membranous organelles are thus more stable after death than commonly supposed. Collidine-buffered osmium fixation followed by Epon embedding. (Courtesy of Dr. S. Ito, Harvard Medical School.)

the time saved. But more importantly, these results offer the encouraging prospect of fruitful applications of electron microscopy to surgical pathology and the likelihood that useful information about the natural history of disease may even be retrieved from autopsy material.

Views have changed greatly with respect to washing after osmium fixation and the correct procedure for dehydration. Washing with distilled water, buffer solution, or saline after fixation was formerly common practice and very gradual dehydration was thought to be essential. Special devices were invented to accomplish dehydration over a period of several hours without abrupt change in concentration of the alcohol or acetone. Washing after veronal-osmium fixation is now regarded as a potentially damaging procedure, and is usually omitted (*183a*). Slow dehydration at room temperature has now been replaced in many laboratories by rapid dehydration with very cold ethanol or methanol, proceeding from 60 through 80 to 95% in a few minutes,

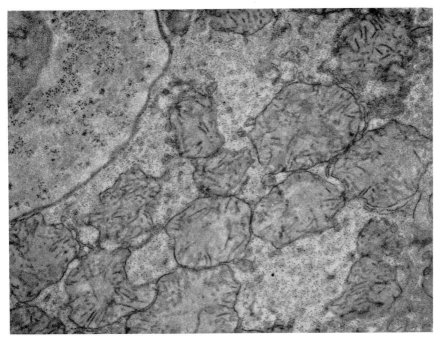

FIG. 23. A corresponding area of a cell from a liver excised and left 14 days at 6°C. The mitochondria are irregularly distorted in shape but still retain their cristae and matrix. The agranular reticulum has fragmented and disappeared but tubular and cisternal profiles of granular reticulum persist. The cytoplasmic matrix contains abundant free ribosomes. (Courtesy of Dr. S. Ito, Harvard Medical School.)

followed by gradual warming to room temperature in 95% alcohol, and a sojourn of 2 hours or more in absolute alcohol (*66*).

2. EMBEDDING MEDIUM

The first embedding media that had a consistency permitting sucessful cutting of ultrathin sections were acrylic plastics (*96*). For nearly 10 years after their introduction, mixtures of *n*-butyl and methyl methacrylates were used almost exclusively in specimen preparation for thin sectioning, usually in a proportion of 8:2, but other mixtures were substituted as the need for harder or softer blocks arose. In the hands of experienced users this method of embedding yielded excellent results and was the basis for many of the classic early studies of normal tissue ultrastructure. It had the serious disadvantage, however, that some tissues were seriously disrupted or distorted during polymerization of the plastic. This damage could be controlled, in part, by conditions favoring rapid polymerization, such as high concentrations of catalyst, high temperature, and a nitrogen atmosphere (92). Prepolymerization before introducing the tissue and addition of uranyl nitrate (172) were also partially successful in minimizing this source of artifact, but the results continued to be highly variable and unpredictable. When methacrylate sections were subjected to heat in the electron beam of the microscope, a portion of the plastic sublimed. Although this resulted in improved contrast in the image, it also permitted membranes to collapse and other components to be displaced. Such distortions could be avoided by coating the section with carbon or with a thin layer of methacrylate so that it was sandwiched between protective films (176). These additional steps in specimen preparation were time consuming and provided increased opportunities for technical errors.

The most important contributions to the recent general improvement in the quality of biological electron microscopy have been the introduction of Araldite (57) and of Epon (51, 84) as embedding media. The use of these and related epoxy resins has largely eliminated artifacts and distortions associated with polymerization and subsequent sublimation of acrylic plastics in the electron beam. Although these materials, which do not sublime in the microscope, yield images of lower contrast than methacrylate, this has been offset by the concurrent development of heavy metal staining procedures (vide infra). The great stability of epoxy resins eliminates the need for supporting sections on Formvar or celloidin films. Carbon coating and sandwiching techniques are usually unnecessary. Therefore, thicker sections can be used and, since the full thickness of the preparation contributes to the image, better contrast and richer detail can be achieved.

The variety of available embedding media continues to increase with the addition of the polyester, *Vestopal* (72), the water-soluble epoxys, *Aquon* (55), *Durcupan* (160), and *Maraglas* (52), and sundry other related preparations. With the exception of the water-soluble epoxy resins which may be especially desirable in relation to certain histochemical reactions, the others appear to have no great advantage over Epon. It is interesting that electron microscopy in its first decade and a half has developed a greater diversity of embedding materials than was available in the previous 80 years for light microscopy.

3. MICROTOMY AND STAINING

The principles of microtomy are the subject of a separate chapter and will not be considered here except to comment that the cutting of adequately thin sections, free of compression, chatter, furrowing, or general roughening of the surface, is the most challenging part of specimen preparation and possibly the most frequent obstacle to early success in biological electron microscopy. Failures in this step often produce mottling, distortions, and lack of clear definition in the electron micrographs, that are erroneously blamed upon earlier steps of specimen preparation. The newer epoxy-embedding media demand an especially high order of patience and skill in microtomy for they are very much more difficult to section than is methacrylate. Their widespread use places a high premium upon skill in the breaking of plate glass for use as knives. A number of different methods and mechanical devices have been developed to facilitate this important step in preparative technique and to make it possible to break knives with straight edges free of imperfections (1, 168, 180). Glass-cutting edges are rapidly dulled by these materials and relatively few sections can be obtained from a given part of the knife edge before the sections begin to lose the smooth, unroughened surface that is essential for clean staining and for micrographs of good quality. The knife must, therefore, be moved frequently to expose a fresh cutting surface to the block. To conserve the edge at the new site, the block face must be accurately realigned parallel to the cutting edge so that the least possible number of trimming passes will be made before useful sections of the full block face are obtained. A good diamond knife (48a) can save much time in the cutting of epoxy embeddings. In spite of the high initial cost this would be the cutting edge of choice if the makers of diamond knives could achieve a higher degree of reproducibility in their sharpening procedures. An occasional excellent knife will perform well for a year or more but an unfortunately high proportion of diamond knives have poor cutting properties from the outset and this may make the expense prohibitive.

The development of procedures for staining sections has brought great improvement in results by enabling the microscopist to obtain images of adequate contrast from thinner sections. The staining is usually accomplished by exposure of the sections to solutions of heavy metal salts. The metal ions form complexes with certain components of cells thereby substantially increasing the density of their image in electron micrographs. In most instances the staining has little chemical specificity but enhances the contrast of such varied components as membranes, glycogen, and ribosomes. A large selection of methods are available and the number is rapidly increasing. Those now used most widely are solutions of lead hydroxide (*177*), lead cacodylate (*68*), lead tartrate (*88a*), and lead citrate (*139*). All of these produce satisfactory results and the choice among them depends largely on which is most stable and free of precipitates. The lead citrate solution has the advantage of remaining stable for several months whereas the others often lose their staining properties after a few days or weeks.

Although the novice is inclined to blame his initial lack of success upon his instrument, the microscopist of greater experience recognizes that the fault usually lies in the specimen and seldom feels limited by the performance of his microscope. In spite of the impressive advances that have been made, the principal challenge and the key to success in the electron microscopy of thin tissue sections still lies in the preparation of the specimen. This simply cannot be delegated. The investigator who does not at some time become personally involved in this important aspect of the work is not destined to succeed, for he can neither train a technician nor advise one as to the probable cause of failure. Nor can he correctly interpret the electron micrographs obtained unless he has had experience with all of the technical procedures.

There has been steady progress in the resolving power of the electron microscope but the great forward strides in biological electron microscopy in the recent past are not attributable to improvements in performance of the instrument so much as they are to the remarkably rapid concurrent advances in methods of specimen preparation. It is in this area that we may expect the major advances in the years immediately ahead. A few years ago if one considered the number of steps that could fail in the elaborate process of specimen preparation and microscopy, the chances of success seemed slight indeed. The number of excellent micrographs obtained was, in fact, very small in proportion to the time, material, and energy expended. The reproducibility of results was so poor that the validity of findings in experimental investigations which involved comparison of tissue from treated and control animals was always in doubt. Moreover, in interpretation of the micrographs it was often difficult to distinguish between tissue effects of the experimental treatment and distortions introduced by the preparative procedures. The avoidance of artifact occupied far more of the investigator's attention than the biological problem. The situation now is completely changed. The improvements in fixatives, the simplification of tissue processing, the introduction of embedding media free of distortion, and the development of stains to enhance the contrast of the image have vastly improved the reproducibility of the methods and have made it possible to obtain micrographs of good quality in large numbers consistently.

B. Localization of Enzymes at the Subcellular Level

The efforts of functionally oriented morphologists to discover the localization of specific components of tissues by means of histochemical staining reactions have been attended by remarkable success in the past decade. This approach has made significant contributions to our understanding of the histophysiology of complex organs with heterogeneous cell populations—contributions that could not have come from a biochemical approach which has as its first step the destruction, by homogenization, of the distinctive histological topography which is essential to normal function. However, throughout the early part of this period of rapid evolution of histochemical techniques for use with the light microscope, there was great difficulty in obtaining reaction products of sufficient intensity to be clearly visualized, and serious problems of diffusion and nonspecific adsorption of the colored end products. These potential sources of failure left persistent uncertainties as to the specificity of the methods and the validity of the localizations revealed. Ingenious means were found to overcome most of these obstacles, and the accuracy of localization was gradually extended from the tissue down to the cellular level.

In undertaking to adapt these methods for use at the electron microscope level, the difficulties are compounded. The higher resolution of the electron microscope renders intolerable, distortions of cell structure that are scarcely detectable with the light microscope. The limited range of available fixatives imposes severe restrictions on the development of methods for enzymic cytochemistry. The most effective fixatives for preservation of fine structure often inactivate enzymes. If the reactions are to be carried out on blocks of fresh tissue and these subsequently processed for thin sectioning, the reagents must be soluble enough to diffuse into the tissue block, and incubation must be brief to minimize deterioration of fine structure. The necessity for dehydration and embedding in acrylic plastics or epoxy resins imposes the further requirement that the end products of the histochemical reaction be stable to organic solvents. Finally, the requirement of sections a hundredth the thickness of those ordinarily used for histological procedures reduces the amount of the chemical substance or reaction product in the section to levels so low that it may be difficult to demonstrate convincingly in micrographs. To the conservative, the numerous obstacles to successful adaptation of histochemical methods for electron microscopy might well seem so insurmountable as to discourage efforts along these lines. Fortunately, however, there have been investigators of more optimistic nature who were willing to accept the necessary compromise between faithful preservation of fine structure and meaningful localization of function. As a result, development of histochemical methods for use with the electron microscope has progressed far more rapidly than would have been predicted from a consideration of the difficulties involved.

Most of the metal salt techniques used for demonstration of hydrolases in histochemistry for the light microscope have been modified for

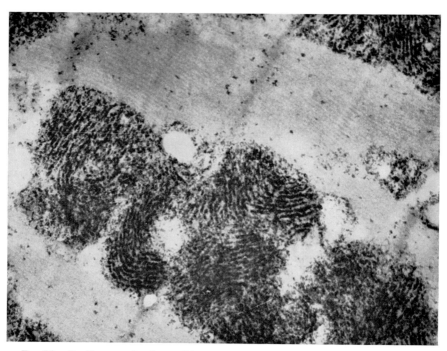

FIG. 24. Cardiac muscle of an albino rat in which the sites of an enzyme splitting glucose-1-phosphate have been localized to the mitochondria. The reaction product, insoluble crystals of lead phosphate, have been deposited on the cristae of the mitochondria. [From Mochizuki *et al.* (*90a*).]

use with the electron microscope. Among the pioneering efforts of this kind was the early adaptation of the Gomori method for alkaline and acid phosphatase for use after brief osmium fixation (*154*). Although reasonably good localization was achieved, the method was applicable only to a few tissues having particularly high activity, for only 5–20% of the original activity is retained after even brief osmium fixation (*98*). Certain improvements in technique permitted Mölbert *et al.* (*91*) to obtain excellent localization of alkaline phosphatase to the brush border and basal labyrinth of renal tubules and to the endothelial cell membranes of the adjacent peritubular capillaries. The acid phosphatase of hepatic cells has been found to reside in certain peribiliary dense bodies that seem to correspond to the lysosomes isolated from cell fractions by de Duve and co-workers (*36, 64*). Methods have also been reported, localizing glucose-1-phosphatase to the cristae of mitochondria (Fig. 24) (*90a*) and ATPase to the Z-band of striated muscle (Fig. 25) (*183b*).

Fig. 25. Enzymic localization of an adenosine triphosphatase at the Z-band of flight muscle from *Phormia regina*. It is of interest that the M-band which was the site of localization of the reaction product in the histochemical method for cholinesterase in Fig. 26, is entirely unstained by this reaction for ATPase. (Courtesy of Dr. H. Zebe and Dr. H. Falk, Zoologisches und Botanisches Institut der Universität Heidelberg.)

In addition to these partially successful demonstrations of the non-specific phosphomonoesterases, a method for the enzyme hydrolyzing adenosine triphosphate (ATP) (*171*) has been modified for localizing this and other nucleoside phosphatases (*99*). Surprisingly precise intracellular localizations and excellent preservation of fine structural detail have been achieved by fixing cryostat frozen sections in formalin, then incubating them in a mixture of specific substrate and trapping agent, followed by osmium postfixation, embedding, and sectioning. With this improved method, the plasma membrane of a wide variety of cells is found to hydrolyze all of the nucleoside mono-, di-, and triphosphates tested. A narrower range of substrate specificities was found in the endoplasmic reticulum where only the diphosphates of guanosine, inosine, and uridine are hydrolyzed at appreciable rates. As might be expected, the nuclear envelope shows the same reactions as the reticulum. The Golgi complex shares the capacity of the endoplasmic reticulum to cleave these substrates and the diphosphates of adenosine and cytidine in addition. In all of these preparations the enzymic activity appears to reside in the membranes rather than in the lumen of the organelles. Although the function of these nucleoside phosphatases in cell metabolism is largely unknown, their localization at the subcellular level may stimulate speculations that can be tested by experiment. Furthermore, the capacity of these reactions to distinguish between the several categories of cellular membranes may prove useful in establishing the identity or ontogenetic relationships of unusual configurations of membranes that might otherwise be difficult to classify.

Useful contrast and localization in electron micrographs can also be attained by using as histochemical agents, certain high molecular weight, insoluble, nonmetallic organic compounds. Thus with suitable modification, the azo dye methods which have proved so useful at the level of the light microscope can also be used for the electron microscope. Sites of succinic dehydrogenase have been demonstrated by several authors with the formazans of tetrazolium compounds (5, 153). A diazo reagent, hexazonium pararosaniline, has been developed which couples with phenolic compounds to produce a deeply colored azo dye, useful in both light and electron microscopy (79). This reagent has not yet been widely used but is said to produce dense crystals no larger than 25 A in size and is therefore capable of yielding localization of enzymic activity with a resolution of about 100 A. Using this diazonium compound and α-naphthyl acetate as substrate, Lehrer and Ornstein (79) have demonstrated cholinesterase activity extracellularly in the myoneural junction between the plasmalemma of the terminal axon and the plasmalemma of the muscle cell. The density of the azo dye deposits is not intense enough to be easily distinguished from other densities resulting from the osmium postfixation employed. The purely extracellular location of the reaction products raises some doubt as to the validity of the localization. Barrnett (6), studying the myoneural junction with thiolacetic acid as substrate and lead nitrate as the capturing agent, found the enzyme associated with the plasma membrane of the axon, the junctional folds of the muscle cell, in the space between the two, and in vesicular structures within the terminal axoplasm.

In an earlier study on the sites of enzymic hydrolysis of thiolacetic acid in the presence of lead ions, Barnett and Palade (7) described a discrete and fine-grained deposit of lead sulfide in the M-band of the myofibrils (Fig. 26). Evidence for the enzymic nature of this reaction was presented, and the suggestion was advanced that it might be detecting the "myosin cholinesterase" which is reported to account for ap-

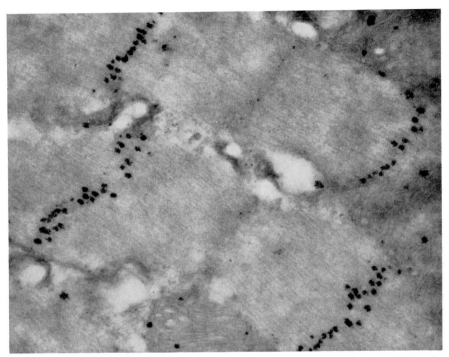

FIG. 26. A section of diaphragmatic muscle incubated in a solution of thiolacetic acid in the presence of lead ions. An enzyme presumed to be cholinesterase has caused hydrolysis of the thiolacetic acid, resulting in deposition of lead sulfide on the myosin filaments at the M-band. [From Barnett and Palade (7a).]

proximately half of the cholinesterase activity of muscle. Although the exact nature of the enzyme demonstrated is in doubt and its physiological significance conjectural, nevertheless, from the point of view of sharpness of localization this work represents one of the more successful histochemical procedures for use with the electron microscope reported to date.

C. Identification of the Nucleoproteins of Cells

Electron microscopic studies of nuclear organization have thus far lagged behind analysis of cytoplasmic components, and there has been considerable uncertainty as to whether the current methods of fixation were adequate for preservation of the nucleic acid protein complexes that comprise the functionally important constituents of the nucleus. To approach this primary problem, Huxley and Zubay (65) studied methods of fixation and staining on a test material consisting of oriented fibers of extracted nucleohistone which had been well characterized by chemical and x-ray diffraction analyses. This material was fixed, embedded, and sectioned as in the preparation of tissues, and stained by methods expected to enhance the contrast of nucleic acid complexes. The orientation of the fibers was well preserved by buffered osmium tetroxide containing added calcium and they were strongly stained by 2% aqueous uranyl acetate. When similar procedures were applied to tissues, an intense preferential staining of the DNA-containing regions of the nucleus resulted. Although the use of uranyl acetate has proven to be highly useful for the general purpose of enhancing contrast of both RNA and DNA complexes in cells, it cannot be regarded as a specific stain and the degree of its selectivity cannot be fully evaluated in tissue wherein other constituents have been blackened by fixation with osmium tetroxide.

A different approach to the same problem has been taken by Watson and Aldridge (178) who have developed a method which takes advantage of the relatively high specificity of trivalent indium for nucleic acid phosphate. To minimize the contrast of non-nucleic acid components of cells an organic fixative, acrolein, is used. Potentially reactive groups in the tissue, other than nucleic acid phosphate, are blocked by acetylation. After dehydration the tissue is stained *en bloc* with a solution of indium trichloride in acetone, then embedded in cross-linked methacrylate, and sectioned. Nucleic acid-containing structures have considerable density while other parts of the cells are unstained. When properly carried out this method appears to have a fairly high degree of specificity.

Identification of cell components by their digestion with specific enzymes has been the basis of several classic cytochemical procedures. The abolition of the Feulgen staining reaction by pretreatment with deoxyribonuclease, and the elimination of cytoplasmic basophilia with ribonuclease have been widely used, standard methods for the light microscopic localization of DNA and RNA, respectively. For electron microscopy, small blocks of tissue previously fixed in cold, buffered formalin can be subjected to nuclease digestion and later embedded in Epon and stained with uranyl acetate (166, 167). Uneven or inadequate penetration of the enzymes into blocks of tissue makes for variable results. The development of water-soluble embedding materials has made it possible to adapt the nuclease digestion procedures for use on the thin sections rather than tissue blocks (74, 75). In thin sections of material embedded in glycol methacrylate there is a rapid and specific digestion of nucleic acid protein complexes with ribonuclease and deoxyribonuclease. Selective staining of nucleoproteins with uranyl or indium used in combination with identification by specific enzyme digestion should prove useful in a wide range of biological problems.

D. Immunohistochemistry at the Ultrastructural Level

Few advances in methods have contributed so much to our understanding of the cellular basis of immunity and hypersensitivity as has the ingenious technique of employing fluorescein-labeled antibodies as sensitive and specific histochemical reagents for the microscopic localization of antigenic macromolecules (24, 86, 87). It is not surprising therefore that there would be vigorous efforts to devise an electron-opaque label for antibody in order to extend this method to localization at the subcellular level. Singer (157) described a method for the conjugation of ferritin to antibody to serve as a marker for detection of the sites of antibody-antigen interaction. For its application to tissues that are to be studied in thin sections, it was necessary to devise means of fixation and subsequent processing that would preserve both the fine structure of the tissue and the antigenicity of the components to be localized, and, at the same time, render the cell permeable to the large antibody-ferritin conjugate. These difficult requirements have been fulfilled in a procedure developed by Rifkind et al. (141, 142) which involves brief fixation in buffered formalin followed by freezing and thawing to permit access of the labeled reagent to the interior of the cells and subsequent exposure to the ferritin-conjugated antibody. The unreacted ferritin complex is then removed by washing and the tissue is fixed in osmium and embedded in Epon. Employing this approach, intracellular globulin of a transplantable plasma cell tumor has been localized by finding the dense particles of ferritin, in electron micrographs, associated with aggregates of moderately dense material within the cisternae of the endoplasmic reticulum and in the lumen of lamellar elements of the Golgi complex (92a). The method has also been applied to studies of viruses and experimental renal disease (2) and promises, in the future, to be an effective histochemical means of identifying and localizing various normal and abnormal products of cells.

E. Autoradiography with the Electron Microscope

When a low-energy β-emitter such as tritium is used for autoradiography with paraffin-embedded sections to be read by light microscopy, a resolution of the order of 1 μ is the best that can be expected. Theoretically, the use of thinner sections and thinner emulsions should

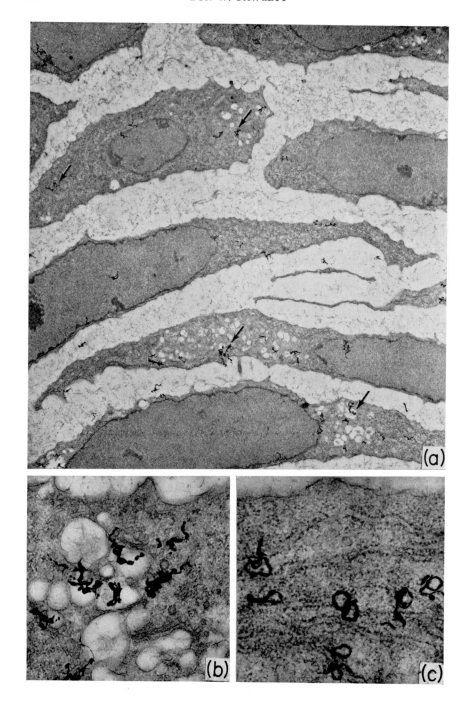

result in improved resolution. The first exploratory efforts at combining electron microscopy and autoradiography were those of Liquier-Milward (80) on tumor cell nuclei labeled with cobalt-60; O'Brien and George (100) on yeast cells labeled with polonium-210; and Van Tübergen's (169) labeling of bacteria with tritium. The resolution achieved in these early studies was not significantly better than could be obtained with the light microscope. The great potentialities of the method for localizing metabolic events within animal cells did not become apparent until Caro (18) used it to trace tritium-labeled leucine through the intracellular pathways of the pancreatic cell to the final secretory product. At early time intervals after administration, the label was localized over the ergastoplasm near the cell base where, presumably, leucine was being incorporated into the newly synthesized specific proteins of the pancreatic secretion. Later the cell base became negative and the label was concentrated in the Golgi region. In animals killed at still longer time intervals after injection of the tritiated amino acid, the reduced silver grains in the autoradiographs were over the zymogen granules at the cell apex or over the secretory material in the lumen of the acini. The results of this study combining electron microscopy and autoradiography provided a gratifying confirmation of the prevailing view that protein synthesis takes place in those regions of the cell occupied by granular endoplasmic reticulum and that the Golgi complex is a site of concentration of the secretory product. It was further shown that these complex biochemical events take place with surprising speed, for the label was already detectable in the Golgi region 20–25 minutes after its intraperitoneal injection.

In the method described by Caro the clarity of the electron microscopic image of the cell was marred by the overlying emulsion. The silver halide crystals are fairly large (0.2 μ) and when the preparation was passed through hypo during processing of the autoradiograph, the extraction of the unreduced silver left conspicuous areas of lower density in the image of the emulsion. This resulted in a distracting mottled ap-

FIG. 27. (a) Electron micrograph of an autoradiograph of developing cartilage from a larval salamander given tritiated proline a half-hour before sacrifice. The dense grains of silver (some indicated by arrows) overlie the endoplasmic reticulum and Golgi complex of the chondrocytes where the labeled amino acid was being incorporated into the precursors of collagen and possibly other components of the cartilage matrix. At later time intervals the label is located over the matrix and is no longer present in the cells. (b) Higher magnification of silver grains over the Golgi complex and secretory vacuoles evidently containing matrix precursors. (c) Similar detail of silver grains over the granular endoplasmic reticulum where amino acid is being incorporated into newly synthesized protein. (Courtesy of Drs. J. P. Revel and E. Hay, Harvard Medical School.)

pearance in the electron micrograph and consequent impaired contrast and resolution of the image of the underlying tissue section. This difficulty was largely overcome in the work of Revel and Hay (1961) who found it possible to remove most of the emulsion from the exposed and developed autoradiography without causing any displacement of the reduced silver grains. This was done by simply exposing the autoradiograph to high pH. By using the highly alkaline lead solution recommended by Karnovsky for staining, the emulsion could be removed and the underlying section stained in the same step. This improvement in the technique has made it possible to localize metabolic events by autoradiography without appreciable sacrifice of resolution in the electron micrograph. By this method, the site of thymidine incorporation into DNA has been localized to a fine filamentous component of the karyoplasm that corresponds in its distribution to the areas of chromatin revealed by Feulgen staining of parallel sections (135). Using tritiated proline the same authors have followed the intracellular pathway of synthesis and release of the precursors of collagen and other components in the basement lamella of regenerating amphibian epidermis (62a). Similar studies have been carried out on developing amphibian cartilage (Fig. 27) (136) and on healing skin wounds of guinea pigs (149). In all of these situations the grains of the autoradiographs, at short time intervals, were located over the endoplasmic reticulum of the fibroblasts or chondroblasts; later, they were over the Golgi complex and vacuoles in the peripheral cytoplasm; and after several hours to several days they were over the collagen fibers and ground substance. These observations provide further evidence for the participation of these cell types in the elaboration of the fibrous and amorphous components of connective tissues and constitute confirmation of our present understanding of the role of the various organelles in the secretory activities of the cells concerned.

The examination of autoradiographs with the electron microscope has proven superior to conventional autoradiography in that it offers (a) an autoradiographic resolution of 0.1 μ, (b) high optical resolution which facilitates identification of the labeled cell component, and (c) a photographic record in which the tissue section and the silver grains are both in sharp focus in the same plane (19). Several modifications of the methods described above have been reported and further improvements will no doubt be forthcoming. Salpeter and Bachmann (1963) obtained high contrast in the specimen and very good resolution by first staining the sections, protecting them with a thin carbon layer and then coating them with an extra fine grained emulsion. Use of a physical developer was also said to result in smaller developed grains. When a chemical constituent can be found which is specific for a particular cell type or is incorporated in unusually high concentration, isotopic labeling of that substance or its precursors will permit its autoradiographic detection and make it possible to trace its movements and ultimate fate. It is already clear that this method will contribute greatly in the future to the morphological identification of the sites of biochemical events in cells.

F. Electron Microscopic Control of Biochemical Studies on Cell Fractions

The study of the biochemical properties of particles isolated by centrifugation of cell homogenates had its inception in the pioneering isolation of mitochondria by Bensley and Hoerr (*10*). The technique was further developed by Claude (*23a*) and Hogeboom *et al.* (*63*) to the point of yielding results of fundamental importance. This fruitful approach to an understanding of the function of cell organelles and smaller particulates continues to be applied to many different organs, and the possibilities for further important discovery by its use appear to be far from exhausted.

The ultimate usefulness of the method of cell fractionation depends upon the cytological identification of the structural components present in the fractions. In the early phases of the development of the method, the identity of the larger particles, such as the nuclei, could be established by phase-contrast microscopy, and mitochondria could be identified by their characteristic supravital staining with Janus green, but fractions consisting of smaller particles could only be defined in terms of the gravitational force applied and the time in the centrifugal field. Unless the sedimentation properties of the particles to be separated were very different a considerable degree of contamination of the fractions was unavoidable. Early in the development of the method it was impossible to determine accurately the degree of homogeneity of the fractions. Consequently, the validity of quantitative biochemical measurements carried out on them was jeopardized. The electron microscope has now greatly extended the usefulness of cell fractionation by making it possible to identify in thin sections of the pellets, small particles that are beyond the reach of the light microscope and thus to monitor the purity of the fractions. The results of much early work done without this control must be reappraised in the light of evidence that the contamination of the fractions analyzed was often greater than previously supposed.

It is still common practice to publish quantitative biochemical results on mitochondrial or microsomal fractions defined only by reference to a flow sheet of the times and gravitational forces used in the isolation procedure. This was permissible when it was the best that could be done, but this clearly is no longer sufficient when it is possible now to examine the fraction with the electron microscope and establish visually its identity and the extent of its contamination. The electron microscope is, therefore, rapidly becoming an essential part of the armamentarium of the biochemist as well as the morphologist and the time cannot be far off when biochemical journals will require electron microscopic evidence of the homogeneity of the fraction as a condition of publication of papers reporting work based upon differential centrifugation.

G. The Negative Staining of Cell Components

Early in the history of biological electron microscopy investigators had to examine fragments of mechanically disrupted cells dried onto a

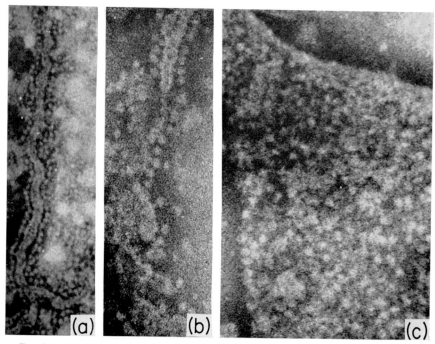

Fig. 28. (a) Negatively stained cristae from unfixed mitochondria. The membranes are studded with small particles about 85 A in diameter which appear to be attached by slender stalks 40–50 A long. (b) Same at higher magnification. A number of particles here have been detached from the membranes. (c) A surface view of mitochondrial membrane showing the large numbers and uniform distribution of the particles. [From Stoeckenius (*163*).]

supporting film because no other method was available to obtain specimens thin enough to be penetrated by the electron beam. To enhance contrast heavy metal was evaporated onto such specimens obliquely. When thin-sectioning techniques were developed, the direct examination of metal-shadowed preparations was largely abandoned in the study of cells, although it continued to be widely used for investigations of viruses, fibers, and other very small particulate matter. We are now witnessing a return to the examination of dissociated frag- ments of cells in order to take advantage of additional details of fine structure that can be disclosed by the method of negative staining. The potentialities of this method were first recognized by Hall (*59a*) and Huxley (*64a*), but its recent popularity is due, in large measure, to the outstanding success of its application by Brenner and Horne (*15a*) and others to the study of the ultrafine structural organization of viruses. The virus particles or cell fragments to be studied are simply suspended

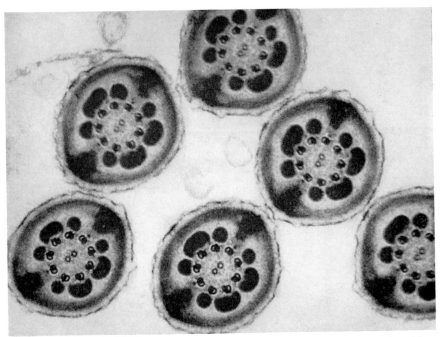

FIG. 29.   Cross sections of guinea pig sperm tails after glutaraldehyde fixation. More of the matrix of the flagellum appears to be preserved than with osmium alone. The distinction between the two subfibers of each doublet in the axial filament complex is clearly shown. The walls of these hollow fibrils have a filamentous substructure not resolved in sections but revealed by negative staining (see Fig. 31).

in a solution of 2% phosphotungstate or other heavy metal and droplets are sprayed onto a carbon-coated grid and allowed to dry in the air or in the vacuum of the microscope column. The phosphotungstate forms a very dense layer when dry and particles embedded in it are sharply revealed by their low contrast relative to their surroundings. As the specimen dries, the heavy metal penetrates into all of the interstices of the particles bringing out much more detail than could be deduced by relying upon the object's own density.

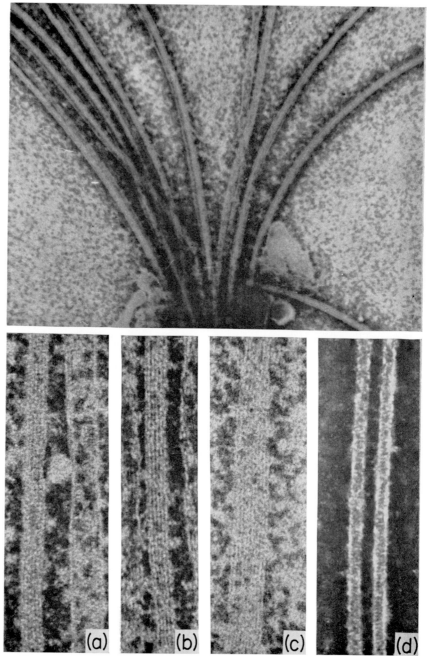

FIG. 30. The frayed out fibrils of the axial filament complex of a sperm tail negatively stained. Compare with Fig. 28 which shows the appearance of such fibrils

The method has been used to advantage in working out the details of surface configuration of isolated myosin and actin filaments of striated muscle (65, 60a). Among its major contributions to studies on cells has been the demonstration referred to earlier in the chapter, of small 85 A particles (Fig. 28) on the membranes of the mitochondrial cristae (49, 159a, 163). This particulate component is destroyed by the usual fixatives, and therefore is absent from sectioned material.

In sections of cilia and sperm flagella (Fig. 29), the nine longitudinal fibrils of the axial filament complex appear as pairs of conjoined tubules. One member of each pair has an interior of low density and appears tubular, while the other has a dense center and appears more solid. No further substructure can be clearly resolved. However, when the fibers of sperm flagella are dissociated and negatively stained (122a), each subfiber of the nine doublets is found to be a hollow tube whose wall is made up of about ten longitudinally oriented filaments 35–40 A in thickness (Figs. 30 and 31). These appear beaded along their length with a regular repeating period of 88 A. The center-to-center spacing of neighboring filaments is 55–60 A and their beads are in register across the entire width of the fibril suggesting that the filaments are cross-linked at these sites. These findings advance our understanding of the structure of flagella to the level of the actual arrangement and inter-relations of the macromolecules. There is every reason to expect that equally penetrating analysis of other cell components will be possible with this valuable technique.

H. Concluding Comment

One can scarcely expect to conclude an assignment such as this with a sense of satisfaction. The application of the electron microscope to histology and cytology has brought such a bountiful harvest of new information that even to catalogue its contributions would be an unending task. The account of the major cell organelles and current concepts of their functions offered here is very superficial and omits discussion of many interesting components of cells. It may, however, serve as an introduction to the interpretation of cell ultrastructure. The reader wish-

---

in thin cross sections. Negative staining reveals additional details of fine structure that escape detection in thin sections. See Fig. 31. [From Pease (122a).]

FIG. 31. (a)–(b) Higher magnifications of negatively stained fibers. Each sub-fibril is found to be a hollow tube whose wall is made up of about ten longitudinally oriented filaments 35–40 A in thickness. The filaments are beaded along their length and the beads are in register across the width of the fibril suggesting that the filaments are cross-linked at these sites. [From Pease (122b).]

ing to penetrate more deeply into the subject is referred to more extensive reviews on the cytoplasmic ground substance (128), mitochondria (97), the Golgi apparatus (27), specializations of the cell surface (45), and cilia flagella (41).

Since the introduction of the electron microscope, the rate of development of methods for revealing the structure of cells more clearly has surely been more rapid than in any comparable period in the long history of morphology. Technical advances occurring from the time of submission of a paper until its appearance in print not infrequently render the illustrations obsolete. Such may be the fate of this chapter. Some of the currently accepted methods described here may well be outmoded when the book is published, and valuable new methods will have been devised. New fixatives, new stains, new embedding media seem to be bringing us ever closer to our goal of preserving cells in a lifelike condition. It must be freely admitted, however, that we have no objective criteria for judging what constitutes good preservation. Perhaps it is more an article of faith for the morphologist, than a matter of demonstrated fact, that an image which is sharp, coherent, orderly, fine-textured, and generally aesthetically pleasing is more likely to be true than one which is coarse, disorderly, and indistinct. Like other matters of faith, this may not withstand logical analysis but it has proven to be operationally sound and has been responsible for much of the progress that has been made in descriptive cytology at the electron microscopic level. To accept any other guiding principle is to encourage carelessness and technical ineptitude.

REFERENCES

1. André, J., J. Ultrastruct. Res. 6, 437-448 (1962).
2. Andres, G. A., Morgan, C., Hsu, K. C., Rifkind, R. A., and Siegal, B. C., J. Exptl. Med. 115, 929 (1962).
3. Bangham, A. D., and Horne, R. W., Nature 196, 952-953 (1962).
4. Barer, R., Joseph, S., and Meek, G. A., Exptl. Cell Res. 18, 179-182 (1959).
5. Barnett, R. J., Proc. 4th Intern. Conf. on Electron Microscopy, Berlin, 1958 2, 91-100 (1960).
6. Barnett, R. J., J. Cell Biol. 12, 247-262 (1962).
7. Barnett, R. J., and Palade, G. E., J. Biophys. Biochem. Cytol. 3, 577-588 (1957).
7a. Barnett, R. J., and Palade, G. E., J. Biophys. Biochem. Cytol. 6, 163-170 (1959).
8. Bennett, H. S., J. Biophys. Biochem. Cytol. 2, 99-104 (1956).
9. Bennett, H. S., and Luft, J. H., J. Biophys. Biochem. Cytol. 6, 113-114 (1959).
10. Bensley, R. R., and Hoerr, N. L., Anat. Record 60, 449-455 (1934).
11. Bloom, W., and Leider, R. J., J. Cell Biol. 13, 269 (1962).
12. Bopp-Hassenkamp, G., Protoplasma 50, 243-268 (1958).
12a. Bopp-Hassenkamp, G., Z. Zellforsch. Mikroskop. Anat. 52, 238 (1960).
13. Brandes, D., Zetterquist, H., and Sheldon, H., Nature 177, 382-383 (1956).
14. Brandt, P. W., Circulation 26, 1075-1091 (1962).

15. Brandt, P. W., and Pappas, G. D., *J. Biophys. Biochem. Cytol.* **8**, 675 (1960).
15a. Brenner, S., and Horne, R. W., *Biochim. Biophys. Acta* **34**, 103 (1959).
16. Burgos, M. H., and Fawcett, D. W., *J. Biophys. Biochem. Cytol.* **1**, 287-300 (1955).
17. Callin, H. G., and Tomlin, S. G., *Proc. Roy. Soc.* **B137**, 367 (1950).
18. Caro, L. G., *J. Biophys. Biochem. Cytol.* **10**, 37 (1961).
19. Caro, L. G., *J. Cell Biol.* **15**, 189 (1962).
20. Caulfield, J. B., *J. Biophys. Biochem. Cytol.* **3**, 827-830 (1957).
21. Choi, J. K., *J. Cell Biol.* **16**, 53-72 (1963).
22. Christensen, A. K., and Fawcett, D. W., *J. Biophys. Biochem. Cytol.* **9**, 653-670 (1961).
23. Claude, A., *J. Exptl. Med.* **84**, 51-58 (1946).
23a. Claude, A., *Biol. Symposia* **10**, 111 (1943).
24. Coons, A. H., and Kaplan, M. H., *J. Exptl. Med.* **91**, 1 (1950).
25. Copeland, D. E., and Dalton, A. J., *J. Biophys. Biochem. Cytol.* **5**, 393-396 (1959).
26. Curtis, A. S. G., *Biol. Rev. Cambridge Phil. Soc.* **37**, 82-129 (1962).
27. Dalton, A. J., *in* "The Cell" (J. Brachet and A. E. Mirsky, eds.), Chapter 8, pp. 603-618. Academic Press, New York, 1959.
28. Dalton, A. J., and Felix, M. D., *Am. J. Anat.* **94**, 171 (1954).
29. Dalton, A. J., and Felix, M. D., *in* "Fine Structure of Cells," pp. 274-293. Noordhoff, Grøningen, 1955.
30. Danielli, J. F., *J. Cellular Comp. Physiol.* **7**, 393 (1936).
31. Danielli, J. F., and Davson, H. A., *J. Cellular Comp. Physiol.* **5**, 495-508 (1935).
32. De Robertis, E., and Pellegrino de Iraldi, A., *J. Biophys. Biochem. Cytol.* **10**, 361-372 (1961).
33. Dourmashkin, R. R., Dougherty, R. M., and Harris, R. J. C., *Nature* **194**, 1116-1119 (1962).
34. Enders, A. C., *Anat. Record* **139**, 225 (1961).
35. Epstein, M. A., *J. Biophys. Biochem. Cytol.* **3**, 851-858 (1957).
36. Essner, E., and Novikoff, A. B., *J. Cell Biol.* **15**, 289-312 (1962).
37. Essner, E., Novikoff, A. B., and Masek, B., *J. Biophys. Biochem. Cytol.* **4**, 711-716 (1958).
38. Farquhar, M. L., and Palade, G. E., *J. Cell Biol.* **17**, 375 (1963).
39. Fawcett, D. W., *J. Natl. Cancer Inst.* **15**, Suppl., 1475-1491 (1955).
40. Fawcett, D. W., *J. Biophys. Biochem. Cytol.* **2**, 403-406 (1956).
41. Fawcett, D. W., *in* "The Cell" (J. Brachet and A. E. Mirsky, eds.), Vol. I, Chapter 4, pp. 218-292. Academic Press, New York, 1959.
42. Fawcett, D. W., *Exptl. Cell Res.* Suppl. **8**, 174-187 (1961).
43. Fawcett, D. W., *Lab. Invest.* **10**, 1162-1188 (1961).
44. Fawcett, D. W., *Circulation* **26**, 1105-1125 (1962).
44a. Fawcett, D. W., and Revel, J. P., *J. Biophys. Biochem. Cytol.* **10**, Suppl., 89-109 (1961).
45. Fawcett, D. W., *in* "Physiology and Pathology of Peripheral Blood Vessels," Chapt. 2. Williams & Wilkins, Baltimore, Maryland, 1963.
46. Fawcett, D. W., and Wittenburg, J., *Anat. Record* **142**, 231 (1962).
47. Fernández-Morán, H., *Exptl. Cell Res.* **1**, 143-149 (1950).
48. Fernández-Morán, H., *Exptl. Cell Res.* **5**, 255-256 (1953).
48a. Fernández-Morán, H., *J. Biophys. Biochem. Cytol.* **2**, Suppl., 29 (1956).
49. Fernández-Morán, H., *Circulation* **26**, Suppl., 1039-1065 (1962).
50. Fernández-Morán, H., and Finean, J. B., *J. Biophys. Biochem. Cytol.* **3**, 725-747 (1957).

51. Finck, H., *J. Biophys. Biochem. Cytol.* **7**, 27-30 (1960).
52. Freeman, J. A., and Spurlock, B. O., *J. Cell Biol.* **13**, 437-444 (1962).
53. Gasser, H. S., *J. Gen. Physiol.* **38**, 709-728 (1955).
54. Geren, B., *Exptl. Cell Res.* **7**, 558 (1954).
55. Gibbons, I. R., *Proc. 4th Intern. Conf. on Electron Microscopy, Berlin, 1958* **2**, 55-58 (1960).
56. Glauert, A. M., Dingle, J. T., and Lucy, J. A., *Nature* **196**, 953-955 (1962).
57. Glauert, A. M., and Glauert, R. H., *J. Biophys. Biochem. Cytol.* **4**, 191-194 (1958).
58. Green, D. E., *Harvey Lectures* **52**, 177-227 (1958).
59. Gritzka, T., *Anat. Record* in press.
59a. Hall, C. E., *J. Biophys. Biochem. Cytol.* **1**, 1 (1955).
60. Hama, K., *J. Biophys. Biochem. Cytol.* **7**, 575-578 (1960).
60a. Hanson, J., and Lowy, J., *Proc. 5th Intern. Conf. on Electron Microscopy Philadelphia, 1962* 0-9 (1962).
61. Hay, E. D., and Revel, J. P., *Proc. 5th Intern. Conf. on Electron Microscopy Philadelphia, 1962* O-7 (1962).
62. Hay, E. D., and Revel, J. P., *J. Cell Biol.* **16**, 29 (1963).
62a. Hay, E. D., and Revel, J. P., *Develop. Biol.* **7**, 152 (1963).
62b. Hendler, R. W., Dalton, A. J., and Glenner, G. C., *J. Biophys. Biochem. Cytol.* **3**, 325 (1957).
63. Hogeboom, G. H., Schneider, W. C., and Palade, G. E., *J. Biol. Chem.* **172**, 619 (1948).
64. Holt, S. J., and Hicks, M., *J. Biophys. Biochem. Cytol.* **11**, 47-66 (1961).
64a. Huxley, H. E., *Proc. Stockholm Conf. on Electron Microscopy, 1956* p. 260 (1957).
65. Huxley, H. E., and Zubay, G., *J. Biophys. Biochem. Cytol.* **11**, 273-296 (1961).
66. Ito, S., *in* "The Interpretation of Ultrastructure" (R. J. C. Harris, ed.), pp. 129-148. Academic Press, New York, 1962.
67. Ito, S., and Winchester, R. J., *J. Cell Biol.,* **16**, 541 (1963).
68. Karnovsky, M. J., *J. Biophys. Biochem. Cytol.* **11**, 729-732 (1961).
69. Karnovsky, M. J., *Proc. 5th Intern. Conf. on Electron Microscopy, Philadelphia, 1962* Q-9 (1962).
70. Karnovsky, M. J., and Himmelhoch, S. R., *Am. J. Physiol.* **201**, 781-785 (1961).
71. Kaufmann, B. P., Gay, H., and McDonald, M., *Intern. Rev. Cytol.* **9**, 77-127 (1960).
72. Kellenberger, E., Schwab, W., and Ryter, A., *Experientia* **12**, 421-422 (1956).
73. Kuff, E. L., Hogeboom, G. H., and Dalton, A. J., *J. Biophys. Biochem. Cytol.* **2**, 33 (1956).
74. Leduc, E. H., and Bernhard, W., *J. Biophys. Biochem. Cytol.* **10**, 437 (1961).
75. Leduc, E. H., and Bernhard, W., *in* "The Interpretation of Ultrastructure" (R. J. C. Harris, ed.), pp. 21-45. Academic Press, New York, 1962.
76. Lehninger, A. L., *Harvey Lectures* **49**, 176 (1955).
77. Lehninger, A. L., *Pediatrics* **26**, 466-475 (1960).
78. Lehninger, A. L., *in* "Biological Structure and Function" (T. W. Goodwin and O. Lindberg, eds.), Vol. II, p. 31. Academic Press, New York, 1961.
79. Lehrer, G. M., and Ornstein, L., *J. Biophys. Biochem. Cytol.* **6**, 399-406 (1959).
79a. Lewis, W. H., *Bull. Johns Hopkins Hosp.* **49**, 17 (1931).
80. Liquier-Milward, J., *Nature* **177**, 619 (1956).
81. Littlefield, J. W., Keller, E. B., Gross, J., and Zamecnik, P. C., *J. Biol. Chem.* **217**, 111 (1955).
82. Luft, J. H., *J. Biophys. Biochem. Cytol.* **2**, 799-801 (1956).
83. Luft, J. H., *Anat. Record* **133**, 305 (1959).

84. Luft, J. H., *J. Biophys. Biochem. Cytol.* **9**, 409-414 (1961).
85. Luft, R., Ikkos, D., Palmieri, G., Ernster, L., and Afzelius, B., *J. Clin. Invest.* **41**, 1776-1804 (1962).
86. Marshall, J. M., Jr., *J. Exptl. Med.* **94**, 21 (1951).
87. Marshall, J. M., Jr., *Exptl. Cell Res.* **6**, 240 (1954).
88. Meyer, G. F., *Proc. European Reg. Conf. on Electron Microscopy, Delft, 1960* (1961).
88a. Millonig, G., *J. Appl. Phys.* **32**, 1637 (1961).
89. Millonig, G., *J. Biophys. Biochem. Cytol.* **11**, 736-739 (1961).
90. Millonig, G., *J. Appl. Phys.* **32**, 1637 (1961).
90a. Mochizuki, Mölbert, E. R. G., and von Deimling, O., *Beitr. Pathol. Anat. Allgem. Pathol.* **126**, 202 (1962).
91. Mölbert, E. R. G., Duspiva, F., and von Deimling, O., *J. Biophys. Biochem. Cytol.* **7**, 387-390 (1960).
92. Moore, D. H., and Grimley, P. M., *J. Biophys. Biochem. Cytol.* **3**, 255-260 (1957).
92a. Morgan, C., Rifkind, R. A., Hsu, K. C., Holden, M., Siegal, B. C., and Rose, H. M., *Virology* **14**, 292 (1961).
93. Moses, M. J., *J. Biophys. Biochem. Cytol.* **2**, 215 (1956).
93a. Moses, M. J., *J. Biophys. Biochem. Cytol.* **2**, Suppl., 397 (1956).
93b. Moses, M. J., *Proc. 4th Intern. Conf. on Electron Microscopy, Berlin, 1958* **2**, 230 (1960).
94. Muta, T., *Kurume Med. J.* **5**, 167-185 (1958).
95. Nebel, B., *Radiation Res.* Suppl. **1**, 431-452 (1959).
96. Newman, S. B., Borysko, E., and Swerdlow, M., *J. Appl. Phys.* **21**, 67 (1950).
97. Novikoff, A. B., in "The Cell" (J. Brachet and A. E. Mirsky, eds.), Vol. II. Academic Press, New York, 1961.
98. Novikoff, A. B., Beaufay, H., and de Duve, C., *J. Biophys. Biochem. Cytol.* **2**, Suppl., 179-184 (1956).
99. Novikoff, A. B., Essner, E., Goldfischer, S., and Heus, M., in "The Interpretation of Ultrastructure" (R. J. C. Harris, ed.), p. 149. Academic Press, New York, 1962.
100. O'Brien, R. T., and George, L. A., *Nature* **183**, 1461 and 4667-4676 (1959).
101. Odland, G. F., *J. Biophys. Biochem. Cytol.* **4**, 529-538 (1958).
102. Palade, G. E., *J. Exptl. Med.* **95**, 285-298 (1952).
103. Palade, G. E., *Anat. Record* **114**, 427-451 (1952).
104. Palade, G. E., *J. Appl. Phys.* **24**, 1424 (1953).
105. Palade, G. E., *J. Biophys. Biochem. Cytol.* **1**, 567-582 (1955).
106. Palade, G. E., *J. Biophys. Biochem. Cytol.* **2**, Suppl., 85-98 (1956).
107. Palade, G. E., in "Electron Microscopy in Anatomy" (J. D. Boyd, F. R. Johnson, and J. D. Lever, eds.), pp. 176-206. Williams & Wilkins, Baltimore, Maryland, 1961.
108. Palade, G. E., *Circulation* **24**, 368-384 (1961).
109. Palade, G. E., and Farquhar, M., *J. Biophys. Biochem. Cytol.* in press.
109a. Palade, G. E., and Porter, K. R., *J. Exp. Med.* **100**, 641-656 (1954).
110. Palade, G. E., and Siekewitz, P., *J. Biophys. Biochem. Cytol.* **2**, 171-200 (1956).
111. Palade, G. E., and Siekewitz, P., *J. Biophys. Biochem. Cytol.* **2**, 671-690 (1956).
111a. Palade, G. E., in "Subcellular Particles" (T. Hayashi, ed.). Ronald Press, New York, 1959.
112. Palade, G. E., Siekewitz, P., and Caro, L. G., in "The Exocrine Pancreas" (A. V. S. de Reuck, and M. P. Cameron, eds.), p. 23. Little, Brown, Boston, Massachusetts, 1962.

113. Palay, S. L., *J. Biophys. Biochem. Cytol.* **2**, Suppl., 193-203 (1956).
114. Palay, S. L., ed., "Frontiers in Cytology" Yale Univ. Press, New Haven, Connecticut, 1958.
115. Palay, S. L., *Exptl. Cell Res.* Suppl. **5**, 275-293 (1958).
116. Palay, S. L., and Palade, G. E., *J. Biophys. Biochem. Cytol.* **1**, 69-88 (1955).
117. Palay, S. J., McGee-Russell, S. M., Gordon, S., and Grillo, M., *J. Cell Biol.* **12**, 385-410 (1962).
118. Pallie, W., and Pease, D. C., *J. Ultrastruct. Res.* **2**, 1-7 (1958).
119. Parpart, A., and Ballentine, R., *in* "Modern Trends in Physiology and Biochemistry" (E. S. G. Barrón, ed.), pp. 135-148. Academic Press, New York, 1952.
120. Peachey, L. D., and Rasmussen, H., *J. Biophys. Biochem. Cytol.* **10**, 529-553 (1961).
121. Pease, D. C., *J. Histochem. Cytochem.* **3**, 295-308 (1955).
122. Pease, D. C., "Histological Techniques for Electron Microscopy." Academic Press, New York, 1960.
122a. Pease, D. C., *J. Cell Biol.* **18**, 313 (1963).
123. Peters, A., *J. Biophys. Biochem. Cytol.* **8**, 431-446 (1960).
124. Philpott, C. W., and Copeland, D. E., *J. Cell Biol.* **18**, 389 (1963).
125. Policard, A., and Bessis, M., *Compt. Rend.* **246**, 3194 (1958).
125a. Porter, K. R., Claude, A., and Fullam, E. F., *J. Exptl. Med.* **81**, 233 (1945).
125b. Porter, K. R., and Kallman, F. L., *Ann. N.Y. Acad. Sci.* **54**, 882 (1952).
126. Porter, K. R., *J. Exptl. Med.* **97**, 727 (1952).
127. Porter, K. R., *Harvey Lectures* **51**, 175 (1957).
128. Porter, K. R., *in* "The Cell" (J. Brachet and A. E. Mirsky, eds.), Vol. II, Chapter 9, pp. 621-675. Academic Press, New York, 1961.
129. Porter, K. R., *in* "Biological Structure and Function" (T. W. Goodwin and O. Lindberg, eds.), Vol. I, pp. 127-155. Academic Press, New York, 1961.
130. Porter, K. R., and Bruni, C., *Cancer Res.* **19**, 997-1009 (1959).
131. Porter, K. R., and Machado, R. D., *J. Biophys. Biochem. Cytol.* **7**, 167-180 (1960).
132. Porter, K. R., and Palade, G. E., *J. Biophys. Biochem. Cytol.* **3**, 269-300 (1957).
133. Porter, K. R., and Yamada, E., *J. Biophys. Biochem. Cytol.* **8**, 181-205 (1960).
134. Revel, J. P., *J. Cell Biol.* **12**, 571-588 (1962).
135. Revel, J. P., and Hay, E. D., *Exptl. Cell Res.* **25**, 474-480 (1961).
136. Revel, J. P., and Hay, E. D., *Z. Zellforsch. Mikroskop. Anat.* **61**, 110-144 (1963).
137. Revel, J. P., Ito, S., and Fawcett, D. W., *J. Biophys. Biochem. Cytol.* **4**, 495-496 (1958).
138. Revel, J. P., Fawcett, D. W., and Philpott, C. W., *J. Cell Biol.* **16**, 187-196 (1963).
139. Reynolds, E. A., *J. Cell Biol.* **17**, 208-211 (1963).
140. Rhodin, J., *Intern. Rev. Cytol.* **7**, 485-534 (1958).
141. Rifkind, R. A., Hsu, K. C., Morgan, C., Siegal, B. C., Knox, A. W., and Rose, H. M., *Nature* **187**, 1094 (1960).
142. Rifkind, R. A., Morgan, C., and Rose, H. M., *Proc. 5th Intern. Conf. on Electron Microscopy, Philadelphia, 1962* L-1 (1962).
143. Ris, H., *Can. J. Genet. Cytol.* **3**, 95-120 (1961).
144. Robertson, J. D., *J. Biophys. Biochem. Cytol.* **1**, 271-278 (1955).
145. Robertson, J. D., *J. Biophys. Biochem. Cytol.* **3**, 1043-1048 (1957).
146. Robertson, J. D., *Biochem. Soc. Symp. (Cambridge, Engl.)* **16**, 3-43 (1959).
147. Robertson, J. D., *Progr. Biophys. Biophys. Chem.* **10**, 343-418 (1960).
148. Robertson, J. D., *in* "Electron Microscopy in Anatomy" (J. D. Boyd, F. R. Johnson, and J. D. Lever, eds.), pp. 74-99. Williams & Wilkins, Baltimore, Maryland, 1961.

149. Ross, R., and Benditt, E. P., *Abstr. Am. Soc. Cell Biologists* (1963).
150. Sabatini, D. D., Bensch, K. G., and Barrnett, R. J., *Anat. Record* **142**, 274 (1962).
150a. Salpeter, M., and Bachmann, L. *Science* (in press).
151. Schneider, W. C., *J. Histochem. Cytochem.* **1**, 212-228 (1953).
152. Sedar, A. W., *J. Cell Biol.* **14**, 152 (1962).
153. Sedar, A. W., and Rosa, C. G., *J. Ultrastruct. Res.* **5**, 226-243 (1961).
154. Sheldon, H., Zetterquist, H., and Brandes, D., *Exptl. Cell Res.* **9**, 592-596 (1955).
155. Siekewitz, P., and Palade, G. E., *J. Biophys. Biochem. Cytol.* **4**, 203-218 (1958).
156. Siekewitz, P., and Palade, G. E., *J. Biophys. Biochem. Cytol.* **4**, 309-318 (1958).
156a. Siekewitz, P., and Palade, G. E., *J. Biophys. Biochem. Cytol.* **7**, 619-630 (1960).
157. Singer, S. J., *Nature* **183**, 1523 (1959).
158. Sjöstrand, F. S., *Nature* **171**, 30-32 (1953).
158a. Sjöstrand, F. S., *J. Ultrastruct. Res.* **8**, 517 (1963).
159. Slautterback, D. L., and Fawcett, D. W., *J. Biophys. Biochem. Cytol.* **5**, 441-452 (1959).
159a. Smith, D., *J. Cell Biol.* **19**, 115-138 (1963).
160. Stäubli, W., *Compt. Rend.* **250**, 1137 (1960).
161. Stoeckenius, W., *J. Biophys. Biochem. Cytol.* **5**, 491-500 (1959).
162. Stoeckenius, W., *in* "The Interpretation of Ultrastructure" (R. J. C. Harris, ed.), pp. 349-367. Academic Press, New York, 1962.
163. Stoeckenius, W., *J. Cell Biol.* **17**, 443 (1963).
164. Stoeckenius, W., Schulman, J. H., and Prince, L. M., *Kolloid-z.* **169**, 170 (1960).
165. Strauss, E. H., *J. Cell Biol.* **17**, 597 (1963).
166. Swift, H., *Brookhaven Symp. Biol.* **12**, 134 (1959).
167. Swift, H., and Adams, B. J., *Proc. 5th Intern. Conf. on Electron Microscopy, Philadephia, 1962* O-4 (1962).
168. Tokuyasu, K., and Okamura, S., *J. Biophys. Biochem. Cytol.* **6**, 305-308 (1959).
169. Van Tübergen, R. P., *J. Biophys. Biochem. Cytol.* **9**, 219 (1961).
170. Verwey, E. J. W., and Overbeek, J. T. G., "Theory of the Stability of Lyophobic Colloids." Elsevier, Amsterdam, 1948.
171. Wachstein, M., and Meisel, E., *Am. J. Clin. Pathol.* **27**, 13 (1957).
172. Ward, R. T., *J. Histochem. Cytochem.* **6**, 398 (1958).
173. Warner, J. R., Rich, A., and Hall, C. E., *Science* **138**, 1399-1403 (1962).
174. Warshawsky, H., Leblond, C. P., and Droz, B., *J. Cell Biol.* **16**, 1-28 (1963).
175. Watson, M. L., *J. Biophys. Biochem. Cytol.* **1**, 257-270 (1955).
176. Watson, M. L., *J. Biophysic. Biochem. Cytol.* **3**, 1017-1022 (1957).
177. Watson, M. L., *J. Biophys. Biochem. Cytol.* **4**, 727-730 (1958).
178. Watson, M. L., and Aldridge, W. G., *J. Biophys. Biochem. Cytol.* **11**, 257-272 (1961).
179. Webster, H. deF., and Spiro, D., *J. Neuropathol. Exptl. Neurol.* **19**, 42-68 (1960).
180. Weiner, S., *J. Biophys. Biochem. Cytol.* **5**, 175-177 (1959).
181. Wissig, S., *Anat. Record* **142**, 292 (1962).
182. Yamada, E., *J. Biophys. Biochem. Cytol.* **1**, 445-458 (1955).
183. Yamada, E., and Ishikawa, T. M., *Kyushu J. Med. Sci.* **11**, 235-295 (1960).
183a. Yasuzumi, G., and Ishida, H., *J. Biophys. Biochem. Cytol.* **3**, 663 (1957).
183b. Zebe, H., and Falk, H. (personal communication from E. R. G. Mölbert) (1963).
184. Zeigel, R. F., and Dalton, A. J., *J. Cell Biol.* **15**, 45-54 (1962).

CHAPTER 7

In Bacteriology

EDWARD KELLENBERGER AND ANTOINETTE RYTER

I. Introduction

Bacteria, or more generally microbial cells, have provided the experimental basis for a majority of the more recent contributions to our knowledge of the basic phenomena in metabolism, biochemistry, and fundamental genetics. This is due not only to the simplicity of their organization but mainly to their accessibility to very precise experimentation. They grow easily in well-defined media. For genetic studies they provide a high number of generations in a short time interval. The quantitative methods are simple, precise, and reproducible. Electron microscopy has two main roles in this field of research on microorganisms: (1) to collaborate intimately with the biochemist and geneticist to help construct valid models of the processes investigated by joint effort; and (2) to provide comparative studies on the microbial cells in respect to other higher cells and thus prepare the way to generalization of results. Comparative studies can be done independently, but it should be emphasized that the interpretations are of value only if they are based on a thorough knowledge of microbial biochemistry and genetics. It is most deleterious to progress if the bacterial cell is considered simply as a miniature execution of the "higher cell." Certainly, the basic vital processes and functions are the same, but the very much smaller size of the bacteria has the consequence that these processes have to be made with a minimum expenditure of materials. For example, the genetic

TABLE I

COMPONENTS OF THE BACTERIAL CELL

Particle in Fig. 1	Description	Discussed in Section:	Main references for electron microscopy
R	Cytoplasm, matrix with ribosomes	III, A	79, 166, 192
N	Nucleoid, nucleus	II, A; III, B	29, 34, 56, 59, 62, 75, 85, 87, 91, 94, 98, 102, 105, 130, 145, 153, 154, 170, 172, 173, 198, 201, 202
M	Mesosome (chondrioid)	III, D	19, 40, 47, 55, 58, 59, 62, 89, 91, 102, 113, 126, 135, 137, 146, 160, 179, 180, 200, 201
L	Lipid granules	III, A	No thorough investigation
G	Glycogen granules (in *Escherichia coli*)	III, A	31
CM CW	Cytoplasmic membrane Cell wall	III, C	33, 35, 47, 50, 55, 59, 60, 62, 65, 73, 76, 77, 92, 126, 139, 140, 143, 160, 165, 194, 201, 209, 214
V	Metachromatic granules	III, A	102, 103, 136, 184
Ch	Chromatophores	III, A	25, 53, 57, 72, 178, 204
—	Plastids	III, A	25, 57, 147, 154, 178
—	Flagella, pili, capsules	III, E	20, 22, 23, 44, 45, 78, 108, 109, 110, 123, 138, 164, 174, 206, 210, 217

information of a bacterial virus is stored in less than 10^5 nucleotide pairs, in bacteria in 10^7, and in a liver cell in 10^{10}. It is obvious that it is much more difficult to organize the deoxyribonucleic acid (DNA) of a liver cell to make a functioning chromosome than that of a bacterium or even of a phage. It is obvious, also, that it will be easier to understand the division of "higher" chromosomes once the division of the genetic material of phage and bacteria is understood.

Electron microscopy of microbial cells can and must be carried out as supplementary or corollary investigations with other methods. Purely descriptive work is easy to perform, but should be limited to a strict minimum.

To make further discussions easier, we have summarized our descriptive knowledge in the form of a drawing of a "superbacterium" (Fig. 1) (Table I). The reference to papers where each structure has been described is found in the legend.

This contribution does not make pretention of being complete. The reader is referred to the excellent reviews by Murray (140) and Robinow (156). In this chapter we have chosen for discussion some results which, in our opinion, illustrate the use of the electron microscope as a tool in broader research projects. There is a variety of methods and techniques for investigating microbial cells. The observation of entire, unsec-

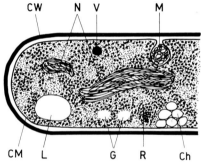

FIG. 1 Various schematized internal structures of an idealized "superbacterium." For explanation see Table I.

tioned cells is able to provide some information on the surface structure and on the appendages of the cell. For internal structures, however, the obtainable resolution is very little above that of the optical microscope. All problems of internal organization, therefore, have to be solved utilizing thin sections. Owing to the small size and the general experimental accessibility of microorganisms, the information obtained on sections can easily be related to those obtained on homogenates, on which parallel biochemical investigations are made. The techniques applied to the study of the constituents of disrupted cells are the same as those applied to macromolecular constituents in general and are discussed in Chapters 3 and 8 of the present book. Among the newer techniques, the method of embedding in potassium phosphotungstate, improved and generalized by Brenner and Horne (17), the pseudo-replicas on mica, introduced by Hall and Litt (66), and finally the use of protein films spread on water (99) have been revolutionary. Their applications to specific bacterial problems will be discussed in Section III, B.

The first part of this chapter will be devoted to a discussion of some recent methods based mainly on thin sections. These example have been selected not only because they have given results in the field of bacteria but also because they offer great promise for future contributions and should stimulate the development of new methods.

II. New Methodological Approaches

A. Fixation and Embedding

It is now well known that the methacrylate polymerization frequently produces swelling and distortion of the embedded material (see Chapter 4). For several years this "explosion phenomenon" was interpreted as due to inadequate fixation. In the case of bacteria it happened so frequently and so extensively that here, at least, it was obviously not due to fixation alone. The micrographs showed very clearly that the swelling was so pronounced that the cells burst. This swelling can be explained as follows: The methacrylate probably first polymerizes inside the cell because of some cellular substances acting as accelerators, unpolymerized monomer from the outside of the cell is then taken up by the polymer inside and induces the swelling and eventual bursting of the cell. However, the conditions of fixation do seem to influence the outcome of the swelling process. The frequency of this artifact and its obvious occurrence in the case of bacteria explain the interest in new embedding media. Maaløe and Birch-Andersen (9, 122) introduced the use of epoxy resins. Araldite is one of the well-known representatives of this group (61). Kellenberger et al. (93) investigated the group of polyester resins and found that Vestopal W (159) has the required properties for embedding and sectioning. Other representatives are the epoxy resin, Epon (118) and the Japanese polyester, Rigolac (106).

Epoxy resins and Vestopal are both copolymers. Their polymerization proceeds with great regularity and is insensitive to outside influence. These qualities probably prevent any swelling regardless of the previous physiological state and the fixation of the biological material. The thermosetting properties of these resins give the sections a behavior under the electron beam which is very different from the thermoplastic methacrylates (159). The behavior of methacrylate can be changed by the addition of a copolymerizing agent, like divinylbenzol (107); systematic studies of this new procedure in respect to explosion phenomena are not yet available.

Fixation

Once the polymerization artifacts had been eliminated it became evident that the bacteria are very sensitive to the conditions of osmium fixation. The content of the bacterial nucleus in particular was observed in different aspects. At one extreme the nucleus appeared to be a plasm composed of fine fibrillae (30–60 A thick) and at the other extreme as a vacuole containing one to several electron-opaque bodies of very variable shape swimming in an electron-translucent sap (see Kellenberger, *85* for references). All degrees of intermediate stages could be produced. In the cytoplasm, the observed differences were not as striking. Systematic studies on the conditions of osmium fixation have been made (*54, 160*). Owing to the great number of parameters influencing the observed effects, there arose some disagreement in interpretation. The results are summarized in Table II and in the discussion which follows.

A scale of four letters, A to D, is introduced in Table II to evaluate the appearance of the nucleoplasm. The appearances resulting from the conditions in the main fixation and the posttreatment are both indicated. The main results on the nucleus may be summarized as follows: (1) The so-called R-K conditions of fixation (see Table III) alone are sufficient to produce D. (2) When uranyl acetate (UA) posttreatment is applied, the conditions of the main fixation are apparently not important. This latter conclusion was not recognized in the paper of Ryter and Kellenberger (*160*), although it could be deduced from their results. It has been "rediscovered" independently by Schreil (*172*), Koike and Takeya (*102*), and Schlote (*171*).

If D is assumed to be the true representation of a DNA-plasm, then the combination of the R-K conditions of OsO_4 fixation combined with UO_2 postfixation is obviously an efficient and reliable combination (see Table III).

The different fixatives have been tested macroscopically (*87, 173*). A concentrated solution of DNA of honeylike consistency was subjected to different fixatives. It was found that UA treatment produces almost immediate gelation of the sol without flocculation. The R-K conditions of OsO_4 fixation produce gelation within a few hours. When either one or both of the two critical additions (Ca^{++}, amino acids) are omitted, the gelation does not take place.

Fixed solutions of DNA nucleohistone and nucleoprotamine (called DNAc for DNA complexes) either alone or with admixed bacteria have been observed in the electron microscope (*172, 173*). The results show unambiguously that such solutions can be fixed either in a fibrillar state or under different forms of coarse figures (Figs. 2a and b). In this case the interpretation is obvious. Only the fibrillar state corresponds approximately to what is expected from a colloidal sol. The coarse figures are aggregations which are produced during the dehydration. It is well

TABLE II

EFFECT OF SOME COMBINATIONS OF CRITICAL CONDITIONS OF Os FIXATION ON THE ASPECT OF DNA-PLASM OF BACTERIAL NUCLEOIDS[a,b]

Main fixation: 1% OsO_4 within the following additives[b]						Posttreatment: 1 hour with the following additives				Result[c]
pH	PO_4^{3-}	Ca^{2+}	La^{3+}	UO_2^{2+}	Amino acids	Ca^{2+} (pH 6)	La^{3+} (pH 6)	UO_2^{2+} (pH 2.5)	Versene (pH 6)	
6	−	+	−	−	++	+	0	0	−	D
6	−	+	0	0	++	0	+	0	−	D
~	~	~	0	−	~	0	0	+	−	D
6	+	+ or −	0	−	++	+	0	−	+	B
6	−	+	−	−	−	−	−	−	−	B
6	−	0	−	−	−	+	−	−	+	B–C
7–8	−	~	−	−	−	−	−	−	−	A
6	−	~	~	+	~	~	~	~	~	D

[a] Extracted from Table I in Ryter and Kellenberger (161), from Kellenberger and Ryter (91), Schreil (172), and from unpublished results of Schreil and Kellenberger. All treatments have been made in Veronal-acetate buffer. There is no claim, however, that other buffers cannot be used; however, for phosphate buffer it has been shown that the PO_4 ions interfere with the calcium requirement.

[b] Explanation: +, present; −, absent; in cases where the importance of the presence or absence has been demonstrated; 0, absent, in cases where the importance of the presence or absence has not been investigated; ~, probably unimportant (available experimental data are limited).

[c] Scale of evaluation of aspect of the DNA-plasm of the bacterial nucleus: A, very coarse; B, coarse; C, intermediate; D, fine fibrillae.

known that DNA, nucleohistone, and nucleoprotamine flocculate when some water-miscible solvent replaces 50–70% of the water.

If one now treats bacteria and DNA or DNAc containing solutions simultaneously under different conditions of osmium fixation, it then can be observed that the content of the DNA-plasm of the bacteria produces exactly the same figures as the DNA or DNAc outside of the cell (Fig. 3).

TABLE III

FIXATION OF BACTERIA

R-K fixation[a]:	Michaelis buffer pH 6; 1% OsO_4; 0.1% $CaCl_2$; 0.1% tryptone or casamino acids; fixation for 4–15 hours depending on material
Posttreatment:	Before dehydration, in one of the following solutions [the best is (b) which is both a fixative and stain for nucleic acids]
	(a) Directly in 25% acetone-water or a few minutes in Michaelis buffer pH 6, 0.1% $CaCl_2$
	(b) 1–2 hours in Michaelis buffer with 0.5% uranyl acetate (pH drops to 3.5)
	(c) 1–2 hours in Michaelis buffer pH 6, 1% La $(NO_3)_3$

[a] The R-K conditions of osmium fixation are: presence of 0.1% $CaCl_2$, 0.1% casamino acids or tryptone, and pH 6. The posttreatment in $UO_2{}^{2+}$ is not part of the R-K conditions, although its application is recommended.

We can now discuss which aspect of the nucleoplasm of the bacteria is correct. It can be concluded that uranyl acetate and osmium fixation under R-K conditions are fixatives for solutions of DNA and DNAc. But it is not immediately evident that they are also good fixatives for complex chromosomes. It is possible that these fixatives first destroy such structures and swell them, and then they are fixed in the swollen state. If this happens, none of the figures of nucleoplasm shown are correct. Indeed, the compact structures are certainly due to aggregation phenomena, even if they come from swollen chromosomes, otherwise they would not be identical inside and outside the bacteria when fixed simultaneously.

Further arguments are necessary to exclude the swelling artifact. The subject is discussed in detail in (87), and only a summary will be given here. It has been shown (Section III,G) that growing phage exists first as a vegetative particle in a highly hydrated pool (Fig. 18). The first step of maturation consists in a condensation of the DNA before the protein coat is formed on this "condensate." Both the highly hydrated pool and precursor particles are observed with the R-K fixation combined with either Ca, La, or uranyl acetate posttreatment. When other conditions are used these two states are no longer easily distinguishable. In the dinoflagellate *Amphidinium elegans*, chromosomes exist in an expanded and condensed state depending on certain physi-

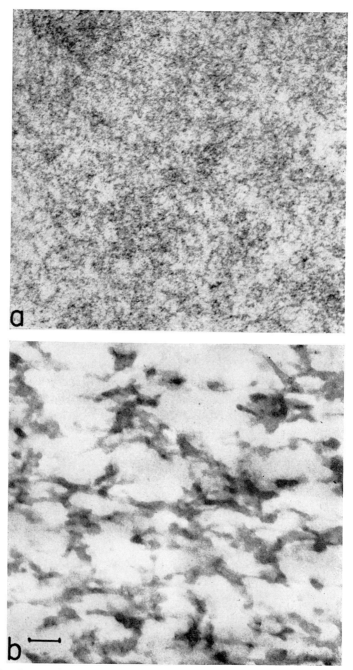

FIG. 2. Preparation of herring-sperm DNA, embedded and sectioned after two different osmium fixations: *a,* under the R-K conditions (calcium and amino acids in the main fixative at pH 6) and with uranyl acetate posttreatment; *b,* under usual conditions of osmium fixation at pH 7 and washed in Versene. Preparation and micrographs by Dr. W. H. Schreil.

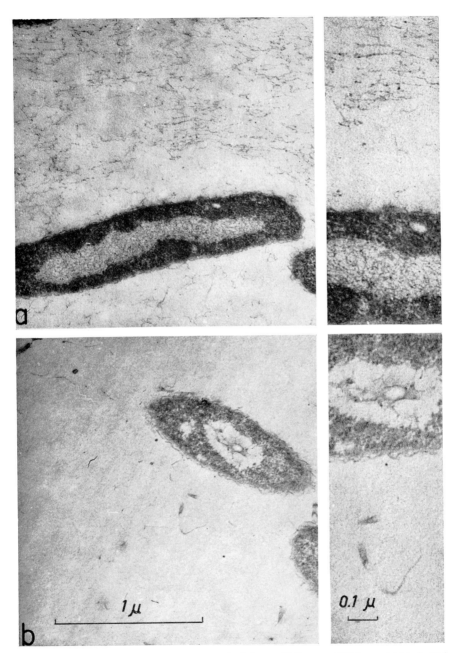

FIG. 3. *Escherichia coli* cell surrounded by calf-thymus DNA, embedded and sectioned after two different osmium fixations: *a*, posttreated with uranyl acetate; *b*, washed in Versene after fixation. Preparation and micrographs by Dr. W. H. Schreil.

ological conditions (*41, 87*). Both forms are represented distinctly with the same fixative (R-K-osmium fixation with uranyl acetate posttreatment). It is obvious that in these two cases at least one form of the chromosome (the condensed one) is preserved without gross swelling.

Other fixatives not based on OsO$_4$, such as the permanganate fixation (*117*), when applied to bacteria (*47, 130, 197*) also produce a fibrillar nucleoplasm.

In conclusion, these arguments together with many others summarized in Kellenberger (*85, 87*), favor a fibrillar character as an adequate description of the bacterial nucleus. All other interpretations need complicated assumptions which have not been established by any solid observations or arguments.

Protoplasts cannot be fixed by osmium fixation because the fixative induces immediate lysis. Hofschneider (*73*) found that fixatives containing bichromate and acetone or formaldehyde and followed by uranyl acetate postfixation yield acceptable results. The nucleoids though not always observed to be extremely fine are, at least, not coarsely aggregated. Strangely enough, these fixatives usually do not give good results with bacteria.

To avoid harmful effects of the centrifugation, like anaerobiosis, the bacteria are usually prefixed before being spun down. The main fixation is then done on the bacteria resuspended in a small volume, with the advantage that only a small amount of fixative is needed. Prefixation is done mostly in 0.1% OsO$_4$. Other successful prefixatives are formaldehyde vapors for 1 hour (*113*), and formaldehyde (4% in liquid) for 3 hours (*26*).

B. Specific Differentiation

Great effort has been made in the past few years to develop methods in electron microscopy which would allow specific identification of substances in thin sections of cells. Four methods are being used at present: specific coagulation, staining, digestion, and recognition of cellular enzymes by reaction with a substrate.

These differentiating actions can be applied at various phases of the embedding process (see also Chapter 4): (*a*) Action on the cells before fixation or after only prefixation. This step is usually performed on thick sections of tissues obtained on the freezing microtome. (*b*) Action after fixation, but still in aqueous solutions. (*c*) Action in one of the dehydration baths. (*d*) Action on the finished sections. These techniques are described in detail in Chapter 4 of this book.

One major complication in specific staining is introduced by the fact that osmium fixation—which is adequate for the preservation of most ultrastructures—is by itself a powerful stain. Therefore, it is frequently necessary either to use other nonstaining fixatives like formaldehyde, or to remove the osmium from the tissue before applying the staining reaction. The situation is not very different for enzymic reactions, where the osmium stain may interfere with the action of the enzyme. Applied in the aqueous phase, the enzymic action may destroy structural linkages and produce as consequence artifacts of arrangement. The use of water-soluble resins for the embedding has some promising prospects (111). These resins stay very hydrophilic even after polymerization and allow better penetration of enzymes or other reactives. However, this advantage is partly balanced by the disadvantage that aggregations of structures may occur in the water-swollen resin.

1. Specific Coagulation

DNA-plasms such as the bacterial nucleus withstand dehydration and embedding without collapsing only if their physical and chemical state has been modified by fixation. This modification occurs in a sufficiently irreversible manner only under certain definite conditions, for example, by the R-K fixation (see Section II, A). The presence of Ca^{++} or Mg^{++} is one of the required conditions.

On the basis of this cation requirement the so-called Versene test has been devised. This test is effective for hydrated plasms exclusively, the cytoplasm being practically unaffected. In the normal fixation procedure (Table III) the washing bath (which contains either Ca^{++}, La^{+++}, or UO_2^{++}) is replaced by a solution of 9.3% (0.25 M) of disodium ethylendiamintetraacetate (Versene or Complexone III) in the normal Veronal-acetate buffer. By this treatment the behavior of the DNA is affected in such a way that coarse aggregations are produced during dehydration.

We have standardized this procedure in the following way: The agar blocks containing the specimen to be studied are split into fractions after the main fixation; one is washed in Versene, the other in the usual uranyl acetate solution. The comparison of these two fractions is then called the "Versene test." It is called positive when the fractions show a difference, negative if there is no obvious difference. It is clear from the foregoing that the positive outcome of the Versene test indicates the presence of a hydrated, DNA-containing plasma. This test has shown the following positive cases: solutions of pure DNA, of nucleohistone, pool of vegetative phage, nuclei of bacteria (94, 172, 173), of the dinoflagellate A. elegans (41, and quoted in 94), and of blue-green alga (154).

Although this is not yet complete proof for the specificity of the reaction, nevertheless it is a very strong evidence and encourages further use.

It may be possible to develop similar coagulation tests for other hydrated plasmas of different substances. The specificity may also be improved so that, for example, a distinction may become possible between pure DNA in a salt configuration and other DNA derivatives like nucleohistones.

2. Staining and Digestion

Very little is known about the specificity of OsO_4 as a stain (3, 4) mainly because substances not stained are probably overlooked in most of the cases. Cellulose and its derivatives, as well as starch and glycogen, are not stained appreciably by osmium.

Even less is known about the quantitative aspect of osmium uptake in different cellular constituents. A substance at the limit of visibility in a section may be assumed to become visible if the electron scattering from the substance is doubled. With proteins, calculations show that the quantity of osmium needed is approximately equal to the mass of the protein. To what degree these conditions can be accomplished by stoichiometric reactions has not been determined, but would seem difficult to achieve. Since such increased contrasts are obtained experimentally, it is possible that osmium precipitates physically as well as chemically. Some amino acids and small proteins in solution may reduce some OsO_4 to metallic particles which then precipitate down on all available surfaces. Serious consideration must be given to reactions on such structures as ribosomes and membranous components.

One of the stains in current use on bacteria is uranyl acetate, which also acts as a fixing agent on DNA-plasms (see Section II, A). This substance has been shown to react with nucleic acids of both types (80). Hence, it probably stains both ribonucleic acid (RNA) and DNA.

Lanthanum salts also seem to stain the nucleic acids since they increase the contrast of both intracellular phages and cytoplasm (94). However, they are less specific than the uranyl acetate. Indeed, some observations indicate that they may also stain polysaccharides like glycogen (161) and sporecortex (128, 129). These experiments allow no definite conclusions. Glycogen granules seem to be stained also by lead salts (30).

Singer (181, 182) describes a particularly interesting method of "staining" which is based on the specific antibody-antigen reactions. Since the antibody itself would scarcely increase the contrast of an antigen, the antibody is conjugated with ferritin particles and becomes easily recognizable in the electron microscope. Morgan et al. (133) have demonstrated the applicability of the method to sections containing viruses. This technique has been applied also to bacteriophage-infected bacteria (*112*). To obtain penetration of antibody into the cell, infected spheroplasts were used which demonstrated that the ferritin-conjugated antibody is located around the phages and in the cytoplasm but never in the pool of DNA. This technique has also been applied to uninfected bacteria and to antigenic reaction on the bacterial surface (*183*).

3. Specific Digestion

The techniques based on specific removal of substances before dehydration have given disappointing results, at least in the case tried: RNase treatment applied to *Escherichia coli* (*11*).

(1) The biochemical controls show that the digestion depends greatly on the removal of the fixative before treatment with the enzyme.

(2) The digestion is satisfactory though not quite complete after osmium prefixation.

(3) The digestion is very poor and often inhibited after formaldehyde; it can be improved by washing with weak alcohol. But unfortunately formaldehyde does not preserve the ultrastructure of bacteria in a satisfactory state.

(4) The perturbations introduced by the digestion by RNase on the fine structure of the bacteria are not constant. They modify the nucleus as well as the cytoplasm. They do not bring distinct informations of the kinds of modifications having taken place and seem to depend very much on the procedures of fixation and dehydration.

All these observations indicate clearly that the method is not yet refined enough to be applied at the structural level for bacteria. Action on finished sections of bacteria has not yet been reported. This approach has the serious disadvantage that it does not allow any chemical control of the enzymic reaction.

4. Localization of Enzymes by Substrate Reaction

When a suitable substrate is added to a cell some cellular enzymes may react specifically with the substrate. This reaction product, if insoluble, will be deposited in the neighborhood of the enzyme and reveal its presence. This method is of fundamental importance because it can give information about cellular functions (*5*), and its use is being rapidly developed. Several attempts have been made to localize enzymes of the respiratory system in bacteria. Two methods can be used: (1) Tellurium salts give rise to insoluble crystals which are strongly electron scattering (*5*). (2) Tetrazolium salts become insoluble in aqueous solutions after reduction to formazan but most formazans are soluble in acetone and alcohol; therefore their presence in manifested on thin sections by an empty space. A successful application of this latter technique is reported in Section III, D in the investigation of the function of mesosomes (200). The use of tetranitro blue-tetrazolium introduced by Sedar et al. (177) will probably permit a more precise localization of the succinic dehydrogenase reaction sites in bacteria because this salt is insoluble in the dehydration solutions.

C. Serial Sectioning and Reconstruction

1. STUDY OF RATHER LARGE CELLULAR STRUCTURES

A thin section of thickness 450–500 A represents 1/15–1/20 of a longitudinally cut bacterium. According to the level and the plane of the section, cellular components which are much larger than 500 A will present variable shapes and sizes. It is thus obvious that a single section cannot give precise information on shape and size of these organelles and that even the observation of a great number of sections will be of little help. In such cases one is forced to use serial sections. This technique is difficult and requires fastidious work which is not undertaken with any great pleasure. The formation of good ribbons and recovery of the sections are delicate operations which add to the difficulty of locating the same bacterium on successive sections. However, in many studies serial sections give so much useful information which neither single thin sections nor observations of the whole bacterium are able to supply that the extra effort is well rewarded.

For instance, in the case of the bacterial nucleus, the light microscope gives pictures which are difficult to compare to those obtained on thin sections. In the optical microscope the cell presents generally two or more nuclei of a very characteristic shape (dumbbell, U or V, or sticklike). On thin sections, it shows 1–4 nuclear vacuoles of shapes which seldom resemble those of the optical pictures. In the early period of the sectioning technique, when it had not yet been established that the nuclear vacuoles contained the nuclear material, Birch-Andersen (8) demonstrated with serial sections that the reconstruction of these vacuoles from thin sections did indeed give the same shape as that observed in stained light microscope preparations. He thus proved that they are actually the true nuclear equivalents.

Another case which could be solved only by use of serial sections and subsequent reconstruction was that of the "fragmented" nucleus of irradiated bacteria. When E. coli are irradiated with ultraviolet light and then incubated in a growth medium, they undergo typical nuclear transformations (83, 84). Examination of samples taken 30-40 minutes

after irradiation by either staining and light microscopy or observation
in the electron microscope of the whole organism shows that the nucleus
becomes enlarged and appears to be composed of many little "pieces" or
fragments. A single thin section shows an increased number of smaller
vacuoles tending to confirm the idea that the nucleus is actually
fragmented, but serial sections reveal that all the vacuoles are connected
with each other. This shows that the "fragmented" nucleus is in fact a
continuous very large chromosome endowed with numerous intrusions

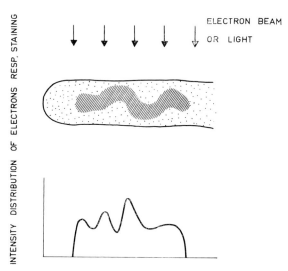

Fig. 4. Schematic drawing explaining the density distribution in the nucleus of
stained bacteria viewed in the light microscope or of over-all specimens observed in
the electron microscope. The orientation of the chromatin material simulates denser
patches alternating with less dense areas.

and protrusions (157). Hence, irradiations do not produce ruptures, at
the electron microscope level, of the bacterial chromosome.

The "wrong" picture of a fragmented nucleus is simulated by the
variations in thickness of the nuclear material. Indeed, in electron
microscopy and phase-contrast microscopy the different shades of half-
tones in the micrograph are directly dependant upon the product $d \times \rho$,
where d is the thickness, and ρ the mass-density in gm/cm^3 of the specimen. The density of the cytoplasm is different from that of the nucleus.
It may be seen in Fig. 4 how a complicated nuclear structure results in
variable apparent densities, thus explaining the apparently fragmented
appearance. For stained preparations for light microscopy, the same
conditions apply; instead of ρ, one has to introduce the absorption
coefficient of the specific stain used.

Such complicated nuclei can be reconstructed from serial thin sections. A drawing on transparent gray film is made of each serial section, and the nuclear vacuoles are cut out. By superposition of these films one arrives at exactly the same picture of a fragmented nucleus as that observed on the whole bacterium, thus confirming the explanation given previously for the fragmented appearance of the nucleus. It becomes obvious now that most of the stained preparations of bacterial nuclei showing "fragments" can be explained on this basis, and there is really no evidence in favor of a multitude of individual chromosomes.

2. Study of Very Small Intracellular Structures

The shape and size of particles having a diameter of the order of the thickness of the section can be deduced rather easily by observation of single sections. Nevertheless many variations in electron opacity and shape are artifacts.

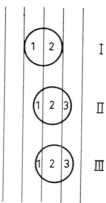

Fig. 5. Schematic representation of three different cases of serial sections through a sphere. In case I the sphere is distributed on only two sections, whereas in the two other cases it may appear on 3 successive sections. For case III it is possible that portion 1 does not give enough contrast to be visible in the electron microscope.

Let us consider spherical viruses homogeneously filled with an electron-opaque material and measuring 1000 A in diameter. The thickness of the sections may be 500 A. They may be cut at different levels as schematically represented in Fig. 5.

In case I, the virus appears in the first and second sections, and shows similar opacity since both sections contain the same amount of viral material. In case II, the second section presents a virus of the same opacity as in case I, but in the first and third sections the virus segment is of half the opacity. In case III, the second and third sections show viruses of only slightly different opacity while the first section contains a particle of very low opacity. There may not even be sufficient contrast in the first section to make the particle recognizable in the electron micrograph. The various virus segments in these sections thus show several degrees of opacity while the viruses themselves have exactly the same constitution. And while in this ideal case of spherical particles, the

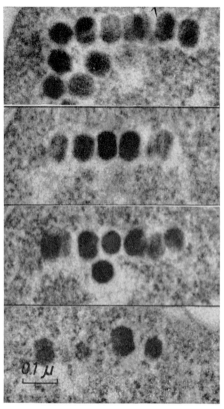

FIG. 6. Four serial sections through a cluster of intracellular T2 phages. Notice the different aspects produced solely by the different levels of sectioning. Embedding is in Vestopal.

variations in opacity would be accompanied by very slight variations in size, even this would not hold true in the case of polyhedral bodies. It is then obvious that one cannot interpret variations in opacity as representing, for example, different stages of virus maturation. Indeed, looking at a section, one cannot distinguish a segment of a possibly immature virus of lower density from a thinner segment of a mature, denser virus. The maturation of intracellular viruses, then, cannot be studied simply by examining random thin sections. Elaborate quantitative considerations of the distribution of particles in serial sections must form the basis for conclusions.

To study the intracellular growth of bacteriophage T2, Séchaud *et al.* (*176*) established a quantitative method which gives a partial answer to this problem. They determined a numerical factor which allows the calculation of the mean number of particles per cell from the mean number of particles seen in sections. To obtain this factor, both the frequency of appearance of the virus in consecutive sections and the thickness of the sections had to be known. The frequency of appearance of the phages was deduced from serial sections. The identification of the same phage on consecutive sections was rather difficult (Fig. 6) but this problem was solved by drawing the viruses on transparent film in a different color for each section. The superimposition of three or four of these drawings permitted the determination of the number of times the same phage appeared. It was found that 37% of the phages were seen only once, 56% twice, and 7% three times. This relatively large difference is explained by the following facts: (1) The phages studied are polyhedral rather than spherical and measure along the two axes 750 and 525 A. The frequency of appearance varies, therefore, with the plane of the section. (2) The minimum thickness which will still allow sufficient contrast for the particle to be visible in the electron microscope is not known precisely enough and introduces an uncertainty.

Taking into account the first factor and estimating the minimum visible thickness to be 50 A, the authors calculated the thickness of the sections to be about 400 A. With these data, it was then possible to establish the correlation which exists between the mean number of phages contained in the whole bacterium and the mean number of the visible phages in the cut bacterium. The maturation of phage was studied with the help of this correlation (see Section III, G).

This quantitative technique acquires general interest because of its application not only to the study of virus-infected bacteria but also to the study of animal and vegetal viruses and to the study of other intracellular particles.

Further application of serial sectioning procedures are made in the autoradiographic technique discussed in Section II, D.

D.   Autoradiography

Autoradiography is limited in its resolution by the length of the track produced by the radioactive particle, by the geometry of the specimen, and the size of the silver bromide grains in the emulsion. Increased resolution can be attained by decreasing the track length artificially by the use of a very thin layer of photographic emulsion together with thin sections of the specimen. Recently this technique has been introduced in electron microscopy (27, 30, 151, 152, 203). On thin sections a layer of photographic nuclear emulsion is spread so thin that the silver halide crystals form only a single layer. In an improved technique, the film of emulsion is produced on a wire loop before being put on the section (27, 30). Section and photographic emulsion are stored together to obtain an appropriate amount of radiation counts from the isotopically labeled organelles. They are developed, fixed, and observed in the electron microscope. The attainable resolution is in the order of the size of the silver bromide crystal. Indeed every exposed crystal is transformed into the well-known random aggregates of silver threads. The nonexposed grains are removed in a photographic fixative. For the time being, the resolution in locating the radioactivity is of the order of 0.1 μ; it is achieved by use of emulsions with silver bromide crystals of the order of 0.1 μ and of development procedures which reduce the silver thread to a very small size (28). Some improvements may hopefully still be reached, either by use of smaller silver halide crystals, or by use of other radiation-sensitive systems. Most important would be, however, to find a biologically suitable substance emitting particles of still lower energy than the electron of tritium.

An approach different from the direct localization of label has been introduced by Caro et al. (29). Two methods, both based on statistical counts, have been proposed. In the first, a normal autoradiograph is made of a 0.2 μ thick section containing a large number of bacteria. The photographic grains per bacterial cross section are counted in the optical microscope and plotted. The curves, giving the number of cross sections of cells showing a given number of grains as a function of the latter number, can be predicted theoretically to be of different types. If the label is uniformly distributed all over the cell, then the curve must correspond to a Poisson distribution. If the label is confined only to some parts of the cell, then the curve must be significantly different from a Poisson distribution. This is indeed what Caro et al. (26, 28, 29) (Fig. 7) found when studying cells in which the DNA contained tritium-labeled thymidine. Assuming a given geometrical form of the nucleus, they have calculated a distribution and compared it with the distribution found experimentally. They found a good correspondence.

In the second method introduced by the same authors, grain counts are made on successive serial sections about 0.2 μ thick. Only cross sections perpendicular to the cell axis are considered, and selection introduced for the first nongrazing section. The distribution of the grain counts is as expected.

In two more recent papers (*26, 28*) these very elegant techniques have been developed further. It was shown, for example, that the morphological change of the nucleus in chloramphenicol-treated cells is reflected in the distribution curves. Analyzing further different possibilities of the techniques, the authors conclude that using the first method (random cross sections of a population), the Poisson distribution offers three possibilities in interpretation: (1) The label is distributed randomly in

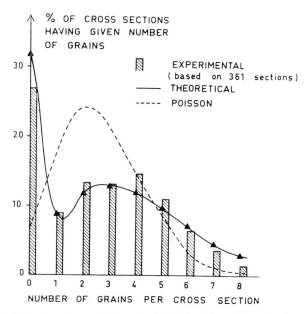

FIG. 7. Individual sections of bacteria labeled with tritium in the thymidine of their DNA are submitted to radioautography. The number of grains per section is counted and the statistical distribution plotted. It is seen that the experimental curve deviates clearly from a random labeling and corresponds to a situation where the label is confined only to the nuclear region of the cell. [From Caro *et al.* (*29*).]

the cytoplasm. (2) The label is distributed randomly in the cytoplasm and the nucleoplasm. (3) The label is distributed in a thin surface layer of the cell. By use of serial sections condition (3) may be distinguished from conditions (1) and (2). This is easily understood in the following example: If a label is located exclusively in the cell wall, then polar sections will contain much more labeled material than the subsequent sections. The serial sections must therefore show a marked, characteristic distribution pattern. Conditions (1) and (2), however, cannot be distinguished significantly.

In a case in which the statistical counts obtained by the first method give a distribution which deviates from the Poisson curve, three possibilities can be envisaged: (1) The label is confined exclusively to the nuclear region. (2) The label is distributed throughout the cell but with a large concentration in the nuclear site. (3) The label is restricted to small regions of the cell appearing in thin sections as vacuoles or granules.

Possibilities (1) and (3) are easily recognizable because (1) gives a more spread curve than (3). Serial sections also give different curves for each of the two cases. Possibility (2) is very difficult to distinguish from (1).

The distribution of RNA may be expected to fall into this difficult category (2) if one assumes that it is produced in the nucleus and then spreads into the cytoplasm. To get some insight into this problem Caro and Forro (28) used pulse experiments with H^3-labeled uridine under the experimental conditions where it enters RNA only. When the pulse is very short (1 minute) and the bacteria immediately fixed, the curve obtained deviates strongly from Poisson's curve; when, after the short pulse of uridine, the bacteria are incubated for 20 minutes, then the distribution corresponds to Poisson's curve. These results indicate that the labeled-RNA is first located in the region of the nucleus and is subsequently distributed into the cytoplasm.

III. Discussion of Some Results

A. The Cytoplasm and Its Inclusions

The most striking features of the bacterial cell cytoplasm are its extreme over-all density and the small number of organelles. Essentially the cytoplasm appears to be constituted of granules of a diameter of approximately 100–200 A. It is agreed now that these granules are *ribosomes*. Biochemical studies of disrupted cells have shown that the ribosomes contain about equal parts of protein and RNA (166, 196). By centrifugation in a sucrose gradient (121) several fractions can be isolated with the following sedimentation constants: 32 S, 51 S, 70 S, and 100 S (121). Their respective proportions vary with the Mg^{++} concentration, thereby indicating that the heavier particles are composed of smaller ones (15, 195). Electron microscopy (79) confirms these results by showing that the 70 S particles are not symmetrical but are formed by fused 51 S and 32 S particles and that the 100 S particles are constituted of two 70 S particles. In thin sections, since the appearance of the ribosomes is neither uniform nor constant, it is not possible to distinguish these different sorts of particles. It is likely that fixation and dehydration alter their size and shape; for instance, after reaction with the fixative, soluble proteins may

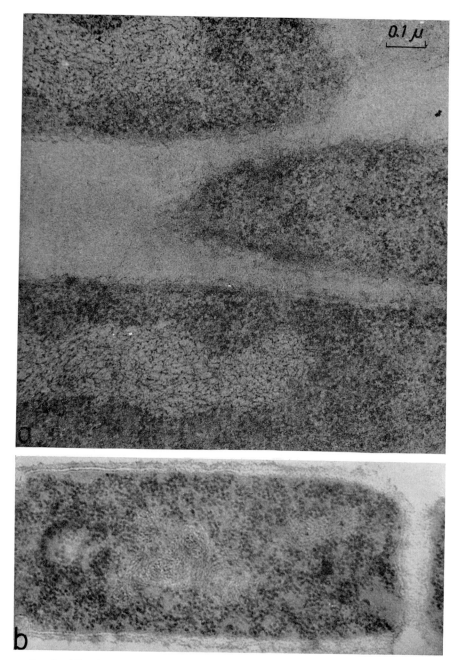

FIG. 8.   The density pattern of the cytoplasm: *a,* as seen on *Escherichia coli* when fixed in OsO_4 and posttreated with uranyl acetate; *b,* as seen on *Bacillus subtilis* fixed

perhaps adsorb onto the ribosomes and increase their apparent diameter.

In very thin sections, where the ribosomes are particularly well visualized, one can see that they are not evenly distributed throughout the cytoplasm but rather are grouped in clusters separated by homogeneous, less dense areas (Fig. 8). The concommittant scattering from the material which forms this diffuse cytoplasmic matrix leads to a lack of contrast. By staining the sections with lead salts the ribosomes become very distinct (Fig. 8b). Systematic experimental studies on the fixation of ribosomes are still lacking. The R-K fixation, which preserves the nucleus well, is perhaps not the best fixative for preserving the fine structure of the cytoplasm.

Both whole bacteria and thin sections of bacteria observed in the electron microscope show two or more cytoplasmic regions of lesser density which correspond to the chromatin bodies and which are termed "nuclear vacuoles," "nucleoids," or simply "nucleus." Thin sections reveal that the nuclear vacuoles are not separated from the cytoplasm by any membrane. When treated by the R-K fixation they are filled with a fine, stranded material. Further discussion of the *nucleus* will be found in a later section.

The *glycogen particles* appear as small round "vacuoles" of rather diffuse outline and without limiting membrane. They seem to be empty, but this appearance reflects rather the very low electron-scattering power of all polysaccharides of which glycogen is a representative. Good evidence for its identification has been given by Cedergren and Holme (*31*). Generally *E. coli* contains a rather small amount of glycogen which can be increased when the cells are fed with a suitable carbon source under conditions of nitrogen starvation. In this case the final amount of glycogen reaches 25% of the total dry weight of the cell and the micrographs of thin sections show bacteria crowded with vacuoles. This parallel increase in number of vacuoles and in chemical amount of glycogen is rather convincing for identification.

In *Bacillus megaterium* and *B. cereus,* inclusions of hydroxybutyric acid are found, which look like "empty vacuoles" (*127*); they have been frequently assimilated to lipids. In thin sections, the vacuoles are rather large with well-defined limits but with no membrane separating them from the rest of the cytoplasm. Their emptiness is probably again only simulated. It is probable that this polymer with a chemical structure similar to that of polysaccharides has also a very low electron-scattering

---

the same way, but in this case the sections have been floated on H_2O_2 and contrasted with lead hydroxide. It is clearly apparent, that the "ribosomes" are not regularly distributed. Embedded in Vestopal. Micrographs: *a,* Dr. W. H. Schreil, *b,* A. Ryter.

power. True *lipidic granules* have not yet been investigated carefully on thin sections.

Metachromatic granules have been observed, mainly in whole cells, as very dense bodies which are easily sublimated and deformed under the electron beam (*103, 184*). The granules have frequently been confused with the chondrioids. In thin sections they appear as dense granules which are entirely different from the mesosomes; they are not limited by a membrane and show no internal structure (*102*).

In the beginning of ultrathin sectioning techniques, few organelles were found which even slightly resembled the typical membranous structures called mitochondria. With the improvement of fixation and embedding techniques, however, lamellar or tubular bodies were suddenly observed in several species: bacilli (*55, 62, 160, 201*), streptomyces (*59*), *Mycobacterium tuberculosis* and *M. leprae* (*19, 102, 179, 190, 220*), and *Spirillum serpens* (*200*). In all these species, these structures seem to arise from an invagination of the cytoplasmic membrane. In *S. serpens,* the invaginations appear as small discrete tubules while in the other species they are more developed, forming a well-defined organelle (Fig. 9). Depending on the plane of the sections, they seem to be constituted either of approximately concentric lamellae or of small vesicles or tubules. Both the membrane which limits these organelles from the cytoplasm and the membranes of the internal tubules have the same appearance and dimensions as the cytoplasmic membrane. The neutral term of *mesosome* has been proposed for these membranous organelles by Fitz-James (*47*). In Section III, D, studies connected with the function of these mesosomes will be described more fully.

Unusual organelles—the *chromatophores*—are present only in photosynthetic bacteria and appear to be related to the photosynthetic abilities. The aspect of the chromatophores may vary from one species to the other but a basic similarity seems to exist among them all. In *Rhodospirillum* species (*R. rubrum* and *R. spheroid*) and in some strains of *Chromatium* and *Chlorobium,* the cells contain vesicles with a diameter of 300–700 A which are limited by a membrane (*72, 204*). In some micrographs they seem to be filled with a rather homogeneous material of low density while in others they appear to be empty. Their number increases with the age of the culture (*72*). A recent publication by Boatman and Douglas (*12*) shows that the chromatophores arise from the cytoplasmic membrane as vesicles which are presumably released into the cytoplasm by a "pinching-off" process when mature. These observations would then explain why in disrupted cells the chromatophores do not leave the cell immediately after disruption but only progressively (*6, 186, 199*).

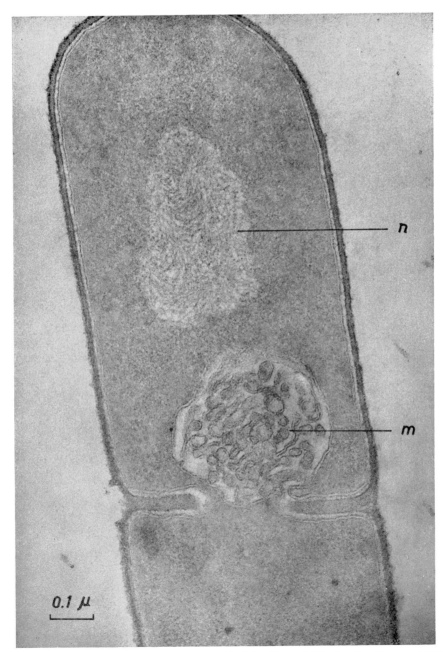

FIG. 9. Partial view of a section of a cell of *Bacillus subtilis* showing the mesosome (m), the nucleoid (n), the cell envelopes, and a beginning of septum formation. [From Eiserling and Romig (*45a*).]

Fractional centrifugation of disrupted photosynthetic bacteria (*R. rubrum*) shows that one fraction contains flattened discs of about 1000 A in diameter on which the photosynthetic pigment is located (*150*). These particles are considered to correspond to the particles observed in thin sections (*53*).

In *R. molischianum*, multilamellar bodies are visible which are rather similar to the grana of the chloroplasts. They are formed by an invagination of the cytoplasmic membrane and seem to remain linked to this membrane for the whole life of the cell (*57*).

Blue-green algae contain lamellar structures which vary in appearance and placement with the species observed. Resembling somewhat the chloroplasts but without possessing their individuality (*25, 147, 154, 178*), in some species the lamellar structures form a network throughout the cells while in others they occupy a more precise location in the cell.

B. The Bacterial Nucleus

1. INTRODUCTION

To facilitate discussion of the biological plasms containing DNA (DNA-plasm) the following definitions have been introduced (*87*). The *chemical* state of the DNA refers to the substances present which neutralize the acidic groups of the DNA. The *physical* state concerns the DNA molecule itself, for example, its single, double, or multiple-strandedness. The *organizational* state concerns the whole DNA-plasm. Electron microscopy aids in investigations of the physical state but is used mainly for studies of the organizational state. One of the parameters which describes the organizational state of DNA-plasms is its hydration; differences up to factors of 15 may occur in the physiological process of condensation (*86, 95*). The process exists in phages and presumably in higher chromosomes but not in bacteria. This parameter of hydration can be studied by electron microscopy more easily than by any other means; in general, hydrated or expanded DNA-plasms respond positively to the Versene test (see Section II, B).

Other aspects of the organizational state relate to the spatial arrangement of the chromofibrils. Electron microscopy, together with genetic observations and investigations of the physical state of the DNA, helps in constructing usable models of the "chromosomes." The bacterial nucleus is most likely to be a single chromosome in a perpetual interphase state. (Interphase is defined here as the state in which DNA replication normally does occur.) DNA content is small in comparison to that of the chromosomes of higher cells, and its genetics is easily accessible for experimentation. It can be assumed, therefore, that the organizational state of the DNA is relatively simple in contrast to the complexity of the "higher chromosomes" with their multiple coiling and bipartite nature (heterochromatin, euchromatin). A still more primitive organizational state is found in viruses, particularly in the bacteriophages.

2. THE FIBRILLAR COMPOSITION OF THE BACTERIAL DNA-PLASM

In Section II, B problems concerning the fixation of the DNA-plasm of the bacterial nucleoids have been discussed. The OsO_4 fixation under the R-K conditions has been widely applied to numerous microorganisms. Usually uranyl acetate postfixation has been used simultaneously (*47, 62, 94, 98, 102, 113, 160, 202*).

After treatment with these fixatives, the DNA-plasm, in all these instances, is composed of fibrillae of a diameter between 30 and 80 A. The specific appearances vary with the authors as much as with the species. In some cases individually visible fibrils are finer than in others; and, although an arrangement in bundles is most frequent (Fig. 10), an aspect similar to a network also is encountered. The mean density of the DNA-plasm, compared to that of the cytoplasm, is also variable; in some cases the nuclear region can be distinguished from the ribosomes only because of its fibrillar structure, in other cases it is much less dense. These differences must be attributed to small variations in techniques not yet under sure control. It is easy, however, to find explanations for the differences since by its nature fixation produces aggregation in variable degree. It may be, also, that the fibrils are thickened by deposit of material on their surfaces and, as a consequence, the staining is of different intensities. Both R-K fixation and uranyl acetate do add substances to the DNA. Finally, both section thickness and the optical characteristics of the microscope can be responsible for differences in the appearance of the DNA-plasm.

That the fibrils represent DNA or DNA complexes (DNAc) becomes evident from the observation of isolated DNA and DNAc (Figs. 2 and 3 and Section II, B).

The variabilities described above must come under experimental control and the techniques become more refined. It is not yet possible, for instance, to visualize directly the production of RNA in the nucleus. This localization is strongly supported by the experiments of Caro and Forro (*28*) obtained by radioautographic techniques as described in Section II, D.

It was indicated in Section II, A that hydrated DNA-plasm is most likely to be a significant and adequate representation of its natural state in spite of a possible swelling which cannot be excluded. The former belief that coarse bodies in otherwise empty vacuoles represented DNA-

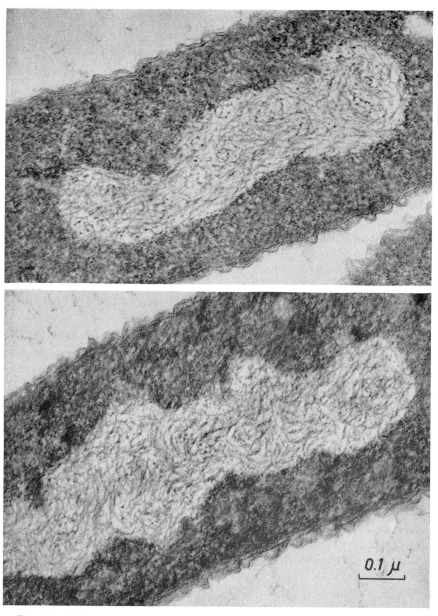

FIG. 10. High-magnification micrographs of some bacterial nucleoids obtained after osmium fixation and uranyl acetate posttreatment. Preparation and micrographs by Dr. W. H. Schreil.

plasm need not be discussed except to label them as artifacts of aggregation. Further discussion and references may be found in (*85, 87*). In fact, a slightly swelling artifact actually would provide a welcome means to distinguish individual chromofibrils. It is well known that in "dense" chromosomes fine structure has never been revealed despite the high resolving power of the microscope. A swollen chromosome would permit the investigation of its intimate organization even though there is some slight disorder.

What is the functional signification of this highly hydrated state? For bacteria, it is known that DNA synthesis occupies at least 80% of the generation time (*1, 120, 167*). Is high hydration a necessary condition for replication? One can easily imagine that this state is favorable for the penetration of enzymes and precursors to the sites of synthesis. In the following, the basis for this working hypothesis will be explored.

In the late interphase or early prophase of mitosis of higher cells, Moses (*134*) has observed chromosomes composed of an electron-opaque core surrounded by filamentous material. In normal interphase, De Robertis (*43*) has observed a filamentous plasm which is visible as such only after fixation in presence of calcium. In the dinoflagellate, which shows an abnormal nuclear division without formation of a spindle, the chromosomes are in general in an organizational state very similar to bacteria (*56, 63, 64*). Thorough investigation of the appearance of the dinoflagellate after fixation has shown that it is similar to that of bacteria (*41, 85, 87, 153*). There is no doubt, however, that systematic studies of these higher cells are urgently needed. In particular, morphological studies of DNA-plasms must be done in connection with measurements of DNA synthesis.

3. THE VARIABILITY OF THE NUCLEAR SHAPE

That there are variations in the shape and size of the nuclear vacuoles of the different species is not astonishing when one considers that, even for *E. coli*, different strains have a distinctive nuclear morphology. For two such strains, C, which is globular in its general aspect, and K12, which is bacillar, genetic recombination is possible (*115*). Each strain shows a quite different nuclear morphology which is inherited independently from the cell shape. In the recombinants, one can find bacillary strains with the nuclear arrangement of C and globular cells with the nuclear arrangement of K12. However, not only genetically inherited factors but also the ionic conditions of the growth medium condition the shape and arrangement of the nucleoids. Optical microscopy has shown that high NaCl concentrations produce globular nucleoids with sharp outlines, while either low concentrations or no

NaCl result in diffuse or "dispersed" nuclei (216). This observation
has been confirmed by electron microscopy (94) (Fig. 11). A discrepancy
in interpretation of these results has arisen, however, which must be
solved by further experiments. The latter authors have found a clear-cut
difference between cells growing without NaCl and those in 2% NaCl
and concluded that the nuclei are already different in the growing state.
Changes in the salt concentration of the fixative did not materially

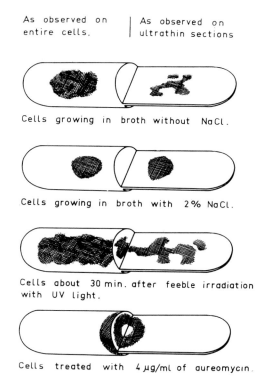

FIG. 11. Schematic drawing of some typical nuclear shapes of *Escherichia coli.*
[From Kellenberger (85).]

alter the shape. The former authors, however, think that fixation may
first alter the permeability of the cell so that different salt concentrations
in the outside are propagated inside. Recent experiments (144) are not
yet consistent; depending on specific conditions, the response may be in
favor of either interpretation. Again, a better understanding of the
process of fixation is necessary.

Other environmental influences are reflected in morphological changes
similar to those of the "salt effect." Most antibacterial drugs produce
such specific effects. Ultraviolet irradiation and x-rays initiate changes

which are similar to those of low salt concentration but greater. Indeed, in the over-all picture, the nucleus seemed to be fragmented (83, 84). Reconstruction experiments based on thin sections (157), however, have shown that there is no fragmentation but rather an increase of extrusions and intrusions in the limits between cytoplasm and nucleus (see Section II, C). This effect is only partly dependent on the salt concentration. A very specific action, which is also independent of salt, is produced by even sublethal doses of aureomycin and chloromycetin (Fig. 11) (91, 94). In this instance, the nuclear material assumes a regular spherical or ellipsoidal shape; sometimes a body is enclosed exactly in the center.

In Section III, G a few cases of virulent viruses in which the phage infection results in a typical nuclear breakdown are reported. Most other phages, however, and all temperate phages produce only unspecific changes which can be induced equally well by reversible metabolic perturbations.

4. EXTRACTION OF NUCLEI

Obviously, the availability of isolated bacterial nuclei would facilitate correlated biochemical and morphologic investigations. Unfortunately, the isolation of bacterial nuclei from disrupted cells becomes a problem quite different from that of the isolation of the nuclei of higher cells. The bacterial nucleus is not a physical entity as is the nucleus of a higher cell with its membrane. In the preceding discussion of the great variations in shape and size of the bacterial nucleus it was concluded that its shape must be the result of complicated interactions between cytoplasm and nucleoplasm. That the nucleus tends to disperse its constituents as soon as it is free of the surrounding cytoplasm can, therefore, be expected. The prediction can be made that all those factors which prevent dispersion are unnatural chemical and physical conditions which produce a system of cross-links among the chromofibrils.

By gentle lysis of spheroplasts (lipase digestion and several cycles of centrifugation), Spiegelman et al. (185) succeeded in concentrating all DNA in one body. Subsequent fraction of these DNA-containing bodies revealed also, however, an equal amount of RNA and three times as much protein. Unfortunately, no proof was provided to show that every "nuclear body" contained the RNA and protein, or whether the fraction was nonhomogeneous and contained for example "DNA-bodies" as well as "protein-RNA bodies." Nor is the electron microscopy of these bodies as yet convincing. Using similar techniques, Nisman and Fukuhara (148) have isolated bodies from E. coli and have begun their physical investigations (38).

In a different approach, the nuclear material is not consolidated but its organization is made available for observation before complete dispersion (98, 99). These authors have devised an ingenious technique in which protein films are formed by spreading on water. DNA admixed to the protein remains adsorbed to the film and becomes easily visible after circular shadowing. This technique is applied to *in situ* studies of lysing spheroplasts. Conditions are chosen so that the spheroplast is lysed just prior to the spreading of the film and in such a way that the entire DNA of one spheroplast can be observed on an area of convenient size (Fig. 12). All fibers are seen to be connected. Free ends are hard to find. There are starlike points from which fibers emerge. Interpretation is still uncertain since whether the central body of the star is natural or artifactual has not been ascertained.

5. A Model of the Bacterial Nucleus

Convincing evidence exists that the genetic map of the chromosomes of bacteria is circular (see Jacob and Wollman, 81). The circular map becomes linearly stretched in the so-called high-frequency mutants. Most likely this circularity is related to the physical arrangement. These genetic facts have to be taken into account when building a model.

The crucial but unsolved problem is the physical length and constitution of the DNA. Meselson and Stahl (131) have determined a molecular weight of 7×10^6 for bacterial DNA and, therefore, a bacterial nucleus would contain about 500 such molecules or subunits. From the foregoing genetic evidence, the conclusion is drawn that these molecules are linked together to form a linear, circular chromosome. (The assumptions made are that every molecule carries other information and that each does contain information, which means that there is no "nonsense DNA"; they are likely but by no means proved.) Thus were postulated "linkers" which would be different in nature from the DNA. The natural length of DNA in organisms is, as has been said, a matter of conflicting opinions. For phage T-even, it has been proposed that 10 molecules of 14×10^6 would account for its DNA content (132). More recent experiments have shown that most carefully extracted DNA from this phage stays linked together in one piece (71). Kleinschmidt *et al.* (100) have confirmed this result with beautiful micrographs of preparations obtained by their special technique of spread-surface films (Section III, B). On the other hand, careful investigation of the physical means necessary to fragment this DNA revealed that "linkers" or predetermined sites of breakage are not necessary to explain the results (114). Since sound scientific practice does not admit the existence of something new without strong evidence to support it, further developments must give a final answer to the question of whether in all chromosomes the DNA is

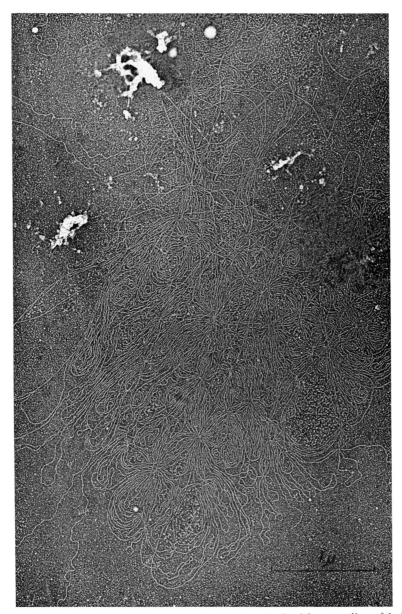

FIG. 12. Nuclear DNA of *Micrococcus lysodeikticus* obtained by spreading of lysing protoplasts. Prepared in a solution of cytochrome at pH 5 and spread on a solution at pH 5. The contrast is enhanced by circular shadowing, which is the reason for the thick appearance of the DNA fibrils. It is especially noteworthy, that only very few free ends are visible. Preparation and micrograph by Dr. A. Kleinschmidt, Hygiene-Institut der Universität Frankfurt.

formed of one continuous, homogeneous molecule or if it consists of an assembly of subunits. If the former is true, the difficulties of replication and separation are obvious. These difficulties are not encountered in the "linker" theory since the DNA segment between each two linkers could rotate freely around its axis and replicate independently.

How much can electron microscopy help in elucidating these problems? The observations of Kleinschmidt and Lang (98) provide convincing evidence that the DNA in bacteria is connected in a continuous structure. This is in agreement with the genetic evidence. The authors cannot easily exclude the existence of linkers.

Observed on thin sections of normal cells (Fig. 10), the parallel arrangement of the fibrils, the occurrence of volutes, and possible cross sections suggest a bundled arrangement of the DNA. The bundles would make 1–3 crude helical turns. This helix being more or less tight would explain the wide variabilities in the form of the nucleoid. That cells treated with aureomycin or chloromycetin show nucleoids of a spherical or ellipsoidal shape has already been seen. With a linked model, this geometrically defined form could be easily explained by assuming all linkers to be in the center with the DNA segments each forming a loop outside.

From these observations, a tentative model of the bacterial nucleus or chromosome has been proposed which assumes a linker system without polyteny[1] (85). The model reflects the genetic and metabolic observations satisfactorily. This, and other models such as a third-order helix (56) or polytenic bundles (163, 170) cannot be proved or disproved by the observation of individual sections alone.

It is believed that electron microscopy can contribute to this problem by reconstruction experiments using serial sections but that this work will be really fruitful only when the question of the existence and nature of the linkers is definitely solved. In this inquiry, specific antibody techniques (as described in Section II, B) could be of invaluable help.

The understanding of nuclear division also depends on a knowledge of molecular organization. Obviously the division process is reflected in changes in the shape of the nucleus. Interpretation of such changes is

---

[1] It has been pointed out earlier (94) that, under the assumption of several, nonidentical linkage groups and random distribution on the daughter nuclei, polyteny would be the only way to assure genetic continuity. In considering carefully the genetics of E. coli, where it had been shown clearly that only one linkage group exists, this hypothesis was not maintained (85, 87). Since the calculations of the genetic length from the data of Jacob and Wollman (81) give approximatively the same values as those of the chemical length, there is no longer any need to introduce polyteny.

made difficult by variabilities in shape introduced by preparatory techniques. Thus, there is no general agreement on these matters: results vary from species to species, strain to strain, and laboratory to laboratory.

C. The Cell Envelopes

Since membranous structures are the cell parts which are the most insensitive to fixation conditions, investigations utilizing electron microscopy are capable of revealing valuable information. This is as true for bacterial cells as for higher cells. The property of insensitivity, or mechanical and chemical stability has permitted extensive and promising biochemical examinations of cell envelopes. In this section biochemical and morphological findings will be related since it is increasingly urgent that the two approaches be conducted in parallel. Indeed, the interpretations of results obtained from both approaches are for the moment not sufficiently convergent, a consequence of the fact that the two types of investigations are rarely pursued in the same laboratory.

There is general agreement that cell envelopes can be separated into two classes: the components of cell wall and those of the cytoplasmic membrane. This division may be somewhat artificial and may be subject to revision, particularly in respect to the functions which are believed to be attributable to each class. The main function ascribed to the cytoplasmic membrane is that of selective permeability. It is also believed that the cytoplasmic membrane contains many enzymes (for references see Section III, D) and thus must be considered in all questions of cellular metabolism. The cell wall, however, is rather inactive metabolically; its main role is believed to be mechanical, conferring to the cell its form, rigidity, and resistance to the high internal osmotic pressure created by the selectivity of the cytoplasmic membrane. Many optical microscope observations, such as those of plasmolyses and of the formation of spheroplasts, are in favor of this functional differentiation.

Unfortunately, in some papers a distinction is not made between cell walls and cytoplasmic membranes and the definitions used are not always indicated. In the reports of Weidel, for example, the cytoplasmic membrane is considered to be a layer of the cell wall and the whole is called "Zellmembran." Therefore caution is a prerequisite in comparing and correlating the results of different authors.

In the following paragraphs, morphological observations will be described separately and later related to the biochemical findings.

Electron microscopy of cell envelopes can be done on two types of preparation: observation of the entire envelopes after disintegration and chemical interaction and observation of thin sections. These observations are complementary and should be used jointly, as will be seen below.

Observation of thin sections of *E. coli* shows convincingly the existence of two mechanically separable envelopes: the outer, called the cell wall, and the inner, the cytoplasmic membrane which always stays in contact with the cytoplasm (*92, 139*). The cell wall has the "double" structure typical of biological membranes, an inner unstained layer about 30 A thick sandwiched between two opaque layers. The cytoplasmic membrane of 60 A thickness was shown to be stained homogeneously in a first paper (*92*). Later results (Fig. 18) reveal that the cytoplasmic membrane is also frequently visualized as a double structure of dimensions similar to those of the cell wall. The differences of aspect are probably due to variations in fixing and staining conditions.[2]

The cell walls of bacilli and many other species are generally much thicker, 150–250 A (Figs. 9 and 16) than those of *E. coli* (*55, 62, 126, 139, 160, 201*). Usually they do not present a layered structure. Depending on the conditions of fixation and postfixation treatment, separated layers might be revealed. If this is the case, difficulty would ensue in determining whether the double membranes reflect a characteristic chemical structure for each layer or whether the layered effect is produced artificially by deposits of osmium.

That the cytoplasmic membrane of *Bacillus* species appears to be comparable to that of *E. coli* may be seen in Fig. 9. The same conclusion has been reached by van Iterson (*201*) on plasmolyzed cells. In most other micrographs, this situation cannot be recognized as clearly and leads to other interpretations (*47*).

The process of septum formation is still relatively unknown. In some species (bacilli, some cocci, and streptomyces), the septum seems to be constituted immediately of the cytoplasmic membrane and of the cell wall (*34, 55, 60, 160, 202*) (Fig. 9), whereas in other species first a double cytoplasmic membrane seems to be formed and then the cell wall is built between its components (*33*). Mesosomes have frequently been found near newly forming septa, and it has been proposed that they are implicated directly in the synthesis of envelopes (*202*). In Section III, D the metabolic function of mesosomes is discussed in more detail.

Observation of envelopes isolated from disrupted cells has been done

---

[2] These differences are certainly not due to resolution—since the dimensions are not markedly different for wall and cytoplasmic membrane—and therefore raise the question of whether double structures are real or artifacts. It has already been pointed out (see Section III, A) that the soluble parts of the cell may precipitate on surfaces after reacting with the fixative. This may also be true for other reaction products, such as the MnO_2 produced after reduction of permanganate by cell sap.

so far mainly on shadowed preparations. A comparison of the results obtained from sections (Fig. 13) with those from shadowed preparations reveals immediately that, in the latter, the cytoplasmic membrane is usually difficult to identify. Thin sections of preparations of supposedly pure walls, however, show clearly the presence of cytoplasmic membranes. This is true for envelopes isolated from *E. coli*; those obtained from *B. subtilis* were apparently pure wall fractions (*14*). This particular situation has an important bearing on the interpretation of biochemical data.

The study of isolated envelopes has produced interesting observations on the ultrastructure of some of the component layers. In several species, an internal layer is composed of visible subunits, on Spirillum species (*76*); on *R. rubrum* (*165*); on *Halobacterium halobium* (*77, 108*). Recently Murray (Fig. 14) discovered a complicated structure in an inner envelope layer of a tetrad-forming *Micrococcus* species after embedding in phosphotungstate. The figure shows this nice superposition pattern which, so far, has not been completely explained. In *E. coli*, subunits have not been made visible. By chemical removal of some constituents of the wall, a layer of small globular elements becomes apparent, an observation to be discussed later.

The biochemistry of cell envelopes has been extensively investigated in many laboratories. To supplement the limited outline of results which is included here, the reader is referred to reviews by Staub (*187*), Salton (*163, 164*), Weibull and Bergström (*209*), and Westphal and Lüderitz (*215*). However, the role of electron microscopy in this field will be analyzed in some detail.

All envelopes studied contain as main constituents lipopolysaccharides and mucopolysaccharides of complex composition which, in details, vary with the species investigated. Glycosamines and some amino acids are always found; in particular, diaminopimelic acid seems to be a very specific amino acid heretofore not encountered in proteins. *Escherichia coli* envelopes contain supplementary lipoproteins, a feature which seems to be specific for gram-negative cells, particularly the Enterobacteriaceae (*213*). These lipoproteins can be extracted by phenol (*214*) and by lauryl sulfate (*13*). By appropriately combined chemical or enzymic actions, envelopes can be differentially extracted in successive steps (*214*). These observations led to the idea that the envelopes are made up of successive layers of different chemical constitution. This idea was tested by electron microscopy with the following results.

After treatment of *E. coli* cells in a Mickle disintegrator, the isolated envelopes contain both cell wall and cytoplasmic membrane (Fig. 13a). Treatment with trypsin does not remove the membrane (Fig. 13b). Treat-

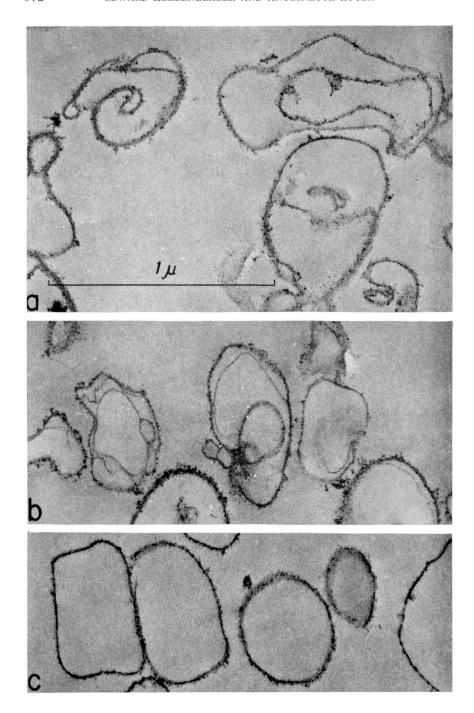

ment with lauryl sulfate removes the cytoplasmic membrane but no change is visible in the structure of the wall (Fig. 13c). Hence these chemical extractions cannot be related to a morphologically visible layer of the cell wall, but only to the removal of the cytoplasmic membrane.

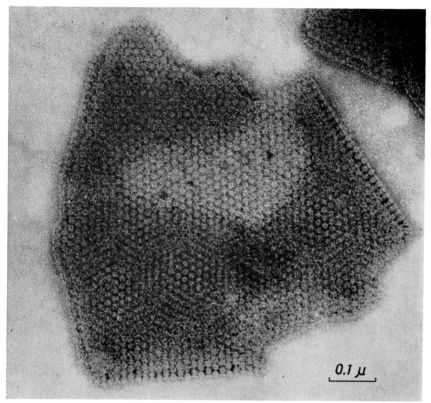

Fig. 14. Envelopes of disrupted cells of the tetrad-forming *Micrococcus* (sp. *sarcina*) enclosed in postassium phosphotungstate. Preparation and micrograph by Dr. R. G. E. Murray.

Furthermore, great care must be taken in following in each case the morphological fate of the cytoplasmic membrane. There is no doubt that the previous deduction (*13*) that lauryl sulfate extracts a layer of

Fig. 13.   Thin sections of cell envelopes of *Escherichia coli,* obtained by treatment of the cells in the Mickle desintegrator: *a,* without further treatment; *b,* digested with trypsin; and *c,* treated with lauryl sulfate. It becomes obvious, that there is a double system of envelopes (wall and membrane); the membrane is removed only by the lauryl sulfate treatment. Preparation by Dr. A. Bolle; micrograph by E. Boy de la Tour.

the cell wall must be revised. The existence of an outer lipoprotein layer in *E. coli* must also be reconsidered. Weidel concluded its existence from the observation that its removal destroyed the ability of some phages to adsorb. The O-antigen, supposed to be a surface antigen, is a mucopolysaccharide (*215*). The implication is that the polysaccharides

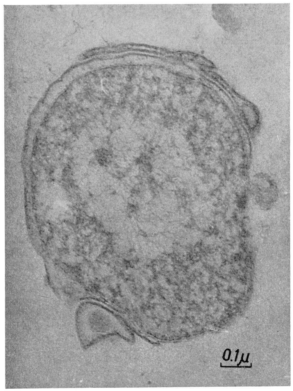

FIG. 15. Spheroplasts of *Escherichia coli* obtained by treatment with lysozyme and Versene. Fixed in acetone-bichromate mixture and posttreated in uranyl acetate. The cell wall is distorted, but normally still adherent to the protoplast. Preparation and micrograph by Dr. P. H. Hofschneider, Max-Planck-Institut für Biochemie, Munich.

also reach the surface. Perhaps these different chemical components intermingle and, therefore, possibly cannot be related directly and specifically to the "double structures" of the electron micrographs.

It is tempting to assume the existence of a supplementary outer layer of cell wall which may be invisible. The observation of thin sections of walls coated with antiserum does not show an interval, but a supplementary new layer is observed, the thickness of which (150 A) does not depend on the concentration of antiserum. The intensity of staining of the layer, however, *is* proportional to the concentration of antiserum (*14*). The dimension, 150 A, corresponds roughly to the generally accepted size of the long axis of globulins.

The important role of thin sections as a tool in the investigation of cell envelopes becomes obvious from the previously mentioned observations. The use of shadowing techniques, however, should not be discredited. Starting with a skeleton of the cell wall (after lauryl sulfate and phenol extraction) Weidel *et al.* (*214*) were able to study the chemical and morphological constitution of the so-called rigid layer of *E. coli* walls composed of lipopolysaccharide and some 13 amino acids. A special mechanical-chemical procedure of extraction revealed a very thin structure (called R-layer) made up of spheres measuring about 200 A. With lysozyme treatment the spheres became unlinked. Chemically they are not composed of a lipopolysaccharide, but of a still undefined composite containing the nonspecific amino acids mentioned previously. The lysozyme-sensitive linkages, however, seem to be composed of groups containing diaminopimelic acid, muramic acid, and glucosamine.

An erroneous concept has been introduced in regard to protoplasts. By definition a protoplast is the protoplasm enclosed in the cytoplasmic membrane (*18*). Unfortunately every bacterium transformed into a globular body has been called a protoplast and assumed to be devoid of cell wall material. Only thin sections can reveal whether walls are present or not, and only by sectioning has it been possible to show that for *E. coli* cells, real protoplasts can never be produced (*73*, *113*) (Fig. 15). The cell wall adheres to the protoplast and only very infrequently some area of a spherical body is seen denuded of cell wall. For these spherical bodies, the term spheroplasts is, therefore, more appropriate. For bacilli species, in only one case were true protoplasts obtained (*194*).

These findings challenge the investigations made on the so-called cytoplasmic membranes, obtained after lysis of "protoplasts."

Electron microscopy of thin sections shows the existence of a cell wall and a cytoplasmic membrane in most cases. The chemical characterization of each membrane is not definitively established, however, because the fractions used have not always been identified morphologically by adequate means. With the use of methods outlined previously, a clarification will soon be reached.

D. The Localization of the Respiratory System in Bacteria

The discovery of the mesosomes (see Section III, A) has the advantage of reconciling two divergent opinions on the cellular localization of the respiratory enzymes of bacteria. Mudd *et al.* (*137*) describe this situation with all necessary references. A summary of various pertinent investigations follows.

Fractions which apparently contained only the cytoplasmic membrane (but actually included several layers of the cell envelopes) gave biochemical reactions proper to the respiratory cycle (39, 188, 211). The conclusion was, then, that the respiratory enzymes are located in the cytoplasmic membrane. This hypothesis was supported mainly by the biochemists but opposed by the bacterial morphologists who believed in distinct intracellular reduction sites. Morphologists went so far as to call these sites "mitochondria" (40, 135) or "chondrioids" (89). Their evidence came from light microscope observations and included the use of mitochondrial stains and the reduction of tetrazolium salts. Distinct organelles were also visible with other microscopic techniques. Using phase contrast, dark granules were found in starved cells and in lysed spheroplasts (116, 208). If sufficiently careful techniques were employed, the granules were also visible in electron micrographs (116).

There is no longer a contradiction between the chemists and morphologists since most investigators now have dependable evidence that the mesosomes are invaginations of one or several inner layers of the cell envelopes. The cytoplasmic membrane is therefore certainly implicated in the structure of the mesosome with these consequences: (1) Enzymes found in the mesosome in relatively high concentrations may also be found in the cytoplasmic membrane. (2) It can be predicted that the mesosomes cannot be separated readily from the cytoplasmic membrane without concomitant destructions. Indeed, attempts already made to purify mesosomes have not been very successful (180). The granules found in ghosted cells or ghosted spheroplasts are also easily explained since it is likely that they represent mesosomes which remained attached to the cellular envelopes.

With this new understanding, the technical means which allow the investigation of the function of these organelles merit description. A feature of the mesosomes is their ability to reduce chemicals to an insoluble form which remains fixed to the structure. Most widely employed are the tetrazolium salts. Two reactions can, in fact, be distinguished, one a specific and the other a nonspecific deposit of insoluble formazan (90). The specific reaction occurs in competition with oxygen. In aerated cultures the supply of oxygen must be arrested for the reaction to occur. Only if these conditions are realized will results be comparable to those already published (7). The unspecific reaction occurs in a much slower and unpredictable way. It consists of a deposit of numerous very small formazan crystals on the surface of the cell. This reaction is not in any manner a preliminary step of the other reaction as was claimed. The unspecific reaction has been one of the reasons for the theory of the reductional sites being linked to the cell surface (207).

Niklowitz (146) has shown that reduction of tetrazolium salts can be used in electron microscopy since formazan crystals can be dissolved in acetone or alcohol, leaving a characteristic empty space. The author observes in E. coli a darker and more homogeneous area beside this space which he thinks to be the chondrioid he is looking for. These experiments have been repeated by Vanderwinkel and Murray (200) with similar results. However, despite the use of improved techniques, the organelles usually are not visible in the untreated cell and therefore any conclusions for E. coli are premature. In Bacillus and Spirillum species, the same investigators found a clear association with the mesosomes. Depending on the size of the formazan crystal formed, a larger or smaller "empty" area was observed in or just beside the mesosome. The kinetics of the amount of formazan extracted exactly parallels these findings and so furnishes strong evidence that the mesosome is actually the site of reduction. Since the term "chondrioid" was introduced to characterize an organelle detectable because of the ability to reduce tetrazolium salts (89), now the statement that mesosomes are chondrioids can be safely made.

That mesosomes are implicated in the cross-wall formation has been proposed (55, 62, 201). This hypothesis is not excluded by their identification with the reduction sites. Further experiments must show, however, that the presence of mesosomes in areas of septum formation or of spore formation is not simply the expression of an increased local energy requirement.

E. The Cell Surface (Flagella, Pili, and Capsules)

The number and location of the *flagella* vary with strains and species. Some species have only one flagellum and others are nearly covered with them. The flagella often have the tendency to form large bundles, which in the optical microscope suggest the presence of a sort of tail (76, 78, 217). The observations made by Weibull (205) on isolated and purified flagella also show the bundles and these assume a helicoidal arrangement. When the flagella have been broken and are shorter, they form surface films presenting periodic arrangements of parallel flagella which appear as waves (205). The latter observation was made with the electron microscope and was manifest only on highly purified preparations. Presumably the wavelike appearance is related to the chemical structure of the flagella. Chemical analysis revealed that the flagella are essentially composed of proteins (101, 206). In examining mutants of Salmonella, which have large amounts of certain amino acids in the flagella, Kerridge (96) observed that the growth of the flagella depends on the presence of these amino acids. The absence of other amino acids does not prevent the growth of flagella on otherwise nongrowing bacteria.

Very recently, preparations of flagella made in phosphotungstate revealed regular packing arrangements of possibly globular subunits about 25 A in diameter (97). The diameters of flagella are reported to be between 110 and 150 A.

The flagella are considered to be instruments of locomotion (45) but the rationale of their movement is still unknown. Their chemical constitution does not permit an analogy with muscle contraction; indeed they contain no myosin components (206).

In some micrographs, especially those of carefully lysed cells, small intracellular spherical bodies (basal bodies) have been observed from which the flagella seem to arise (78, 217). The inspection of shadowed cells does not prove that the spheres are really in the cytoplasm because it is impossible to be sure that the flagella pass through the cell wall. Ultrathin sections should provide an answer. So far no such observations are available, probably because the contrast of flagella on thin sections is too poor.

The pili, or fimbriae, were first noted by Houwink and van Iterson (78) and later by several authors (20, 23, 44, 123, 174, 193). Pili can be distinguished from the flagella by thinner diameter (50–80 A) and greater rigidity. Covering the whole surface of the cell and growing continuously like hair, they form a sort of capsule. The pili are fragile and easily broken or detached, so fragments are often observed on the preparations. A comparative study of the motility of piliated and nonpiliated strains has shown that these structures do not play any active role in the motility of the cell (45).

On the other hand, electrophoretic mobility measurements showed that piliated bacteria are "slower" than nonpiliated (20, 23). This difference in mobility can be explained as a difference in viscosity; the slowest cultures possess an intrinsic viscosity 3.3 times as great as that of a "fast" culture. Treatment of piliated bacteria in a blender (which does not affect the viability of the cells) removes all the pili, and changes the electrophoretic mobility from typically slow to typically fast. Therefore, the electrophoretic mobility is directly correlated with the piliation. In growing cultures, the cells from which the pili are removed recover their former piliation after a few hours.

Preparations of purified pili show their tendency to form little bundles resembling needles of a paracrystalline aspect. High magnification has not yet revealed fine structure (21, 193).

The interest of pili has recently been shown by genetic experiments (22, 24, 123, 124, 125). Piliation can be transferred from a piliated strain to a nonpiliated strain by transduction with phage or by sexual recombination. By the latter procedure, the gene of piliation has been located on the genetic map (24, 125).

Chemically, pili seem to be a rather simple protein or polypeptide (21), and may provide an easily accessible experimental system for the study of the pathway of polypeptide synthesis.

An electron microscope survey of bacteria possessing a *capsule* or a slime has not revealed any particular fine structure. The capsules present a homogeneous and diffuse aspect. The lack of interesting results in this field is probably due to technical limitations. Studies employing modern and more adequate techniques should give new information.

Two reports should be mentioned, however. The presence of large fibers forming a capsule was observed in a strain of *E. coli*. The fibers showed cross striations with a periodicity of about 200–290 A (109).

Bacterium xylinum is surrounded by a diffuse slime out of which grow many cellulose fibers 250 A in diameter (138). The length and the number of these fibers increase with the age of the culture and finally are so numerous that they form a rigid network in which the bacteria are enclosed.

F. Sporulation

At the end of their period of growth and under specific conditions, several species of bacteria form a spore within their protoplasm. The completed spore protected by several layers of envelopes is set free by disruption of the mother bacterium.

Both the process of sporulation and the morphology of the spores have stimulated the interest of many bacteriologists. Ultrathin sections, first used for the study of these problems by Robinow (155) and later by Chapman (32), should help resolve some of the controversial points raised by observations in the light microscope.

Spore structure. The spores of different species of bacteria seem to resemble each other in their internal organization but differ in the degree of elaboration of their envelopes. The apparent differences among the species may decrease and the similarities increase with progressively refined techniques.

The core of the spore, which contains cytoplasmic and chromatic material, is diffuse and generally featureless. A few areas of low density may be distinguished near the surface of the core and may correspond to the sites of chromatic material (156).

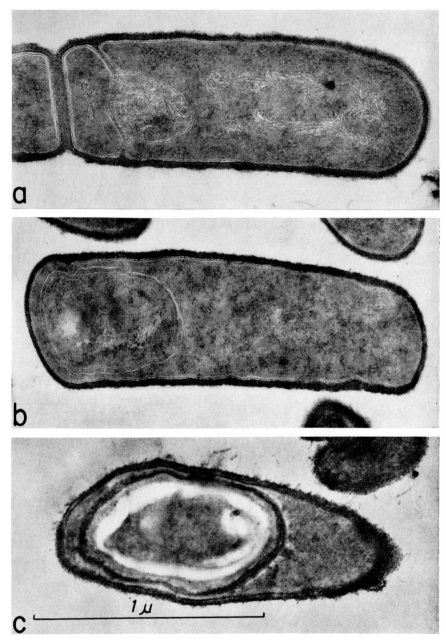

Fig. 16. Sporulation of *Bacillus subtilis*. *a*, A septum (constituted of cytoplasmic membrane) begins to enclose a portion of cytoplasm and nuclear material. A very large mesosome is "linked" to this septum. *b*, In a later step the forespore has taken

In the spores of several species, the core has been seen to be surrounded by a delicate envelope which is often difficult to see. Robinow called it "spore wall" because observations during germination seemed to indicate that the envelope becomes the wall of the cell; but the quality of the micrographs is not sufficient to show this evolution clearly. The spore is generally surrounded by two or even three further layers (Fig. 16c): cortex, spore coat, and, in some strains, an exosporium. The cortex lies close to the spore wall and is distinguished from the other envelopes by its thickness and by its low electron scattering power. Usually the cortex of normal spores lacks any internal structure. Mayall and Robinow (128), however, have shown a lamellation of the cortex when spores of *Bacillus megaterium* are treated with acid and stained afterward with lanthanum nitrate. Since in developing spores of *B. cereus* the cortex shows a laminated aspect even without acid and lanthanum treatment, these authors think that the structure is not an artifact.

The appearance of the one or two spore coats surrounding the cortex varies considerably from one species ot another. They are often composed of several layers (198), and sometimes many grooves give a very special and typical aspect to the spore surface (46, 49, 52, 74). In some strains of *B. megaterium* and *B. cereus*, the spores are wrapped in a delicate bag, the exosporium (48, 68, 149). The general belief has been that the exosporium is the remainder of the cell wall of the bacterial cell. Ultrathin sections have shown that it is formed inside the protoplasm of the mother cell (68, 149).

Spore formation. Recent studies (47, 219) on *B. cereus* and *B. megaterium* and observations on *B. subtilis* (158) have revealed how the envelopes of the spore are formed. The earliest definitive sign of a developing spore is an invagination of the cytoplasmic membrane at the periphery of the bacterium which corresponds to an annular septum. Growing, it finally becomes a transverse septum constituted of two cytoplasmic membranes which partitions from the mother cell a portion of the cytoplasmic and chromatic material (Fig. 16a). During septum formation, a mesosome is often seen adhering to the chromatinic material of the forespore and linked to the septum. Later it enters the forespore and becomes a constituent of the spore. Once the septum has completely crossed the cell, the spore begins to bulge; one or two new mesosomes are seen linked to the septum. The ovoid shape of the forespore progressively appears, produced by the movement of the septum toward the pole of the bacterium. Finally, 1–2 hours after the beginning

---

its characteristic ovoid shape. It is still limited by a single "double membrane" only. c, Mature spore showing its system of multilayered envelopes.

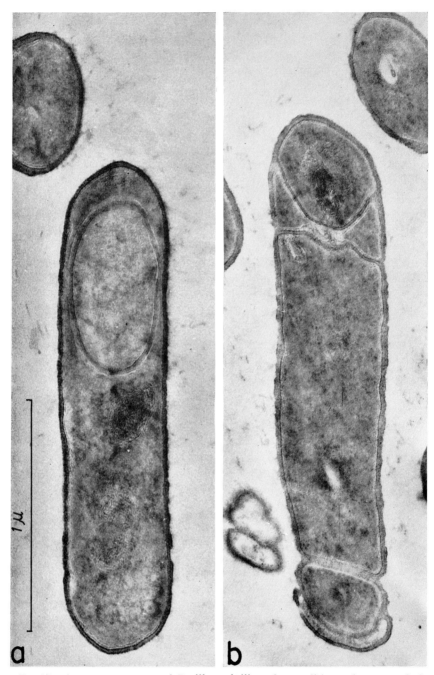

FIG. 17.   Asporogen mutants of *Bacillus subtilis* under conditions where sporulation is initiated in normal cells. *a*, In this mutant the progress of sporulation is inhibited

of sporulation (the time depends on the species and on the experimental conditions), the forespore is seen within the bacterial cytoplasm as an ovoid body limited by two identical membranes (Fig. 16b). The cortex is formed between these two membranes. When it has developed to approximately half its final width, the beginnings of the spore coat can be detected on the outside of the forespore.

In *Clostridium* species, the formation of the first envelope is rather different. The envelope which appears first is already ovoid and seems to be formed in the cyotplasm of the mother cell (*141, 189*).

The heat resistance of spores increases progressively during the formation of the spore envelopes, but attains its final level at the time of morphological maturation (*70*). The presence of α-dipicolinic acid and calcium seems to be important for the heat resistance, but at the present time the chemical and physical basis of heat resistance is not really understood (*10, 37*).

During sporulation some strains form a protein crystal which may be located in the cytoplasm of the mother cell independently of the spore (*48, 67, 68, 149*), or may be contained in the exosporum of a spore. The protein of the crystals found in some strains is highly toxic to insects. Almost nothing is known of the genetic determinants, the origin, or the physiological role of these proteins.

Germination. When put in a suitable environment, the bacterial spores take up water and undergo a series of changes which culminate in the bursting of the spore coat and the emergence of a growing bacterium. When this process is observed in thin sections, the outer coat and the cortex are seen to be deformed and then are shed by the germinating cell (*36, 128*). The cytoplasm recovers its granularity, the nuclear material its fibrillar structures. Then the cell wall appears, seemingly formed by the thickening of the spore wall.

The studies undertaken by Schaeffer and Ionesco on the Marburg strain of *B. subtilis* are a new approach toward understanding the sporulation process. This strain presents two advantages: It can be transformed, and isolation of its mutants is a very easy task (*168*). If DNA extracted from one asporogenic mutant is given to another asporogenic mutant, the ability to sporulate is generally restored. By these transformations sporulation is shown to be controlled by several genes located in different regions of the chromosome.

The first results of a morphologic study of thin sections of some of

---

after some first steps. *b,* This mutant shows so-called monstrosities: polar and ovoid bodies appear which are surrounded by a complete set of cell envelopes. Numerous abnormal septa are also visible.

these mutants have shown that markedly different types of mutants exist (*162*). Some do not even start sporulation and look like normal cells. Others begin to sporulate but then remain blocked at a stage which corresponds to that observed 1–2 hours after onset of normal sporulation (Fig. 17a). This forespore is ovoid in shape and is limited by an envelope formed by two connected cytoplasmic membranes. Other mutants show drastically abnormal features. In one instance, numerous septa are formed which are not necessarily transverse and which, therefore, enclose cellular areas containing no apparent nuclear material. In another mutant, two polar ovoid bodies are formed which possess cytoplasmic material, nuclear material, and a mesosome; instead of being surrounded by the normal sporal envelopes, the bodies are within a cell wall of normal aspect (Fig. 17b). They are not thermoresistant but are viable and are liberated by lysis of the median part of the cell.

In the future, by relating biochemical studies and those of abnormal morphological behavior, the pathways and genetic determinants of the process of sporulation should be uncovered.

G. Virus-Infected Bacteria

This problem has been extensively reviewed with particular emphasis on the contributions of electron microscopy (*86*). A shorter survey will suffice here.

Phage infection proceeds in clearly defined steps from adsorption of the phage to the cell, to the injection of the head content into the host cell, to the modification of the cellular metabolism in favor of phage synthesis.[3] The techniques of electron microscopy are invaluable for morphologic investigations of all these processes, as long as conclusions are related very carefully with biochemical and genetic results.

Phage is adsorbed to the cell by its tail as was described by Anderson (*2*). Since then, it has been shown that the tail sheath of phage T-even is modified upon contact with empty cell envelopes (*88*). Most likely a contraction of the sheath mediates the penetration of the inner core of the tail through the envelope (see Kellenberger, *86*).

The next step, the injection of the head content is still not understood. The statement can be made, however, that tail-sheath contraction is not directly connected to injection. Unfortunately, misconceptions have resutled from some electron microscope observations that DNA was released as soon as the phage was in contact with the cell wall or even with only a wall extract (*82*). This is not true in many other cases,

---

[3] In the case of lysogeny, however, the phage is transformed into a prophage integrated in the nuclear division cycle of the host cell.

particularly when gentle methods of specimen preparation such as agar filtration are used (88). A possible explanation of these conflicting reports would have to assume that the phages with contracted sheath are much more sensitive to outside influences than the normal phage.

For T-even phages the specific adsorption is probably connected to a very complicated pattern on the cell surface. Not only the tail fibers but also the base plate seem to be involved in the process. This situation is made evident by the neutralization of several distinct antigenic sites all resulting in the prevention of adsorption (51). In other phages, such as T5, the situation may be simpler. Its receptors are extractable as a uniform fraction, the reaction of the receptor sites with the phage T5 has been visualized by electron microscopy. Here also it has been shown that adsorption is not necessarily followed by the release of DNA from the phage (212).

The visible processes induced on the tail of T-even phages by adsorption and those simulated by chemical means have been the basis of extensive biochemical studies by Kozloff and co-workers (104). The chemical changes induced on the cell walls have been investigated by the same group and also by Weidel and co-workers (see 86 for references).

After these preliminary steps of infection, the cells undergo numerous profound modifications in their metabolism. These changes are accompanied by a typical nuclear breakdown in the case of the virulent phages T-even and T5. The changes were first observed by optical microscopy and described in papers, one of which considered most of the T phages (119) and the other the T-even phages (142). The investigations have been repeated and confirmed for T-even phages by different authors using the electron microscope and preparations of whole cells. T-even and T5 have been recently studied in thin sections (86, 95).

The nuclear breakdown initiated by phage T2 ends in typical marginal vacuoles which still contain some Feulgen positive material. The breakdown does not take place in the presence of chloramphenicol in spite of injection of DNA (95) and is not produced by the adsorption of ghosts (16). These findings seem to favor the idea that the agent inducing the nuclear breakdown is the DNA, or something injected with it, and that a protein synthesis is necessary for the process to start. For T5 the breakdown is even more complete. Measurements of DNA and the identical reaction to chloramphenicol indicate that here also injection is necessary to initiate the nuclear changes (see Kellenberger, 86).

All other phages which have been studied carefully do not produce typical nuclear breakdown, but only changes in the shape of the nucleus which are more or less typical. Many of these changes are similar to those obtained by metabolic disturbances, as, for example, starvation (axial nucleus) and salt concentration (see Section III, B). The morphological effects of different mutants of phage λ have been investigated recently in combination with biochemical and genetic measurements (175). For this phage, nuclear modifications are not apparent by any of the methods used. In particular, lysogenization does *not* result in a special nuclear pattern.

For the study of the replication and maturation of phage, electron microscopy has provided essential help. By artificial disruption of the T-even-infected bacteria and by study of these lysates, mature phages were found and also the so-called doughnuts which were rapidly identified as empty heads (42). It was believed that the empty heads were true precursors which later became filled with DNA. By the study of thin sections and quantitative estimates, however, the situation was interpreted differently (86, 95). As soon as phage DNA increases in amount, cytoplasm vacuoles appear which are filled with DNA, as was shown by positive Versene tests (94). There is abundant evidence that this morphologic pool (Fig. 18), constituted of highly hydrated DNA plasma, represents the genetic pool of phage genomes (86).

In the next phase of the multiplication cycle, electron-opaque bodies appear, which are of the approximate size and shape of phage. They are very fragile, and, on opening of the cell, break down. These so-called phage-condensates (phage-precursor particles of the first type) are formed by the phage DNA which has been withdrawn from the pool and condensed into a much less hydrated DNA-plasm. They are still devoid of a protein coat, as made evident by quantitative studies (95). In the subsequent step the protein coat is deposited around each condensate, producing a precursor particle of the second type. These particles are also fragile. Disrupted in lysates, there are found only empty heads or membranes and dispersed DNA. The doughnuts observed in lysates are, therefore, a breakdown-product of the precursor particle of the second type. The final step, of course, is maturation of the precursor particles into infectious particles.

This sequence of the events of replication has been established by a quantitative method as described in Section II, C. Indeed, in thin sections it is not possible to distinguish with certainty between a condensate, a precursor particle of the second type, and a matured phage; their appearances are too dependent upon the plane and the level of the section (see Section II, C and Fig. 6). The number of condensates has been determined, however, in the following way: An estimate of the total number of electron-opaque phagelike bodies has been found from sections; this value integrates the precursor particles of all types as well as matured phages. From the lysate, the total number of coats has been

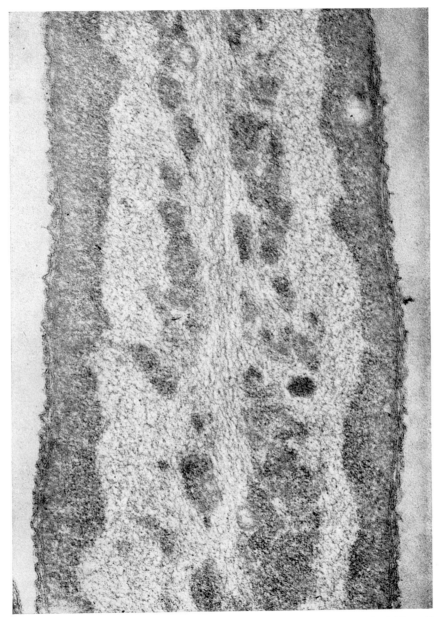

FIG. 18. The pool of vegetative phage in a T2-infected cell of *Escherichia coli*. Chloramphenicol has been added 8 minutes after infection, in order to block the synthesis of proteins. The phage DNA increases, however, at the same rate as without the drug and forms the fibrillar DNA-plasm of the cell. Micrograph by E. Boy de la Tour.

established as the sum of morphologically intact phages and empty heads. The difference between the two values gives the number of condensates.

The process of assembly of the phage tail is not yet known. There are some arguments in favor of its being assembled *in situ* from much smaller subunits (*86*). Unfortunately electron microscope techniques have not yet been able to confirm this hypothesis. The survey of lysates shows that many isolated tails are visible but they are probably artificially separated from the heads of labile precursor particles. On thin sections, where this artifact is avoided, the tails have too little contrast to be visible.

This cycle of intracellular development has not yet been confirmed for phages other than T-even. Very good micrographs of intracellular phages of mycobacteria have been presented (*191*).

ACKNOWLEDGMENTS

Original experimental work reported here and executed in Geneva has been supported by the "Swiss National Foundation for Scientific Research."

During the redaction of this paper we had numerous discussions with Drs. B. Blondel, R. G. E. Murray, W. H. Schreil, and E. Vanderwinkel, to whom we are very grateful.

We very much appeciate that Drs. B. Blondel, W. H. Schreil, and F. Vanderhaege permitted us to use some of their unpublished results.

Our thanks go to all these who have supplied us with micrographs.

REFERENCES

1. Abbo, F. E., and Pardee, A. B., *Biochim. Biophys. Acta* **39**, 478 (1960).
2. Anderson, T. F., *Am. Naturalist* **86**, 91 (1952).
3. Bahr, G. F., *Exptl. Cell Res.* **7**, 457 (1954).
4. Bahr, G. F., *Exptl. Cell Res.* **9**, 277 (1955).
5. Barrnett, R. J., *Exptl. Cell Res., Suppl.* **7**, 65 (1959).
6. Bergeron, J. A., *Brokhaven Symp. Biol.* **11**, 118 (1958).
7. Bielig, H.-J., Kausche, G. A., and Haardick, H., *Z. Naturforsch.* **4b**, 80 (1949).
8. Birch-Andersen, A., *J. Gen. Microbiol.* **13**, 327 (1955).
9. Birch-Andersen, A., *Proc. 4th Intern. Conf. on Electron Microscopy, Berlin, 1958* **2**, 44 (1960).
10. Black, S. H., Hashimoto, T., and Gerhardt, P., *Can. J. Microbiol.* **6**, 213 (1960).
11. Blondel, B., and Vanderhaeghe, F., Unpublished results, 1960.
12. Boatman, E. S., and Douglas, H. C., *Proc. 5th Intern. Conf. on Electron Microscopy, Philadelphia, 1962* RR-7 (1962).
13. Bolle, A., and Kellenberger, E., *Schweiz. Z. Allgem. Pathol. Bakteriol.* **21**, 714 (1958).
14. Bolle, A., and Kellenberger, E., Unpublished results, 1959.
15. Bolton, E. T., Hoyer, B. H., and Ritter, D. B., in "Microsomal Particles and Protein Synthesis" (R. B. Roberts, ed.), p. 18. Pergamon Press, New York, 1958.
16. Bonifas, V., and Kellenberger, E., *Biochem. Biophys. Acta* **16**, 330 (1955).
17. Brenner, S., and Horne, R. W., *Biochem. Biophys. Acta* **34**, 103 (1959).

18. Brenner, S., Dark, F. A., Gerhardt, P., Jeynes, M. H., Kandler, O., Kellenberger, E., Klieneberger-Nobel, E., McQuillen, K., Rubio-Huertos, M., Salton, M. R. J., Strange, R. E., Tomcsik, J., and Weibull, C., *Nature* **181**, 1713 (1958).
19. Brieger, E. M., Glauert, A. M., and Allen, J. M., *Exptl. Cell Res.* **18**, 418 (1959).
20. Brinton, C. C. Jr., *Nature* **183**, 782 (1959).
21. Brinton, C. C. Jr., Personal communication, 1961.
22. Brinton, C. C. Jr., and Baron, L. S., *Biochim. Biophys. Acta* **42**, 298 (1960).
23. Brinton, C. C. Jr., Buzzell, A., and Lauffer, M. A., *Biochim. Biophys. Acta* **15**, 533 (1954).
24. Brinton, C. C. Jr., Gemski, P. Jr., Falkow, S., and Baron, L. S., *Biochem. Biophys. Res. Commun.* **5**, 293 (1961).
25. Brody, M., and Vatter, A. E., *J. Biophys. Biochem. Cytol.* **5**, 289 (1959).
26. Caro, L. G., *J. Biophys. Biochem. Cytol.* **9**, 539 (1961).
27. Caro, L. G., *J. Cell Biol.* **15**, 189 (1962).
28. Caro, L. G., and Forro, F., Jr., *J. Biophys. Biochem. Cytol.* **9**, 555 (1961).
29. Caro, L. G., van Tubergen, R. P., and Forro, F. Jr., *J. Biophys. Biochem. Cytol.* **4**, 491 (1958).
30. Caro, L. G., van Tubergen, R. P., and Kolb, T. A., *J. Cell Biol.* **15**, 173 (1962).
31. Cedergren, B., and Holme, T., *J. Ultrastruct. Res.* **3**, 70 (1959).
32. Chapman, G. B., *J. Bacteriol.* **71**, 348 (1956).
33. Chapman, G. B., *J. Biophys. Biochem. Cytol.* **6**, 221 (1959).
34. Chapman, G. B., and Hillier, J., *J. Bacteriol.* **66**, 362 (1953).
35. Chapman, G. B., and Kroll, A. J., *J. Bacteriol.* **73**, 63 (1957).
36. Chapman, G. B., and Zworykin, K. A., *J. Bacteriol.* **74**, 126 (1957).
37. Church, B. D., and Halvorson, H. O., *Nature* **183**, 124 (1959).
38. Cohen, R., and Nisman, B., *Compt. Rend.* **252**, 1063 (1961).
39. Cota-Robles, E. H., Marr, A. G., and Nilson, E. H., *J. Bacteriol.* **75**, 243 (1958).
40. Davis, J. C., Winterscheid, L. C., Hartman, P. E., and Mudd, S., *J. Histochem. Cytochem.* **1**, 123 (1953).
41. de Haller, G., Rouiller, C., and Kellenberger, E., in preparation.
42. De Mars, R. I., Luria, S. E., Fisher, H., and Levinthal, C., *Ann. Inst. Pasteur* **84**, 113 (1953).
43. De Robertis, E., *J. Biophys. Biochem. Cytol.* **2**, 785 (1956).
44. Duguid, J. P., *J. Gen. Microbiol.* **21**, 271 (1959).
45. Duguid, J. P., Smith, I. W., Dempster, G., and Edmunds, P. N., *J. Pathol. Bacteriol.* **70**, 335 (1955).
45a. Eiserling, F. A., and Romig, W. R., *J. Ultrastruc. Res.* **6**, 540 (1962).
46. Fitz-James, P .C., *J. Bacteriol.* **78**, 765 (1959).
47. Fitz-James, P. C., *J. Biophys. Biochem. Cytol.* **8**, 507 (1960).
48. Fitz-James, P. C., and Young, I. E., *J. Bacteriol.* **78**, 743 (1959).
49. Fitz-James, P. C., and Young, I. E., *J. Bacteriol.* **78**, 755 (1959).
50. Frank, H., and Martin, H. H., *Proc. European Reg. Conf. on Electron Microscopy, Delft, 1960* **2**, 1024 (1961).
51. Franklin, N. C., *Virology* **14**, 417 (1961).
52. Franklin, J. G., and Bradley, D. E., *J. Appl. Bacteriol.* **20**, 467 (1957).
53. Frenkel, A. W., and Hickman, D. D., *J. Biophys. Biochem. Cytol.* **6**, 285 (1959).
54. Giesbrecht, P., *Zentr. Bakteriol., Parasitenk., Abt. I. Orig.* **176**, 413 (1959).
55. Giesbrecht, P., *Zentr. Bakteriol., Parasitenk., Abt. I. Orig.* **179**, 538 (1960).
56. Giesbrecht, P., *Zentr. Bakteriol., Parasitenk., Abt. I. Orig.* **183**, 1 (1961).
57. Giesbrecht, P., and Drews, G., *Arch. Mikrobiol.* **43**, 152 (1962).

58. Glauert, A. M., and Hopwood, D. A., *J. Biophys. Biochem. Cytol.* **6**, 515 (1959).
59. Glauert, A. M., and Hopwood, D. A., *J. Biophys. Biochem. Cytol.* **7**, 479 (1960).
60. Glauert, A. M., and Hopwood, D. A., *J. Biophys. Biochem. Cytol.* **10**, 505 (1961).
61. Glauert, A. M., Rogers, G. E., and Glauert, R. H., *Nature* **178**, 803 (1956).
62. Glauert, A. M., Brieger, E. M., and Allen, J. M., *Exptl. Cell Res.* **22**, 73 (1961).
63. Grassé, P. P., and Dragesco, J., *Compt. Rend.* **245**, 2447 (1957).
64. Grell, K. G., and Wohlfarth-Bottermann, K. E., *Z. Zellforsch. Mikroskop. Anat.* **47**, 7 (1957).
65. Hagedorn, H., *Ber. Deut. Botan. Ges.* **73**, 211 (1960).
66. Hall, C. E., and Litt, M., *J. Biophys. Biochem. Cytol.* **4**, 1 (1958).
67. Hannay, C. L., *J. Biophys. Biochem. Cytol.* **3**, 1001 (1957).
68. Hannay, C. L., *J. Biophys. Biochem. Cytol.* **9**, 285 (1961).
69. Hannay, C. L., and Fitz-James, P., *Can. J. Microbiol.* **1**, 694 (1955).
70. Hashimoto, T., Black, S. H., and Gerhardt, P., *Can. J. Microbiol.* **6**, 203 (1960).
71. Hershey, A. D., and Burgi, E., *J. Mol. Biol.* **2**, 143 (1960).
72. Hickman, D. D., and Frenkel, A. W., *J. Biophys. Biochem. Cytol.* **6**, 277 (1959).
73. Hofschneider, P. H., *Proc. European Reg. Conf. on Electron Microscopy, Delft, 1960* **2**, 1028 (1961).
74. Holbert, P. E., *J. Biophys. Biochem. Cytol.* **7**, 373 (1960).
75. Hopwood, D. A., and Glauert, A. M., *J. Biophys. Biochem. Cytol.* **8**, 267 (1960).
76. Houwink, A. L., *Biochim. Biophys. Acta* **10**, 360 (1953).
77. Houwink, A. L., *J. Gen. Microbiol.* **15**, 146 (1956).
78. Houwink, A. L., and van Iterson, W., *Biochim. Biophys. Acta* **5**, 10 (1950).
79. Huxley, H. E., and Zubay, G., *J. Mol. Biol.* **2**, 10 (1960).
80. Huxley, H. E., and Zubay, G., *J. Biophys. Biochem. Cytol.* **11**, 273 (1961).
81. Jacob, F., and Wollman, E. L., "Sexuality and the Genetics of Bacteria." Academic Press, New York, 1961.
82. Jesaitis, M. A., and Goebel, W. F., *J. Exptl. Med.* **102**, 733 (1955).
83. Kellenberger, E., *Symp. Bacteriol. Cytol., Rome* p. 45 (1953).
84. Kellenberger, E., *Experientia* **11**, 305 (1955).
85. Kellenberger, E., *in* "Microbial Genetics" (W. Hayes and R. C. Clowes, eds.), p. 39. Cambridge Univ. Press, London and New York, 1960.
86. Kellenberger, E., *Advan. Virus Res.* **8**, 1 (1962).
87. Kellenberger, E., *in* "The Interpretation of Ultrastructure" (R. J. C. Harris, ed.), Vol. I, p. 233. Academic Press, New York, 1962.
88. Kellenberger, E., and Arber, W., *Z. Naturforsch.* **10b**, 698 (1955).
89. Kellenberger, E., and Huber, L., *Experientia* **9**, 289 (1953).
90. Kellenberger, E., and Kellenberger, G., unpublished, quoted in Vanderwinkel and Murray (*200*).
91. Kellenberger, E., and Ryter, A., *Experientia* **12**, 420 (1956).
92. Kellenberger, E., and Ryter, A., *J. Biophys. Biochem. Cytol.* **4**, 323 (1958).
93. Kellenberger, E., Schwab, W., and Ryter, A., *Experientia* **12**, 421 (1956).
94. Kellenberger, E., Ryter, A., and Séchaud, J., *J. Biophys. Biochem. Cytol.* **4**, 671 (1958).
95. Kellenberger, E., Séchaud, J., and Ryter, A., *Virology* **8**, 478 (1959).
96. Kerridge, D., *J. Gen. Microbiol.* **21**, 168 (1959).
97. Kerridge, D., Horne, R. W., Glauert, A. M., *J. Mol. Biol.* **4**, 227 (1962).
98. Kleinschmidt, A., and Lang, D., *Proc. European Reg. Conf. on Electron Microscopy, Delft, 1960* **2**, 690 (1961).
99. Kleinschmidt, A., and Zahn, R. K., *Z. Naturforsch.* **14b**, 770 (1959).

100. Kleinschmidt, A. K., Lang, D., Jacherts, D., and Zahn, R. K., *Biochim. Biophys. Acta* **61**, 857 (1962).

101. Kobayaski, T., Rinker, J. N., and Koffler, H., *Arch. Biochem. Biophys.* **84**, 342 (1959).

102. Koike, M., and Takeya, K., *J. Biophys. Biochem. Cytol.* **9**, 597 (1961).

103. König, H., and Winkler, A., *Naturwissenschaften* **35**, 136 (1948).

104. Kozloff, L. M., *Ann. Rev. Biochem.* **29**, 475 (1960).

105. Kran, K., and Schlote, F.-W., *Arch. Mikrobiol.* **34**, 412 (1959).

106. Kushida, H., *J. Electronmicroscopy (Tokyo)* **9**, 113 (1960).

107. Kushida, H., *J. Electronmicroscopy (Tokyo)* **10**, 194 (1961).

108. Labaw, L. W., and Mosley, V. M., *Biochim. Biophys. Acta* **15**, 325 (1954).

109. Labaw, L. W., and Mosley, V. M., *J. Bacteriol.* **67**, 576 (1954).

110. Labaw, L. W., and Mosley, V. M., *Biochim. Biophys. Acta* **17**, 322 (1955).

111. Leduc, E. H., and Bernhard, W., *in* "The Interpretation of Ultrastructure" (R. J. C. Harris, ed.), Vol. 1, p. 21. Academic Press, New York, 1962.

112. Lee, S., *Exptl. Cell Res.* **21**, 249 (1960).

113. Lee, S., *Exptl. Cell Res.* **21**, 252 (1960).

114. Levinthal, C., and Davison, P. F., *J. Mol. Biol.* **3**, 674 (1961).

115. Lieb, M., Weigle, J. J., and Kellenberger, E., *J. Bacteriol.* **69**, 468 (1955).

116. Liebermeister, K., and Kellenberger, E., *Z. Naturforsch.* **11b**, 200 (1956).

117. Luft, J. H., *J. Biophys. Biochem. Cytol.* **2**, 799 (1956).

118. Luft, J. H., *J. Biophys. Biochem. Cytol.* **9**, 409 (1961).

119. Luria, S. E., and Human, M. L., *J. Bacteriol.* **59**, 551 (1950).

120. McFall, E., and Stent, G. S., *Biochim. Biophys. Acta* **34**, 580 (1959).

121. McQuillen, K., Roberts, R. B., and Britten, R. J., *Proc. Natl. Acad. Sci. U. S.* **45**, 1437 (1959).

122. Maaløe, O., and Birch-Andersen, A., *in* "Bacterial Anatomy" (E. T. C. Spooner and B. A. D. Stocker, eds.), p. 261. Cambridge Univ. Press, London and New York, 1956.

123. Maccacaro, G. A., and Angelotti, A., *Giorn. Microbiol.* **1**, 85 (1955).

124. Maccacaro, G. A., and Hayes, W., Personal communication, 1962.

125. Maccacaro, G. A., Colombo, C., Ni Nardo, A., *Giorn. Microbiol.* **7**, 1 (1959).

126. Mach, F., *Naturwissenschaften* **48**, 437 (1961).

127. Macrae, R. M., and Wilkinson, J. F., *J. Gen. Microbiol.* **19**, 210 (1958).

128. Mayall, B. H., and Robinow, C. F., *J. Appl. Bacteriol.* **20**, 333 (1957).

129. Mayall, B. H., and Robinow, C. F., Personal communication.

130. Mercer, E. H., *Nature* **181**, 1550 (1958).

131. Meselson, M., and Stahl, F. W., *Proc. Natl. Acad. Sci. U. S.* **44**, 671 (1958).

132. Meselson, M., Stahl, F. W., and Vinograd, J., *Proc. Natl. Acad. Sci. U. S.* **43**, 581 (1957).

133. Morgan, C., Rifkind, R. A., Hsu, K. C., Holden, M., Seegal, B. C., and Rose, H. M., *Virology* **14**, 292 (1961).

134. Moses, M. J., *J. Biophys. Biochem. Cytol.* **4**, 633 (1958).

135. Mudd, S., Winterscheid, L. C., DeLamater, E. D., and Henderson, H. J., *J. Bacteriol.* **62**, 459 (1951).

136. Mudd, S., Yoshida, A., and Koike, M., *J. Bacteriol.* **75**, 224 (1958).

137. Mudd, S., Kawata, T., Payne, J. I., Sall, T., and Takagi, A., *Nature* **189**, 79 (1961).

138. Mühlethaler, K., *Biochim. Biophys. Acta* **3**, 527 (1949).

139. Murray, R. G. E., *Can. J. Microbiol.* **3**, 531 (1957).

140. Murray, R. G. E., *in* "The Bacteria" (I. C. Gunsalus and R. Y. Stanier, eds.), Vol. 1, p. 35. Academic Press, New York, 1960.
141. Murray, R. G. E., Personal communication, 1961.
142. Murray, R. G. E., Gillen, D. H., and Heagy, F. C., *J. Bacteriol.* **59**, 603 (1950).
143. Murray, R. G. E., Francombe, W. H., and Mayall, B. H., *Can. J. Microbiol.* **5**, 641 (1959).
144. Murray, R. G. E., Blondel, B., and Kellenberger, E., Unpublished results, 1961.
145. Niklowitz, W., *Proc. Stockholm Conf. on Electron Microscopy, 1956* p. 115 (1957).
146. Niklowitz, W., *Zentr. Bakteriol., Parasitenk. Abt. I. Orig.* **173**, 12 (1958).
147. Niklowitz, W., and Drews, G., *Arch. Mikrobiol.* **27**, 150 (1957).
148. Nisman, B., and Fukuhara, H., *Compt. Rend.* **249**, 1725 (1959).
149. Norris, J. R., and Watson, D. H., *J. Gen. Microbiol.* **22**, 744 (1960).
150. Pardee, A. B., Schachman, H. K., and Stanier, R. Y., *Nature* **169**, 282 (1952).
151. Pelc, S. R., Coombes, J. D., and Budd, G. C., *Exptl. Cell Res.* **24**, 192 (1961).
152. Przybylski, R. J., *Exptl. Cell Res.* **24**, 181 (1961).
153. Ris, H., *in* "The Interpretation of Ultrastructure" (R. J. C. Harris, ed.), Vol. 1, p. 69. Academic Press, New York, 1962.
154. Ris, H., and Singh, R. N., *J. Biophys. Biochem. Cytol.* **9**, 63 (1961).
155. Robinow, C. F., *J. Bacteriol.* **66**, 300 (1953).
156. Robinow, C. F., *in* "The Bacteria" (I. C. Gunsalus and R. Y. Stanier, eds.), Vol. I, p. 207. Academic Press, New York, 1960.
157. Ryter, A., *J. Biophys. Biochem. Cytol.* **8**, 399 (1960).
158. Ryter, A., Unpublished results, 1962.
159. Ryter, A., and Kellenberger, E., *J. Ultrastruct. Res.* **2**, 200 (1958).
160. Ryter, A., and Kellenberger, E., *Z. Naturforsch.* **13b**, 597 (1958).
161. Ryter, A., and Kellenberger, E., Unpublished results, 1962.
162. Ryter, A., Ionesco, H., and Schaeffer, P., *Compt. Rend.* **252**, 3675 (1961).
163. Salton, M. R. J., "Microbial Cell Walls," Ciba Lecture in Microbial Biochemistry. Wiley, New York, 1961.
164. Salton, M. R. J., *Bacteriol. Rev.* **25**, 77 (1961).
165. Salton, M. R. J., and Williams, R. C., *Biochim. Biophys. Acta* **14**, 455 (1954).
166. Schachman, H. K., Pardee, A. B., and Stanier, R. Y., *Arch. Biochem. Biophys.* **38**, 245 (1952).
167. Schaechter, M., Maaløe, O., and Kjeldgaard, N. O., *J. Gen. Microbiol.* **19**, 592 (1958).
168. Schaeffer, P., and Ionesco, H., *Compt. Rend.* **251**, 3125 (1960).
169. Schlote, F.-W., *Zool. Anz. Suppl.* **23**, 478 (1959).
170. Schlote, F.-W., *Arch. Mikrobiol.* **40**, 283 (1961).
171. Schlote, F.-W., discussion to Kellenberger (*87*).
172. Schreil, W. H., *Experientia* **17**, 391 (1961).
173. Schreil, W. H., in preparation.
174. Schreil, W. H., and Schleich, F., *Z. Infektionskrankh. Hyg.* **141**, 576 (1955).
175. Séchaud, J., *Arch. Sci. (Geneva)* **13**, 427 (1960).
176. Séchaud, J., Ryter, A., and Kellenberger, E., *J. Biophys. Biochem. Cytol.* **5**, 469 (1959).
177. Sedar, A. W., Rosa, C. G., and Tsou, K. C., *Proc. 5th Intern. Conf. on Electron Microscopy, Philadelphia, 1962* L-7 (1962).
178. Shatkin, A. J., *J. Biophys. Biochem. Cytol.* **7**, 583 (1960).
179. Shinohara, C., Fukushi, K., and Suzuki, J. *J. Bacteriol.* **74**, 413 (1957).

180. Shinohara, C., Fukushi, K., Suzuki, J., and Sato, K., *J. Electronmicroscopy* (*Tokyo*) **6**, 47 (1958).
181. Singer, S. J., *Nature* **183**, 1523 (1959).
182. Singer, S. J., and Schick, A. F., *J. Biophys. Biochem. Cytol.* **9**, 519 (1961).
183. Smith, C. W., Metzger, J. F., Zacks, S. I., and Kase, A., *Proc. Soc. Exptl. Biol. Med.* **104**, 336 (1960).
184. Smith, I. W., Wilkinson, J. F., and Duguid, J. P., *J. Bacteriol.* **68**, 450 (1954).
185. Spiegelman, S., Aronson, A. I., and Fitz-James, P. C., *J. Bacteriol.* **75**, 102 (1958).
186. Stanier, R., Personal communication, 1962.
187. Staub, A. M., *Pathol. Microbiol.* **24**, 890 (1961).
188. Storck, R., and Wachsman, J. T., *J. Bacteriol.* **73**, 784 (1957).
189. Takagi, A., Kawata, T., and Yamamoto, S., *J. Bacteriol.* **80**, 37 (1960).
190. Takeya, K., *Proc. 15th Gen. Assembly, Japan Medical Congr.* **I**, 100 (1959).
191. Takeya, K., Koike, M., Mori, R., and Toda, T., *J. Biophys. Biochem. Cytol.* **11**, 441 (1961).
192. Tecce, G., and Toschi, G., *Nuovo Cimento* [10] **18**, Suppl. 2, 207 (1960).
193. Thornley, M. I., Horne, R. W., *J. Gen. Microbiol.* **28**, 51 (1962).
194. Thorsson, K. G., and Weibull, C., *J. Ultrastruct. Res.* **1**, 412 (1958).
195. Tissières, A., and Watson, J. D., *Nature* **182**, 778 (1958).
196. Tissières, A., Watson, J. D., Schlessinger, D., and Hollingworth, B. R., *J. Mol. Biol.* **1**, 221 (1959).
197. Tokuyasu, K., and Yamada, E., *J. Biophys. Biochem. Cytol.* **5**, 123 (1959).
198. Tokuyasu, K., and Yamada, E., *J. Biophys. Biochem. Cytol.* **5**, 129 (1959).
199. Tuttle, A. L., and Gest, H., *Proc. Natl. Acad. Sci. U. S.* **45**, 1261 (1959).
200. Vanderwinkel, E., and Murray, R. G. E., *J. Ultrastruct. Res.* **7**, 185 (1962).
201. van Iterson, W., *J. Biophys. Biochem. Cytol.* **9**, 183 (1961).
202. van Iterson, W., and Robinow, C. F., *J. Biophys. Biochem. Cytol.* **9**, 171 (1961).
203. van Tubergen, R. P., *J. Biophys. Biochem. Cytol.* **9**, 219 (1961).
204. Vatter, A. E., and Wolfe, R. S., *J. Bacteriol.* **75**, 480 (1958).
205. Weibull, C., *Arkiv Kemi* **1**, 573 (1950).
206. Weibull, C., *Acta Chem. Scand.* **4**, 268 (1950).
207. Weibull, C., *J. Bacteriol.* **66**, 137 (1953).
208. Weibull, C., and Beckman, H., *Nature* **188**, 428 (1960).
209. Weibull, C., and Bergström, L., *Biochim. Biophys. Acta* **30**, 340 (1958).
210. Weibull, C., and Hedvall, J., *Biochim. Biophys. Acta* **10**, 35 (1953).
211. Weibull, C., Beckman, H., and Bergström, L., *J. Gen. Microbiol.* **20**, 519 (1959).
212. Weidel, W., and Kellenberger, E., *Biochim. Biophys. Acta* **17**, 1 (1955).
213. Weidel, W., and Primosigh, J., *Z. Naturforsch.* **12b**, 421 (1957).
214. Weidel, W., Frank, H., and Martin, H. H., *J. Gen. Microbiol.* **22**, 158 (1960).
215. Westphal, O., and Lüderitz, O., *Pathol. Microbiol.* **24**, 870 (1961).
216. Whitfield, J. F., and Murray, R. G. E., *Can. J. Microbiol.* **2**, 245 (1956).
217. Williams, M. A., and Chapman, G. B., *J. Bacteriol.* **81**, 195 (1961).
218. Young, I. E., and Fitz-James, P. C., *J. Biophys. Biochem. Cytol.* **6**, 483 (1959).
219. Young, E., and Fitz-James, P. C., *J. Cell Biol.* **12**, 115 (1962).
220. Zapf, K., *Naturwissenschaften* **44**, 448 (1957).

CHAPTER 8

In Studies on
Biological Macromolecules

CECIL E. HALL

I. Introduction

The term "macromolecule" is applied to repeating units of matter having at least one dimension in the range 20 to 1000 A. This includes natural and synthetic polymers and very many structural and functioning components of biological systems including the smaller viruses. The electron microscope has assumed an indispensable role in structure determination in this range of dimensions and the volume of work that could be classified as electron microscopy of macromolecules is very large indeed. In this section the discussion of applications is confined mainly to examples from the experience of the author and his associates. Viruses, even though they may be classified as macromolecules, are a subject in themselves and are treated separately. The macromolecular structure of intact cells and tissues also becomes part of such subjects as pathology or histology or "ultrastructure." In this section the examples are of isolated systems where the problem is the measurement of size and shape of individual molecules and the observation of the ways they interact with one another. In this application the electron microscope supplements and complements the physical chemical methods customarily applied to the study of such systems.

Although macromolecules may be very small in one dimension, less

than 10 A, the problem of examining them with the electron microscope is generally not one of resolving power but of contrast.
Methods of enhancing contrast by manipulation of the specimen are (*a*)
positive staining, (*b*) negative staining, and (*c*) shadow-casting. The
introduction of phosphotungstic acid (PTA) as a positive stain to show
the macromolecular organization in paramyosin, a muscle protein, was
the first instance where a crystalline structure producing a complex
x-ray diffraction pattern was elucidated by electron microscopy (*14*). In
a later quantitative study, Hall (*7*) investigated conditions for optimal
uptake of several stains using tomato bushy stunt virus (BSV) as a test

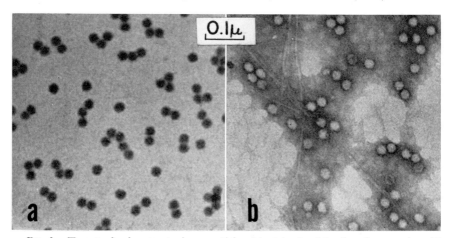

Fig. 1. Tomato bushy stunt virus particles (a) stained with phosphotungstic acid
and platinum chloride; (b) unstained particles embedded in phosphotungstic acid
(negative stain).

object. It was found that the mass of the particles could be increased
by a factor of about 4 although the conditions for this uptake were
rather drastic. The object of the investigation was to find optimal conditions for staining proteins in the hope that smaller macromolecules
could be rendered visible. These methods were unsuccessful when applied to certain typical proteins, however, probably because the mechanics of staining isolated protein molecules is different from that in staining more complex structures. In the same work, however, negative
staining was demonstrated. In this procedure the visibility of a particle
is enhanced by surrounding it with dense material (in this case PTA)
rather than causing it to combine chemically. In Fig. 1a are shown BSV
particles positively stained and in Fig. 1b the same material negatively
stained. In Fig. 1b one sees fine filaments of unknown composition that
stand out clearly, though they are not seen at all in the positively stained

specimen. The smallest of these are only about 25 A in diameter. Huxley (22) later used this technique to demonstrate for the first time by electron microscopy that the tobacco mosaic virus (TMV) was a hollow rod. The development of negative-staining techniques has in fact been one of the most fruitful methods for elucidating the fine structure of viruses (3, 21). Its potentialities have probably not yet been fully realized for the observation of isolated macromolecules in general.

Shadow-casting is an extremely effective method for enhancing the contrast of small isolated particles, and its potentialities were recognized by Williams and Wyckoff when they introduced the technique in 1944 (30). The main difficulty was in finding a suitably smooth substrate for supporting the particles. The mica-substrate technique (8) described below overcomes this difficulty by providing a surface smooth to atomic dimensions. The limitations are in the grain size of the shadow-casting metal and in distortion due to the finite size of the metal coating.

II. Mica-Substrate Technique

In order to make full use of shadow-casting for enhancing the visibility of small particles they should be supported on a substrate that does not have irregularities in the order of the particle dimensions. The smoothest conceivable surfaces are the cleavage planes of crystals, which are flat to the order of interatomic distances over reasonably large areas. Mica is an obvious candidate in this category since it is readily available and is easily cleaved over large areas. It has other properties that are important: it is chemically inert and it is hydrophilic. However, it is not easily split down to thicknesses that can be used directly as a substrate in the electron microscope, thus its use entails a stripping or replica technique. Suspensions are best applied as fine droplets from a spray gun or nebulizer, though this technique can produce diruption of fragile materials. Direct application by medicine dropper or spread-film techniques may be gentler, but the greater thickness of the water layer and impurities that are always present to some extent in water and other reagents make these techniques undesirable. For the same reason, it is not desirable to rinse the surface with water to remove salts or buffers since the wash water usually contains traces of solids that will cling to the surface. This means that materials should be suspended in volatile salts and buffers, although a few thousandths molar of insoluble salts can be tolerated if they are necessary to stabilize materials.

The spray technique is essentially that of Backus and Williams (1) and one of the most useful volatile buffers is a mixture of ammonium acetate and ammonium carbonate introduced by them. When material

is sprayed on to a hydrophobic surface, such as collodion, the droplet
rides on a vapor cushion, shrinking as it evaporates and finally it col-
lapses in a small area. This has the advantage that the contents of an
entire drop can be contained in a small field, but it has the disadvantage
that impurities and suspended molecules are also concentrated into the
final area, thus making it necessary to start with very high dilutions and
very clean reagents. Droplets that ride on a vapor cushion on filmed
grids also tend to migrate to the grid wires and avoid the open, filmed
areas. When sprayed on mica, droplets spread readily over the hydrophilic surface and dry very rapidly. Concentration of protein molecules
may vary from 0.01 mg/ml up to a few tenths mg/ml. Polystyrene latex
spheres are usually added to provide a measure of shadow-to-height ratio
as well as an aid for focusing.

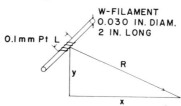

Fig. 2. Geometry for the evaporation of platinum. See Table I for values of
parameters.

Metals for shadow-casting should, of course, be as fine grained as
possible, but there is also the complication that they should separate
readily from the substrate. Although there are metals with a finer grain
than Pt, this metal has been most used because it is easy to evaporate
and strips readily from a mica surface. Shadow-to-height ratios as set
up are from 5:1 up to 10:1, but for computation the ratio is taken from
measurements on admixed polystyrene spheres. It appears that a freshly
cleaved face of mica attracts a monolayer of water molecules, which
subsequently facilitates the entry of water between Pt and mica in the
stripping operation. In fact, if, before shadow-casting, the evaporater
is pumped for too long a time or the surface is baked, the water layer
appears to be lost and stripping becomes difficult or impossible. After
shadow-casting, the Pt film can be backed with carbon or SiO and further strengthened with collodion. The resulting film is scored into convenient squares and floated off on the surface of water to be picked
up over grids.

Since Pt alloys with tungsten, it must be evaporated from a very
heavy filament or distributed in low amount along the filament. A
typical setup for evaporation is shown in Fig. 2 and typical parameters
are listed in Table I.

Any top quality, clear mica appears to be satisfactory. Test runs made on freshly cleaned material on which has been caught a clean aerosol such as carbon black or MgO fail to show any structure attributable to mica itself in between the test particles. Test runs made from even quite pure particulate suspensions in water may be expected to show some background structure because of the impossibility of eliminating traces of contamination absolutely. Aside from extraneous matter, the image of a replicated mica surface will ultimately show some structure. This may be the grain of the metal or the "pebbly" structure of the supporting films that is characteristic of slightly underfocused images. This latter, of course, will appear in shadows. There is no point in taking shadowed micrographs at magnifications so great that metallic

TABLE I

PARAMETERS FOR SHADOW-CASTING[a]

					Platinum 0.1 mm diameter	
	Polystyrene				Wire	
	shadow/	x	y	R	length	L
x/y	diameter	(cm)	(cm)	(cm)	(cm)	(cm)
5:1	3.5–4.5	5.8	1.2	6	1.8	0.4–0.5
10:1	6.5–8.5	5.97	0.59	6	2.4	0.5–0.7

[a] See Fig. 2 for meaning of the symbols.

grain is exaggerated. Most micrographs have been recorded at 15,000 × on Kodak Contrast Lantern Slide emulsion, at which magnification the plates cannot show the resolving power that the instrument is capable of. If one goes to a higher magnification, finer detail may be visible in the metallic film which is unrelated to object structure. It is the same effect that one observes in looking at a halftone reproduction; the printed dots become resolved but the meaningful structure is unimproved or deteriorated. It seems fairly clear that so far as metallic grain is concerned improvement can be expected. Also, if suitable smooth substrates can be made that can be examined by transmission, the stripping operation would become unnecessary and shadowing materials and conditions could be employed that might otherwise be ruled out.

III. Globular Molecules

The shadow-casting process applied on a suitable smooth substrate is exceedingly effective in revealing the presence of globular protein molecules (by which we mean those that are "approximately spherical") down to molecular weights of about 13,000 (e.g., ribonuclease). Accurate measurement of molecular dimensions from such metallized particles is, however, complicated by the fact that what is seen is only the metal cap imposed on the surface which is therefore larger than the particle itself. As the metal is deposited it builds out from the molecule toward the source and also laterally to produce an "acornlike shape." It is not obvious what effect these distortions will have on the relation between the height of the molecule above the substrate and its shadow length for very small particles. In an empirical study of spherical molecules of molecular weight 35,000 to 380,000 (diameter from 44 to 97 A) it was found that the shadow lengths correlated very well with particle diameters (using shadow-to-height ratios measured from admixed polystyrene

Fig. 3. Molecules of yeast alcohol dehydrogenase. Molecular weight equals 75,000.

spheres) but that widths perpendicular to the shadow direction were about 60 A too great owing to the lateral growth of the "acornlike" caps (10). A similar lateral buildup was also measured in the width of TMV rods shadowed end-on. This figure would hold only for the conditions of these particular experiments and would not necessarily be the same for other experiments. In particular, larger distortions would be expected with metals that oxidize in air after deposition, such as uranium. In Fig. 3 is shown a micrograph of the enzyme yeast alcohol dehydrogenase, and a typical set of measurements showing the difference in apparent width and height is reproduced in Fig. 4. If, after allowance is made for the metal, width is still found to be greater than height, one would conclude that the particles are disc-shaped or rod-shaped.

Although measurements of these molecules can be made with fair accuracy and allowance made for the metal, one would not expect to compute a volume with the precision that would be obtainable on a spherical particle by physical chemical methods. The value of electron microscopy here is in showing that molecules are spherical or nearly spherical and thereby resolving ambiguities that may remain in the interpretation of indirect methods.

An elegant method for determining average molecular weights by counting the number of unknown particles relative to the number of a standard species has been used by Williams and Backus (29) to determine the molecular weight of virus particles. The method requires only the identification of the particles and does not require a measurement

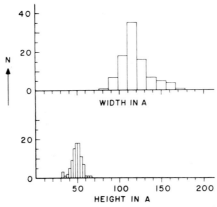

FIG. 4. Widths perpendicular to shadowing direction of shadowed yeast alcohol dehydrogenase molecules and heights calculated from shadow lengths.

of their dimensions. This would appear to be applicable to the smaller observable molecules, but there are serious difficulties: (a) Recognizable standard particles of known weight which are not too different in size from the ones to be determined must be available. The smallest uniform polystyrene latex spheres obtainable commercially average 880 A in diameter, which is much too large to be useful for the measurement of molecules of molecular weight of a few hundred thousand and less. What is needed are small standard particles of the order of 100 A. (b) There should be no interaction between the two species and clumping on the drying pattern should be negligible. When large particles clump, say in a monolayer, they can still be counted, but when small molecules clump they usually lose their identities in the aggregate. Most proteins adsorb to admixed polystyrene spheres, which would result in a false count, but this difficulty could probably be overcome by making counts at two or more relative concentrations and extrapolating the results.

(c) The contents of an entire drop must be counted. With the mica method the drops spread so widely on the hydrophilic surface that it is difficult to contain an entire droplet in one field. This is, however, a technical problem and suitably small droplets can on occasion be produced.

Although these difficulties conceivably might be overcome, the determination of molecular weight of small spherical particles by the counting method does not appear particularly promising at present in comparison with conventional techniques. The chief value of electron microscopy would appear to be in the determination of molecular dimensions and in the observation of heterogeneities rather than average values such as one obtains from the counting method or physical chemical techniques.

IV. Collagen

One of the first observations by electron microscopy of periodic structure in biological material resulting from the regular packing of molecular units was the observation in native collagen fibrils of a 640 A periodicity consisting of alternating light and dark bands (13). Later, fine structure was revealed within the periodicity and eventually it was shown through the occurrence of long spacings in reconstituted collagen (6, 18) and the observation of discrete molecules (12) that the molecule was actually about 4 times the length of the period originally observed. Figure 5 is a micrograph of the individual molecules from acetic acid solution. They are about 13 A thick and, as shown in Fig. 6, they average about 2800 A in length. The breadth of the distribution in Fig. 6 is due to the fact that there is some aggregation and a certain amount of degradation in acid solution. X-ray diffraction results indicate that they are a 3-stranded helix (28). In Fig. 7 are native collagen, fibrous long-spacing (FLS) collagen, and segment long-spacing (SLS) collagen, together with diagrams indicating the way in which the molecules are packed in the three types. The pattern for native collagen results when fibrils form naturally in tissue. It can also be produced by extracting the unpolymerized molecules (tropocollagen) from tissue and warming the extract to promote polymerization. FLS can be produced by treating an acetic acid solution of collagen with glycoprotein before polymerization. SLS may be produced by treating the solution with adenosine triphosphoric acid before polymerization. The SLS and the normal pattern show the asymmetrical nature of the molecule but this feature is lost in the FLS due to the random orientation of the aggregated molecules. The SLS provides a "molecular fingerprint" of the collagen molecule as shown in the high resolution micrograph in Fig. 8. The

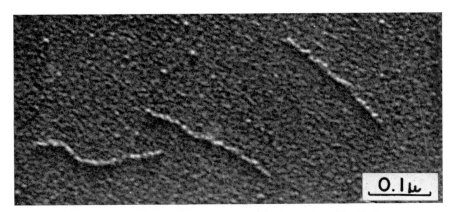

FIG. 5. Collagen molecules (ichthyocol) from acetic acid solution.

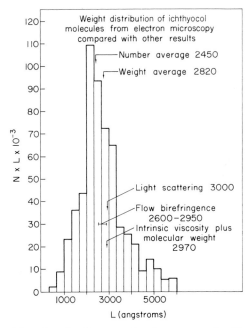

FIG. 6. Measured lengths of collagen molecules compared with results from other methods.

PTA-stained preparations indicate the location of the basic, particularly
the arginine side chains while cationic uranyl salts presumably stain
only the glutamic and aspartic acid residues. The two stains produce

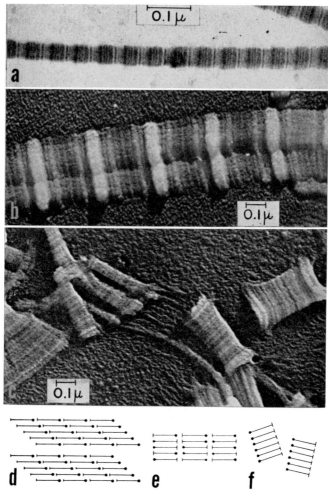

FIG. 7. (a) Native collagen fibril from beef tendon. Note the asymmetry of the
band pattern. (b) Reconstituted fibrous long-spacing collagen. (c) Segment long spacing
collagen. (d), (e), (f) Show diagrammatically how the molecules are packed in the 3
types shown in (a), (b), and (c), respectively. Figures (b) through (f) courtesy of Dr.
Jerome Gross.

bands at identical levels which is consistent with the view that lateral
interaction is primarily through electrostatic bonds between acidic and
basic side chains (20). Hodge and Schmitt (19) have broken the collagen

molecule by varying degrees of sonic irradiation and by forming segment polymers of the fragments have shown where the molecules are broken. This series of studies of collagen constitutes one of the best examples

Molecular Fingerprint of Tropocollagen

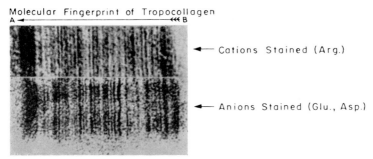

←——— Cations Stained (Arg.)

←——— Anions Stained (Glu., Asp.)

FIG. 8. High-resolution micrograph of stained segment long-spacing collagen. Courtesy of A. J. Hodge and F. O. Schmitt.

of the demonstration of molecular structure and molecular interactions by electron microscopy.

V. Fibrinogen-Fibrin

In the blood-clotting process, fibrinogen is converted to fibers of fibrin by the action of the enzyme thrombin. Fibrinogen is therefore not only a biologically important molecule but, as it turns out, is interesting from the point of view of electron microscopy in that it has a curious structure and mode of polymerization (16). In Fig. 9 is shown

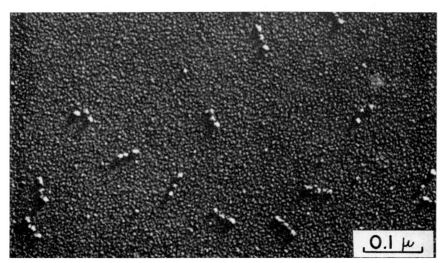

FIG. 9. Bovine fibrinogen molecules.

a typical field from a preparation of purified bovine fibrinogen. The molecule is fragile and easily broken, but the intact molecule has been established by statistical counts as consisting of a string of 3 nodules connected by a very thin strand. Since it has not been resolved clearly, the connecting strand is probably less than 15 A in diameter. It constitutes a small fraction of the volume of protein. The center nodule

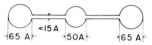

FIG. 10.   Model of the fibrinogen molecule.

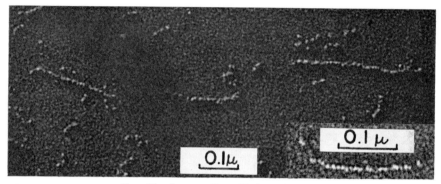

FIG. 11.   Intermediate fibrin polymers.

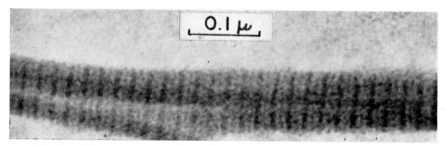

FIG. 12.   Fully polymerized fibrin fibrils stained with phosphotungstic acid.

is slightly smaller than the outer two which are apparently equal. The nodule diameters shown in Fig. 10 in the diagrammatic representation, are consistent with measurements of shadow lengths from electron microscopy and are adjusted slightly to fit the molecular weight of 330,000 which is known accurately from other methods. Since the first study by electron microscopy was reported, it has been found that the length of the molecules vary with pH conditions (H. S. Slayter, 1961, unpublished) and that at the high pH at which the original work (16) was carried out the length tends to be a maximum. It was shown, however, that in polymerization the molecules shrink in length down to about 240 A in the final fibrin fiber. Polymerization begins as an end to end aggregation of trimers, as shown in Fig. 11, which eventually aggregate

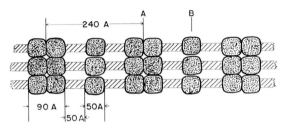

FIG. 13.   Model for the structure of a fibrin fibril.

laterally to form a tough fiber. Stained fibrin appears as in Fig. 12 showing a periodicity of about 240 A consisting of alternating heavily and lightly stained bands. The model for fibrin accounting for the bands and the mode of aggregation of fibrin molecules is shown in Fig. 13. Like the work on collagen, this is an example of the elucidation of details of a molecular structure and interactions that could not be obtained by other methods.

VI. Nucleic Acids: DNA and RNA

Native deoxyribonucleic acid (DNA) appears usually as indefinitely long, fairly stiff strands about 20 A in diameter (Fig. 14). Presumably, these are a double helix, as in the model proposed by Watson and Crick (5), though the helix has not been clearly resolved by electron microscopy. Long DNA is easily fragmented by sonic vibrations or by shear gradients. The ends usually break squarely, indicating that when one nucleotide chain breaks the other breaks at about the same place (12). As shown in Fig. 15, however, frequently the molecules can be seen to fray into two separate and thinner strands, as indicated by the arrow, which is consistent with the double-helix hypothesis. DNA which has degraded on standing or has been degraded by heat appears as "puddles" or random coils (15). Apparently when the two strands become unbonded they become highly flexible and coil up on themselves. DNA degraded by heat and cooled rapidly remains in the coiled state but when it is cooled slowly bands can reform and the double helix is reconstituted to a large degree (27). Figure 16 shows pneumococcus DNA that has been completely denatured by heat and partially reconstituted. In this micrograph, one sees at A a mass which is mainly random coil, at B stiff rods terminating in a "puddle," and the particle at C could consist of 3 strands each pairing with portions of the other 2.

Kleinschmidt *et al.* (*24, 25*) have developed a highly effective method of handling very long DNA molecules. They spread the DNA embedded

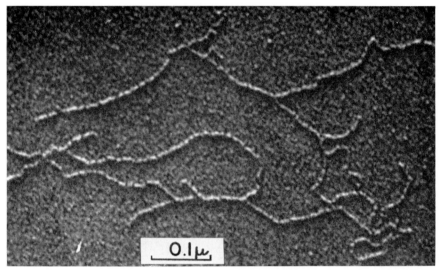

Fig. 14. Pneumococcus DNA.

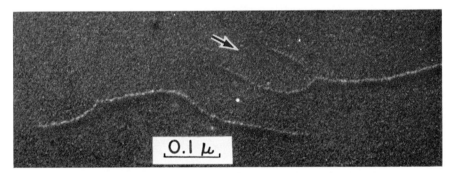

Fig. 15. DNA from salmon sperm fragmented by sonic vibrations.

in a protein monofilm on the surface of a Langmuir trough. The molecules are thus supported by the protein and maintained in a two-dimensional plane from which they can be picked up on support films. They are shadowed with platinum as they are given a rotary motion which causes metal to impinge from all directions. This avoids the difficulty that segments of molecules tend to become invisible when they are in line with the shadow direction. By this method it has been possible to follow extremely long DNA molecules as they twist and turn through the monofilm. A segment of such a DNA molecule is reproduced in Fig. 17.

The extreme length of most native DNA molecules makes the recording of entire unbroken units extremely difficult. By using membranes with suitable absorption properties, however, Beer and Naimark (2)

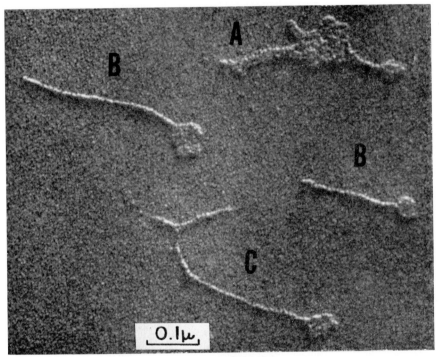

FIG. 16. DNA from pneumococcus which has been denatured by heat and reconstituted by slow cooling. Preparation by J. Marmur and D. Lane.

have successfully recorded in serial exposures the DNA molecule from T2 phage which has a molecular weight of 120×10^6 and is 60 microns long.

DNA from the very small bacteriophage ϕX-174 has been shown to be single stranded. The phage is 250 A in diameter and the molecular weight of the DNA is 1.7×10^6. Application of heat or concentrated salt solutions produces strands of nucleoprotein which show some stiffness as shown in Fig. 18, but the purified DNA is highly flexible and does not generally occur as extended strands (26).

There is also evidence from electron microscopy and other sources

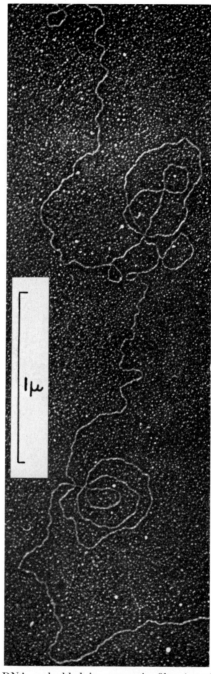

F ɪɢ. 17. Bacterial DNA embedded in a protein film (cytochrome c) and rotated while being shadowed. Courtesy of A. Kleinschmidt, M. Gehatia, and R. K. Zahn.

that DNA from certain rapidly proliferating cells occurs as pairs of double helices joined side by side (*4, 11*).

Ribonucleic acid (RNA) and single-stranded synthetic polynucleotides usually appear as random coils, though there is the possibility that suitable ionic conditions can be attained to keep the molecules extended

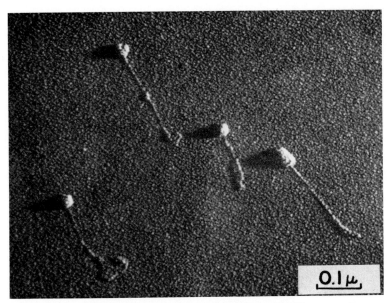

FIG. 18. Bacteriophage ∅X-174 heated at 75°C in 0.18 *M* ammonium acetate, showing extruded strands of DNA.

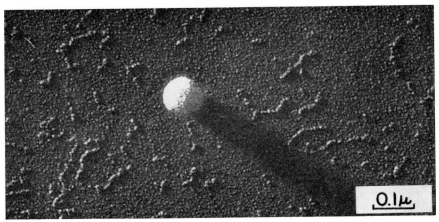

FIG. 19. RNA from microsomes of *E. coli*. Molecular weight equals 500,000. Preparation by W. Möller.

in solution. In a micrograph of purified and deionized microsomal RNA made by Dr. W. Möller at Harvard University (Fig. 19), it is seen that this normally flexible, single chain shows considerable stiffness. Synthetic single-stranded polynucleotides usually appear as random coils or

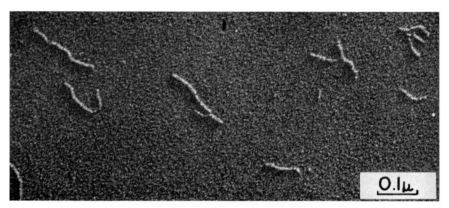

FIG. 20.   Polyinosinic acid.   Preparation by R. Haselkorn.

puddles, but they can be induced to form double or triple helices in which case they show a high degree of rigidity as shown in the example in Fig. 20 (9).

VII. Microsomal Particles

Ribonucleoprotein (RNP) particles or microsomes are involved in protein synthesis and are of roughly the same size from sources differing as widely as liver, pea seedlings, or microorganisms. Extracts of RNP may contain several microsomal fragments characterized by sedimentation constants 100 S, 70 S, 50 S, and 30 S depending upon the magnesium concentration. In a Mg^{++} concentration of $10^{-3} M$ the particles are predominantly the 70 S variety, but if the Mg^{++} concentration is reduced to $2 \times 10^{-4} M$ these particles split into two unequal fragments, one of 50 S and another of 30 S. Electron micrographs (17) of the 70 S particles indicated by arrows in Fig. 21a show that they consist of two granules in close association. The isolated 50 S component consists of particles that are approximately spherical. They are best represented by an oblate ellipsoid 140 A high and 170 A in diameter. The 30 S fragment is best represented by a prolate ellipsoid 95 A wide and 170 A long. These dimensions are in good agreement with molecular-weight data. The 70 S particle which is the unit involved in protein synthesis is therefore a rather peculiar structure consisting of the 50 S unit with the 30 S unit attached like a sort of cap. At higher Mg^{++} concentrations

(0.005 M) the 70 S particles polymerize in pairs with two 30 S particles lodged in between the two 50 S as indicated in Fig. 21b. Huxley and Zubay (23) have demonstrated essentially this same structure by the use of staining techniques.

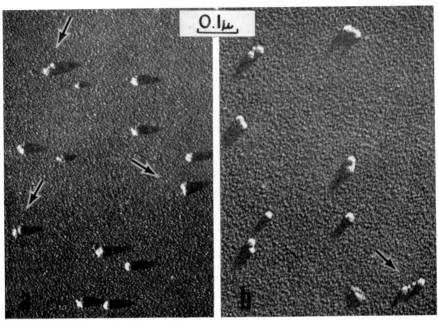

FIG. 21. Microsomal particles from *E. coli*. (a) Predominantly 70 S component (arrows). (b) Predominantly 100 S component (arrows). Preparation by H. Tissières and J. D. Watson.

VIII. Concluding Remarks

In the past decade the improvement in our ability to examine molecular structure with the electron microscope has been truly remarkable and is represented only sketchily within the confines of this section. It is quite clear that the electron microscope has become established as one of the primary instruments to be employed in any broad approach to problems in the field of molecular biology. The present effectiveness of electron microscopy in this application does not stem from the discovery of particularly new principles in recent years but derives, rather, from the cumulative effect of progressively improving techniques in instrumentation, manipulation of materials, and in the understanding of phenomena in the dimensional range that is involved. Actually, although electron microscopy can claim a kind of uniqueness in that it provides direct visualization of biological molecules, its accomplishments are linked to the current rapid expansion of the field of molecular biology in all its aspects. Advances in one direction provide new problems and stimulation for progress in another.

One can scarcely say, however, that the art of electron microscopy is at the stage where, in the field of molecular biology, the full capabilities of the instrument can be effected. The problems in the way of further progress remain basically the same as they always have been since the instrument was first placed in the hands of biologists about 20 years ago: (a) attainment of contrast at high resolution; (b) the quest for substrates with low "noise" levels or other desirable properties; (c) the isolation of materials suitable for significant experimentation; (d) the manipulation of materials for study with regard to preservation or controlled modification of their structure. We can say that we are satisfied that electron microscopy has proved to be of unique value for the elucidation of macromolecular structure, but we are not satisfied that its full capabilities have been demonstrated.

REFERENCES

1. Backus, R. C., and Williams, R. C., *J. Appl. Phys.* **21**, 11 (1950).
2. Beer, M., and Naimark, D., *Program 19th Ann. Meeting Electron Microscope Soc. Am. Pittsburgh, Pa.*, p. 23 (1961).
3. Brenner, S., and Horne, R. W., *Biochim. et Biophys. Acta* **34**, 103 (1959).
4. Cavalieri, L. F., and Rosenberg, B. H., *Biophys. J.* **1**, 317 (1961).
5. Crick, F. H. C., and Watson, J. D., *Proc. Roy. Soc. (London)* **A223**, 80 (1954).
6. Gross, J., Highberger, J. H., and Schmitt, F. O., *Proc. Natl. Acad. Sci. U. S.* **40**, 679 (1954).
7. Hall, C. E., *J. Biophys. Biochem. Cytol.* **1**, 1 (1955).
8. Hall, C. E., *J. Biophys. Biochem. Cytol.* **2**, 625 (1956).
9. Hall, C. E., *Ann. N.Y. Acda. Sci.* **81**, 723 (1959).
10. Hall, C. E., *J. Biophys. Biochem. Cytol.* **7**, 613 (1960).
11. Hall, C. E., and Cavalieri, L. F., *J. Biophys. Biochem. Cytol.* **10**, 347 (1961).
12. Hall, C. E., and Doty, P., *J. Am. Chem. Soc.* **80**, 1269 (1958).
13. Hall, C. E., Jakus, M. A., and Schmitt, F. O., *J. Am. Chem. Soc.* **64**, 1234 (1942).
14. Hall, C. E., Jakus, M. A., and Schmitt, F. O., *J. Appl. Phys.* **16**, 459 (1945).
15. Hall, C. E., and Litt, M., *J. Biophys. Biochem. Cytol.* **4**, 1 (1958).
16. Hall, C. E., and Slayter, H. S., *J. Biophys. Biochem. Cytol.* **5**, 11 (1959).
17. Hall, C. E., and Slayter, H. S., *J. Mol. Biol.* **1**, 329 (1959).
18. Highberger, J. H., Gross, J., and Schmitt, F. O., *Proc. Natl. Acad. Sci. U. S.* **37**, 286 (1951).
19. Hodge, A. J., and Schmitt, F. O., *Proc. Natl. Acad. Sci. U.S.* **44**, 418 (1958).
20. Hodge, A. J., and Schmitt, F. O., *Proc. Natl. Acad. Sci. U.S.* **46**, 186 (1960).
21. Horne, R. W., and Brenner, S., *Proc. 4th Intern. Conf. on Electron Microscopy, Berlin, 1958*, p. 212 (1960).
22. Huxley, H. E., *Program of 15th Ann. Meeting Electron Microscope Soc. Am. Cambridge, Mass.*, p. 5 (1957); *J. Appl. Phys.* **28**, 1369 (1957).

23. Huxley, H. E., and Zubay, G., *J. Mol. Biol.* **2**, 10 (1960).
24. Kleinschmidt, A., Gehatia, M., and Zahn, R. K., *Kolloid-Z.* **169**, 156 (1960).
25. Kleinschmidt, A., and Zahn, R. K., *Z. Naturforsch.* **14b**, 770 (1959).
26. Maclean, E. C., and Hall, C. E., *J. Mol. Biol.* **4**, 173 (1962).
27. Marmur, J., and Lane, D., *Proc. Natl. Acad. Sci. U.S.* **46**, 453 (1960).
28. Rich, A., and Crick, F. H. C., *in* "Recent Advances in Gelatin and Glue Research" (G. Stainsby, ed.), p. 20. Pergamon Press, New York, 1958.
29. Williams, R. C., and Backus, R. C., *J. Am. Chem. Soc.* **71**, 4052 (1949).
30. Williams, R. C., and Wyckoff, R. W. G., *J. Appl. Phys.* **15**, 712 (1944).

Author Index

Numbers in parentheses are reference numbers and indicate that an author's work is referred to although his name is not cited in the text. Numbers in italics show the pages on which the complete references are listed.

Subject Index

A

Abbe theory, of coherent illumination, 38-41

Acrolein, as fixing agent, 304

Adenosine triphosphatase, in cell, 315

Adenosine triphosphate, in cell, 315-316

Airy pattern, 33, 36, 42-44

Alloys,
  electron microscopy of, 238-252
  general antiphase boundaries in, 242-246
  ordered structure studies on, 238-252
  periodic antiphase structures in, 238-242
  thin-film preparation of, 93-95
  transition in, 246-250
  twinning in, 250-252

Aluminum,
  bombardment thinning of, 86, 150
  chemical thinning of, 84
  deformation studies on, 230
  electron-beam dislocation of, 228
  electron microscopy of, 195
  quenching defects in, 195, 201
  radiation defects of, 201, 203

Aluminum-silver alloy, electron microscopy of, 88

Amphidinum elegans, fixation of, 341-342

Antibodies, electron microscopy of, 319

Aquon, as embedding media, 140-141, 310

Araldite, as embedding media, 137, 310, 338

Autoradiography,
  of bacterial cell, 352-355
  using electron microscope, 319-322

B

Bacillus spp.,
  cell wall of, 370-371
  electron microscopy studies on, 356, 357, 359, 380-381
  respiratory system of, 377
  sporulation of, 380-383

Bacteria, virus-infected, 384-388

Bacterial cell,
  autoradiography of, 352-355
  cell envelopes of, 369-375
  cell surface of, 377-379
  chromatophores of, 358
  components of, 336
  cytoplasm of, 355-360

  cytoplasmic membrane of, 336
  DNA-plasm of, 361-363
  electron microscopy of, 335-393
  embedding of, 338-344
  enzyme localization in, 347-348
  fixation of, 113, 338-344
  flagella of, 336, 377-378
  glycogen particles of, 336, 357
  lipid granules of, 336
  mesosomes of, 336, 377
  metachromatic granules of, 358
  nuclear vacuoles of, 363
  nucleoids of, 336, 340, 362
  nucleus of, 348-350, 361-369
    extraction, 365-366
    model, 366-369
  pili of, 378-379
  plastids of, 336
  respiratory system in, 375-377
  serial sectioning of, 348-352
  specific differentiation of, 344-348
    by localization of enzymes, 347-348
    by specific coagulation, 345
    by specific digestion, 347
    by staining and digestion, 346-347
  sporulation of, 379-384
  staining of, 346-347
  virus-infected, 384-388

Bacteriology, electron microscope use in, 353-393

Bacteriophage T2, electron microscopy studies on, 352

Bacteriophage φx-174, DNA of, 409, 411

Bacterium xylinum, electron microscope studies on, 379

Bismuth-telluride, dislocation networks in, 189

Bulk materials, imperfections in, 184-206

Burgers vector determination, in crystal dislocation, 186-187

C

Cadmium, deformation studies on, 232-236

Carbon, as substrate material, 106

Cardolite NC-513, in embedding materials, 139

Cell(s),
  cohesion of, 270-273